CYBERNETICS
FOR THE MODERN MIND

Cybernetics for the Modern Mind

Walter R. Fuchs

with a Foreword by
Professor Yehoshua Bar-Hillel

translated from the German
by K. Kellner

THE MACMILLAN COMPANY
New York

We were sufficiently sophisticated to build the machine and we are too primitive to make it serve us. We carry on world traffic on narrow-gauge mental tracks.

Karl Kraus

CONTENTS

by Professor Yehoshua Bar-Hillel

The problem of the popularization of science has occupied me for a number of years. A rational policy is hardly possible if the 'Establishment' is not sufficiently familiar with, for instance, the scientific bases of modern technology, which form an integral part of our lives. Under such circumstances democracy cannot be expected to work. On the other hand a complete understanding of these bases is simply impossible without a long and specialized University training, and is limited even with such training.

Naturally there is no complete solution to this dilemma. It is important that this should be fully realized and that one should have no illusions in this respect. This does not mean that it is not our duty to contribute to at least a partial solution of the problem.

The situation is by no means eased by the fact that many people, among them also writers and journalists, see it as their business, perhaps even their vocation, to misdirect the desire of many for knowledge and understanding; even to lead them in the opposite direction. Thus, in popular-science books and articles, one can often find references to 'secrets', the solving of which Nature resists with all its power; so that the deciphering of the secret code of Nature, if it can be done at all, can only be done with superhuman efforts. At the same time the impression is given that all the scientific theories, with their jargon and complicated mathematical formulae, can be completely represented in every-day language; as if the formulations in scientific language were only an invention of mystery-mongers and especially thought out for this purpose.

The author of this book has completely succeeded in keeping away from this occupational disease of science popularizers. He has done this in a manner which is almost without comparison. Practically nowhere in the whole book, have I found a statement which is either wrong or unnecessarily misleading. It cannot be avoided that there are readers who are misled by even the best presentations because they see everything through glasses coloured by prejudice, or simply do not possess the minimum basic knowledge, or for some other reason. It cannot be avoided by being silent because even this can be misunderstood. Without haste, with a good deal of humour and by means of amusing and witty illustrations, which never oversimplify matters, the reader is shown some of the achievements of the modern philosophy of languages and of linguistics. This is a brilliant, and sometimes even original, introduction to the theory of information-processing machines. The author's knowledge of the teachings of Ludwig Wittgenstein and Rudolph Carnap has in no small way contributed to this. His skill in using the right quotations in the right places can hardly be surpassed. Although I do not quite share his enthusiasm concerning the importance of Wittgenstein's views for the understanding of language, speaking and thinking, I was near to succumbing to the magic of these quotations.

Many 'deep' and yet so superficial and unreal problems which can turn a discussion about thinking-machines into a very interesting but, on the other hand, completely useless party game have been exposed in a very elegant manner. I hope that nobody after having read this book will show any desire to participitate in discussions about 'can computers think?'; especially since he will know so much more about the perhaps less sensational but more serious question 'how does one think with computers?' or 'how do computers help to solve problems?'.

Norbert Wiener, himself one of the originators of these theories is partly responsible for this secret-mongering in connection with the concept of information and the theories about it. The haze with which Wiener surrounded this concept in order to place it alongside, as equally important and equally fundamental, the concepts of mass and energy can probably be traced back to a mix-up of statistical, communication-theoretical information with semantic information. This was recognized, if somewhat late, but a confusion did result and even nowadays, twenty years later, people still fall for it. It is just in this connection that the author's discussions are particularly clear. Accidents will happen whenever something new is being developed; and it was just one of those small accidents that the name, created in 1928, 'theory of information transmission' was shortened twenty years later to 'information theory'. (We know now that it would have been better had the name 'theory of signal transmission' been used originally.) Thus many people, including Wiener, were under the impression that the statistical theory of information transmission would yield valuable insight into the semantic theory of the information contents of speech.

I found two chapters particularly instructive. Many will have heard that our natural languages, in addition to their many faults about which one likes to complain at cocktail parties, make it possible, even induce one to use redundant expressions. For this reason they cannot be considered as an efficient means of communication, especially not with computers. It cannot be sufficiently stressed that, in such general terms, this is simply not correct. Apart from occasional fluctuations they are almost ideally suited to their various applications. After all one does not only use these languages for scientific writings, but also for letters, novels and poems; one does not use them only to describe facts but one also questions, orders, asks, curses, lies and deceives in them, and also uses them in many other ways in speech. Just because the natural languages serve as an efficient means of communication for the totality of these actions it is evident that they cannot be equally efficient for each one individually. When it comes to executing a particular task efficiently, for instance, to giving instructions to a computer, then one has to expect that the natural language will no longer be the ideal means of communication and that an artificial language containing less redundancy (e.g. the so-called programming language) will be far better suited. Of course redundancy is not the only instance in which programming languages differ from natural languages. It is more important that many, perhaps even all sentences of the natural languages should be intelligible without being ambiguous to men of 'innate intelligence'. In order to achieve this all possible help from available knowledge, and from the special circumstances associated with the speaking of these sentences, is being used. Such possibilities cannot be expected from 'artificial intelligences' within the foreseeable future. Moreover, and one must not be surprised at this, the absence of ambiguity in the sentences of the artificial languages can only be achieved at considerable cost; for a natural language with its manifold uses this cost would be far too high. One of the chapters deals in a particularly impressive way with the meaning of redundancy under normal communication conditions and the possibility of its reduction in special circumstances; this is one of the most important tasks of 'language engineers' and in order to drive this home the author has written the chapter in a particularly redundant style. The last chapter deals with the future of automata. If only for the sake of being able to read this chapter with understanding one should make the effort to work through the previous pages. Every layman who has ever thought about the part played by computers in the future of mankind will be made familiar with well considered thoughts. These should enable him to judge critically not only the irresponsible day-dreams but also the apocalyptic prophecies which one encounters so frequently in this field.

To the extent to which popular-science literature can be successful at all the four ingredients necessary to make a go of it are: technical know-how, common sense, pedagogic skill and a sense of humour. The author shows that he possesses all of these. I have no doubt that many readers will have widened their horizon after having read this book. May I hope, therefore, that some of them will take the opportunity to throw overboard some of the prejudices and misunderstandings based on ignorance?

Y. Bar-Hillel

Professor Yehoshua Bar-Hillel was born in Vienna in 1915, was educated in Berlin and emigrated to Palestine in 1933. In 1938 he obtained an M.A. at the Hebrew University of Jerusalem and a doctorate in 1949. From 1951–3 he worked at the famous Massachusetts Institute of Technology (MIT) in Cambridge, Mass. (USA) mainly on problems connected with the machine-translation of languages. He now holds the chair of Logic and Philosophy of Science at the Hebrew University, is a member of the Israeli Academy of Arts and Sciences and is president of the section for Logic, Methodology and Philosophy of Science of the International Union for History and Philosophy of Science.

'THE BEST WORD I COULD FIND...'

Introducing the magic word 'Cybernetics'

'Cybernetics' has become a popular word of our time. One can hardly open a newspaper nowadays in which this word does not appear in some connection or other; be it in the world of art or science, be it in our natural surroundings or in technology, there is hardly a subject which could not be linked with cybernetics. Biological cybernetics seems as much justified as the combination of 'cybernetics and communication technique' or even 'happening and cybernetics'. Can we regard the 'in'-word 'cybernetics' as a magic word, an 'open sesame' for *all* the problems of contemporary science?

What is cybernetics? No question seems more appropriate; and yet it is just such a narrow, apparently precise 'what is'-type of question like this which can drive the expert to despair. 'What is technology?', 'what is life?', 'what is physics?' Every more or less detailed answer leaves a whole host of questions unanswered. It is simply not possible to give clear, unequivocal definitions. Is there really such a thing as 'the' Cybernetics or 'the' Physics? Or do we have to be content in such cases with statements which the mathematician and logician Paul Lorenzen made about 'the' Physics? 'When we simply speak about physics we use it

only as a collective noun for a multitude of past and present scientific activities. The word "physics" describes one aspect of human activity which, for the moment at least, is given only in historic terms.'

The position, as far as cybernetics is concerned, at least historically speaking, is similar to that of physics with the one important difference that physics, as a modern scientific study, has been pursued since the beginning of the seventeenth century whereas the study of cybernetics did not begin until a few years ago. Living as we do in the age of rapidly expanding exact sciences, with knowledge growing at an ever increasing rate, we find that both these specialized subjects of research are full of unlimited riches for the human observer. Nobody living in the last third of the twentieth century can claim to understand the whole of modern physics or the whole of cybernetics.

Let us try cautiously to draw parallels. From his study of the kinematics of material bodies, a very old subject, the Italian Galileo Galilei (1564–1642), the brilliant experimenter and profound theoretician, developed a completely new science—modern physics. Galileo's amazingly fruitful *dialogue* on experiment and theory has turned natural science and technology into the fertile region of human endeavour that we know today. Galileo elevated the experiment to the highest court of judgement of natural science. The physicists question Nature

The American mathematician Norbert Wiener (1894–1964) is the 'father' of the new science cybernetics.

13

with the help of experiments. In order to develop sound theories about the physical states and their changes, theories which also permit predictions to be made about new phenomena, they use the precise instrumentation of modern mathematics. The physicists have followed the path shown by Galileo; the success of this method has become more than ever apparent today.

In a similar way shortly before the middle of the twentieth century the American Norbert Wiener laid the foundations for a new science 'Cybernetics'. His novel attempts were presented in his book *Cybernetics—or Control and Communication in the Animal and the Machine* published in 1948. Naturally there were other attempts in this field before Wiener, just as there existed pointers towards modern physics before Galileo. But the decisive and revolutionary step in this new and exact discipline stems from Norbert Wiener. Wiener's method, just like Galileo's, seems to be destined to be a great success. If the English communications technologist Colin Cherry, a brilliant exponent of this new exact craft, is of the opinion that cybernetics is merely a revival of very old matters, especially from the seventeenth and eighteenth centuries, but with a completely new orientation and meaning then one has to reply that it is precisely this completely new orientation and meaning which is part and parcel of the decisive achievements in the history of science. This applies to Galileo the Physicist no less than to Wiener the Mathematician.

This was the essential point: Norbert Wiener was first of all a Mathematician, one of the most prolific exponents of this science in our century. His autobiography, recommended to anyone interested in the exact sciences, is appropriately entitled *I am a Mathematician*. Wiener is the most famous mathematician to have emerged from the United States to date. Born in 1894 in the university town of Columbia (Missouri), as the son of a professor of the French and German languages, he grew up as a kind of 'Mozart of the exact sciences' and obtained his doctorate at the early age of nineteen. After further successful years of study at Cambridge, Göttingen and Copenhagen, Wiener became Professor of Mathematics at the most famous technical university of the New World, the Massachusetts Institute of Technology (MIT). Norbert Wiener remained an active mathematician all his life although he himself remarked 'Mathematics is very largely a young man's game. It is the athleticism of the intellect, making demands which can be satisfied to the full only when there is youth and strength.'

Although he made his name as the 'father of cybernetics' it is only proper to refer to his numerous contributions to pure and applied mathematics, theoretical physics and theoretical engineering. Norbert Wiener, who died in 1964, was a real 'life and soul' mathematician. His many publications, which often were aimed at a wide public, stem from the pen of a mathematician.

His *Cybernetics* is a mathematical book throughout; it can only be studied after suitable training and requires considerable concentration and familiarity with mathematical formulae. If Wiener's French colleague Louis Couffignal (born

1902) finds that the book is intelligible to the informed layman, in spite of the many pages of advanced mathematical formulae, then every scientist with common sense must be aware that this is exaggerated, particularly if he seriously tries to find a bridge between exact research and the general public. Few people, whether schoolboys or adults, who try to gain some understanding of the exact sciences, will succeed these days if they are recommended to study original literature from the outset.

Just as no would-be mountaineer should be made to climb the north face of the Eiger, one should not expect a similar tour de force in the case of the exact sciences. Wiener's *Cybernetics* has become a classic of scientific literature in the same way as Heisenberg's *Physical Principles of Quantum Mechanics*, or Russell and Whitehead's *Principia Mathematica*. It is highly specialized literature written by the expert for the expert (see page 85).

It would, however, be wrong to come to the hasty conclusion that the up-to-the-minute aspects of progress in the exact sciences must remain incomprehensible to the outsider. The opposite, in fact, has become necessary. The interested schoolboy, the teacher, the secretary, the politician—they all need to be informed about this new vista of exact knowledge which at an ever increasing rate changes the world we live in.

It is tempting, therefore, for a writer of popular-science books to use as a basis a standard work in the exact sciences, such as Wiener's *Cybernetics*, and to interpret it in the simplest and most understandable way. But the line that a popular-science author has to take differs markedly from that taken in a work in pure science. 'Pop science' follows different rules from 'top science'. Not only is it necessary to explain things in much greater detail and begin with different assumptions but also the emphasis and development of ideas are radically different.

The old rule in popular literature to 'throw out everything that smacks of mathematics' can no longer be applied to a description of any of the exact sciences, least of all to cybernetics. This is because cybernetics *is* mathematics; and to represent 'mathematics without mathematics' would certainly be an absurdity. (Yet there is no lack of attempts to popularize in this direction.)

As a way into this modern field of research Wiener, in his book *Cybernetics* used the basic principles of *statistical mechanics* which is not exactly one of the simplest disciplines of theoretical physics. This, in fact is in step with the line of development of his own researches which we will discuss briefly.

While still a young man, Wiener had developed the neat mathematical apparatus to describe a phenomenon also known to non-physicists, namely *Brownian motion* —the characteristically irregular zig-zag motion carried out by tiny particles in gases or liquids. (This zig-zag motion was first observed and described by the English botanist Robert Brown in 1827 when he looked through a microscope at pollen suspended in a drop of water.)

At the beginning of this century the physicists Perrin and Einstein gave an explanation of this phenomenon; the famous Albert Einstein saw the possibility of a statistical description. Roughly

15

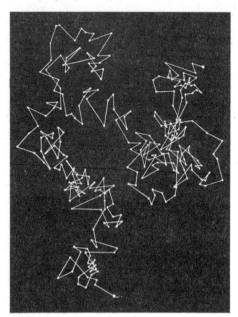

Wiener's mathematical description of the Brownian motion became important to communications technique in the mid-twenties.

statistical assembly of curves with the characteristics mentioned above. Incidentally, a similar kind of motion is carried out by the *free electrons* which, in the form of an *electron gas* fly quite at random through a metal lattice. In this case this movement leads to statistical voltage fluctuations which show up as 'noise' in electronic amplifiers. This phenomenon is known as the *shot effect* and is of utmost importance in radio, radar and television technology. Wiener's mathematical description of these effects (Brownian motion, shot effect) became important to the communications technique in the mid-'twenties. In his autobiography Wiener wrote: 'Previous to my work there had been no thoroughly satisfactory example given of the sort of motion that would correspond to sound or light with a continuous spectrum— that is with energy distributed continuously in frequency instead of being lumped in isolated spectrum lines.' A little later he says: 'I found that it was possible to generate continuous spectra by means of Brownian motion or the shot effect...In other words, I already began to detect a statistical element in the theory of the continuous spectrum and, through that, in communication theory'.

This was in the middle of the nineteen twenties. Almost thirty years later Wiener could say: 'Communication theory is thoroughly statistical, and this can be traced directly back to my work of that time.'

It is this thoroughly statistical communication theory, that forms the basis for a description of any cybernetic system, with which this book is concerned. From

speaking, Einstein's equation for the Brownian motion states that the average path length traversed by a particle can be related to the square root of the time; in other words if the particle traverses a certain distance in one second then it will traverse twice this distance in four seconds and three times this distance in nine seconds. Moreover Einstein's French colleague Jean Perrin interpreted the paths of these tiny particles as being continuous but non-differentiable curves. This means that these microscopic particles in their jerky movements can neither jump over gaps, nor can they at any time move in a clearly defined direction.

Norbert Wiener's theoretical work on an idealized Brownian motion confirmed Perrin's conjecture that the movements of these particles could be regarded as a the purely mathematical point of view this theory of measurable information is still a very young branch of the theory of probability. It is only gradually that we shall develop the statistical and probability aspect of information theory. Because of this, however, we cannot present a popular version of Wiener's deliberations. Is there then another possible scientific approach to this field?

One can say that information theory has been founded by the American scientist Claude E. Shannon (born 1916) whose key works were published during the nineteen-forties. In contrast to Wiener, whose approach was based on continuous phenomena, the communications scientist Shannon started off from discrete phenomena which can be determined by clear cut 'yes or no' decisions (see page 109).

His approach to information theory is decidedly simpler than Wiener's but even so his presentation is not immediately suited to our purposes. Both telegraph and telephone, both radio and television were invented by scientists and worked extremely well even before there existed an information theory. It was not until transmission and handling of information led to more and more complicated problems that the question of measurable information, of the qualitative and quantitative properties of a message, became topical to the technologist.

Primarily the very pertinent analyses of Russian mathematicians have made it possible, in very recent times, to put information theory on an exact foundation and to shape it into a very precise tool of modern mathematics. The outstanding names are A. J. Chinchin and A. N. Kolmogorov. The rather factually thinking engineers, however, find in these brilliant, highly abstract theories a certain lack of applicability.

Claude E. Shannon—who incidentally was one of Wiener's students and like his teacher before him now holds a chair at MIT, the American Mecca of technologists—developed the right tools to control and solve problems arising in communications technology. His information theory makes it possible, so to speak, to sort out the information which is transmitted from place to place either by wire or in the case of radio waves through the 'ether'. In certain respects this is a similar situation to that of the transport of different types of material objects by conveyor belts (see page 172). At first a clear cut and satisfactory way to measure information can only be obtained for very simple communication systems. For this one has to know the total amount of information which the sender is capable of producing and then, in addition, the expectation value of each communication. The detailed explanation of the mathematical treatment of such a simple case is one of the problems which are discussed in this book (see page 161).

We shall always be concerned with the matter-of-fact interpretation of the basic truths, the clarification of the new angle which permits us to see well-known facts. We shall not concern ourselves, however, with the fascinating and fantastic extrapolations, made from this field, which are so immensely popular. They belong to the sphere of science fiction rather than to the solid pursuit of the exact sciences.

Yet it would be remiss of us not to cast a critical eye on what the future holds in store (see particularly page 321 ff).

A matter-of-fact interpretation does not need to be boring. We shall introduce the theory of information as a necessary means of looking at facts from the point of view of cybernetics but not as a purely mathematical subject. It will help us to clarify the recording, encoding, storage, transmission and the dissemination of measurable information between one system and another and also within an individual system. As we are concerned with communication and control we shall call these *cybernetic systems*. So in the broadest sense, cybernetics becomes the mathematics of information processing. Furthermore, in a book about *intelligent machines* we shall also be interested in the technical applications of this. Such technical installations we call *cybernetic machines*. The word cybernetics, however, will not be used more than is necessary.

What is the origin of this word? Let Wiener, who used it as the title of his famous book, explain in his own words:

'...the first thing that puzzled me was what title to choose for the book and what name for the subject. I first looked for a Greek word signifying "messenger" but the only one I knew was *angelos*. This has in English the specific meaning "angel", a messenger of God. The word was thus pre-empted and would not give me the right context. Then I looked for an appropriate word from the field of control. The only word I could think of was the Greek word for steersman, *kybernetes*. I decided that, as the word I was looking for was to be used in English, I ought to take advantage of the English pronounciation of the Greek, and hit on the name *cybernetics*. Later on, I found that a corresponding word had been used since the early nineteenth century in France by the physicist Ampère, in a sociological sense, but at that time I did not know it.'

This reads much more plainly than the many obscure and enigmatical writings on cybernetics which refer to the ancient Greek feast of the Cybernesians and in which Homer and Parmenides, Plato and Lucretius are quoted. It only needs one sentence of Wiener to explode these literary excursions: 'The best word I could find...'. Cybernetics is an artificial word which does not merit any etymological speculations. Those who still find it difficult to free themselves from the idea of 'helmsmanship' of the ancient Greeks, should at least consider what Plato wrote in the dialogue *Georgics*: 'Helmsmanship is unassuming and modest and does not boast and does not behave as if it had done something wonderful...'

Let us sum up. In our opinion cybernetics is the mathematics of information processing and its technical realization. A knowledge of ancient Greek and Roman literature is not necessary. This definition delineates a field within the exact sciences which overlaps with the traditional disciplines. As to the question 'what is cybernetics?' we can extricate ourselves gracefully with the jocular remark made by the mathematician Friedrich L. Bauer: 'Cybernetics denotes what cannot be accommodated in one's own specialized fields'.

Bauer's witticism highlights clearly that cybernetics forms the link between the different subjects of modern scientific activity. In a more poetic way one could speak of 'bridging the gap' between the sciences and the arts. In fact Wiener did address his cybernetics to all kinds of professional groups such as Psychologists, Physiologists, Electrical Engineers, Radio Engineers, Sociologists, Philosophers, Mathematicians, Anthropologists, Psychiatrists and Physicists.

Out of the large field of cybernetics we shall focus our attention on *cybernetic machines* which experts call information-processing devices or information transducers. Our discussions will inevitably lead us to *machines that think* and then on to *computers*. (We shall avoid the misconceptions so dreaded by the expert.)

In this book we shall take a somewhat unusual path to lead us to this goal and which will put the modern techniques into a different and unusual light. The mathematician and physicist Hermann Weyl once said about natural philosophy that 'if it is not the most important, it is the most significant factor in our civilization as distinct from other civilizations'.

But, in the awareness of most people, it does not by any means occupy this high position. The standing of technology is very similar; its achievements are being employed by most people as a matter of course and yet these very same people, in the spoken and written word, deny it its due cultural value and even dismiss it as something to be suspicious of. How effective is the nonsensical caricature of the 'machine which governs man'. Yet in every modern industrial society applied science forms a considerable part of the creative and imaginative field of activity to which man can dedicate himself.

Albert Einstein saw technical activity, which is also a part of the field of cybernetic machines, in these three words curiosity, stimulus and imagination. 'The origin of all technical achievement is the divine curiosity and the stimulus of the experimenting and meditating researcher and no less the constructive imagination of the technical innovator.' Perhaps the following chapters will contribute something towards the clarification of these ideas.

1. THE 'VEHICLE' OF THINKING

1.1 Thinking about thinking, occasionally...
Some thoughts on an important activity of man

Often and everywhere men talk of thinking. People use phrases like 'I wasn't thinking...', 'Just think!', or 'Think nothing of it' in all kinds of situations. Similarly there are many maxims in our everyday speech which also refer to thinking. Many years ago a French politician said: 'I always think, never speak' and a famous compatriot of his who lived more than three hundred years ago coined the now well-known phrase 'I think, therefore I am'. From these clichés which trip so readily off the tongue to real analytical conscious thinking processes there is a very big step. Calculated thought demands our participation and involves everybody to some extent. In all the examples given so far we have merely mentioned aspects of the very large sphere of meaning which the word thinking conveys. But what is *thinking*?

Superficially this seems to be a very simple question, but appearances can be deceptive. Ever since the times of the ancient Greek philosophers men have constantly attempted to make rational reflections about thinking. We have already quoted the conclusion which a French philosopher arrived at: 'I think, therefore I am'. This very well-known sentence was introduced by René Descartes (1596–1650), a man equally famous as mathematician and philosopher. How did Descartes arrive at this startling formula for human existence?

During his search for this one undoubtable truth, which is so important to all philosophers he posed the question: 'Does the material world really exist?' Can I consider my arms and legs, my chest and head, in short the whole body-mechanism, as Descartes himself put it, to be real? Our senses could indeed be deceived. We can at least consider as real the things we can touch and handle. But isn't it true that in our dreams we see and feel familiar objects of this material world which turn out to be nothing but illusions when we wake?

Isn't it conceivable that our surroundings together with our own body-mechanism are dangled before us by some demonic force and in fact do not exist? Could it not be that two people who see and feel alike should be deceived in the same way? Our sense recognition on its own, therefore, is not infallible. From such an uncertain basis is it possible to build up a philosophical argument? In his *Meditations*, Descartes begins to deliberate the following:

'I shall then suppose, not that God who is supremely good and the fountain of truth, but that some evil genius not less powerful than deceitful, has employed his whole energies in deceiving me; I shall consider

Ludwig Wittgenstein (1889–1951); his *Philosophical Investigations* form our guide through the land of thinking and language. Wittgenstein developed a kind of 'chess-game theory' of thinking and speaking.

that the Heavens, the earth, colours, figures, sound, and all other external things are nothing but the illusions and dreams of which this genius has availed himself in order to lay traps for my credulity; I shall consider myself as having no hands, no eyes, no flesh, no blood, nor any senses, yet falsely believing myself to possess all those things.'

Why does Descartes make this extraordinary assumption?

'I shall remain obstinately attached to this idea, and if by this means it is not in my power to arrive at the knowledge of any truth, I may at least do what is in my power, and with resolve avoid giving credence to any false thing, or being imposed upon by this arch-deceiver, however powerful and deceptive he may be.'

But if we are not in a position to recognize 'any truth' 'What remains true?' Descartes gives a resigned yet uncertain answer to this question in his *Meditations*: 'Perhaps just the one thing that *nothing* is certain.' To start thinking along such lines is not being very optimistic.

The structures of the external world, indeed my own body, these are all 'things which one can doubt'. This is the title of the *First Meditation* in which Descartes ponders about the basis of philosophy. What is it then that cannot be doubted? I myself am more than just my body, my body-mechanism. There must be something in me over which the force of evil has no power. 'There is no doubt that I am, also if this force deceives me and let it deceive me as much as it likes but never will it succeed in persuading me that I do

not exist *as long as I think I do.*'

This is Descartes' principal theme. After further carefully thought out sentences he finally reaches this conclusion: 'Here it is—it is thinking. It alone cannot be separated from me. I am, I exist, that is certain.' With this knowledge man becomes 'a thing which thinks' (the '*res cogitans*'). 'I am a real and a really existing thing; but what kind of thing? I have said it already—a thing which thinks! But what do we imagine by a 'thinking thing'? What does it mean?

'It is a thing which doubts, understands, affirms, denies, wills, refuses and which has imagination and feeling. Certainly it is no small matter if all these things form part of myself. But why should they not do so? Am I not that being who now doubts nearly everything, who nevertheless understands certain things, who is of the opinion that this one only is true, who denies all else, who desires to know more, who is averse to being deceived, who sometimes even against his will imagines many things, and who perceives many things as coming from the senses? Even if I were to sleep all the time, even if my creator were to choose to deceive me—is there nothing in all this which is as true as it is certain that I exist? Or can it be said of any one of these things that it can be divorced from myself? Because, that I am the one who doubts, who understands, who wills, is so evident that nothing will make it clearer.'

From such wise meditations Descartes built up a magnificent structure of philosophic thought which is still valid today. From his insight into *thinking things* his path leads to metaphysics, to realizations about the 'Being'. The 'I' becomes the thinking substance.

Let us depart from the field of metaphysics and turn once more to the more matter-of-fact problems we are dealing with in this book; after all in everyday life we are sometimes involved in concentrated thinking as our examples have shown. But in everyday language nobody speaks in terms of 'I as a substance' or of the 'Being'. Is it not possible then to speak of thinking in day-to-day terms in contrast to the great philosophers? Does our common speech not reflect topics which are clearly related to thinking?

'Can one think without speaking? And what is thinking? Don't you ever think? Can't you observe yourself and see what is happening? This ought to be simple. You don't have to wait as for an astronomical event where you may have to make observations in a hurry.'

This challenge, short and to the point, is what another philosopher, Ludwig Wittgenstein, gives as an answer to the question 'what is thinking?' Is thinking really so remarkably simple that we only have to observe ourselves? The simplicity of Wittgenstein's remark is even more startling when one considers that the author of the precise *Tractus Logico— Philosophicus* (1921), of the meditating *Philosophical Investigations* (1953) and the notable *Remarks on the Foundations of Mathematics* (1956) belongs to the most careful, passionate and probing thinkers of the first half of our century.

Lugwig Wittgenstein, who was born in 1889 in Vienna and died in 1951 in Cambridge, will surprise us quite frequently in this book with his clear and startlingly simple thoughts which are mostly collected in brilliant aphorisms. Among the philosophers inspired by his theory that one should first observe thinking in a simple manner and then reflect upon it is Gilbert Ryle. (It is specifically the school of philosophy within the English speaking communities that has been strongly influenced by Wittgenstein.) In an essay entitled *Thinking* (1953) Ryle argued in a manner seemingly quite unusual for a philosopher:

'Men breathe, and grow arthritic however little or much they know about respiration, digestion and arthritis. But people do not play cricket without knowing a lot about cricket—and this is not because they first find themselves playing cricket and then start investigating what they are doing. To play cricket is to do a variety of things all of which one has to learn to do. Cricket is a complex of knacks and techniques, or of drills and skills. It is a truism that a man cannot play cricket who does not know how to play cricket, and what he knows is all that cricketing consists of. There are no hidden ingredients of cricket, though there are all sorts of inevitable and fortuitous concomitants of playing cricket, like panting and perspiring.'

The fact that venerated philosophers should be concerned with ball-games is perhaps not quite so unusual in England. But what connection is there between ball-games, which are apparently so insignificant, and thought, which is so momentous? Let Ryle explain in his own words:

'The word "thinking" covers a wide

Gilbert Ryle compares thinking with cricket: 'multiplying, translating and theorising, like cricket, have to be learnt and practised; people have to acquire a liking for doing them, and to attend to what they are doing when doing them. To be able to do them is to know what they consist of.'

variety of things, some, but not all of which embody, in differing degrees and respects, such things as drills, acquired knacks, techniques and flairs. It is just in so far as they do embody such things that we can describe someone's thinking as careless or careful, strenuous or lazy, rigorous or loose, efficient or inefficient, wooden or elastic, successful or unsuccessful. Epithets like these belong to the vocabularies of coaches and umpires, and are inapplicable to such natural processes as digesting. We cannot be clever or

stupid at digesting, nor yet conservative or independent.'

The careful pinpointing of the diversity of our thinking about games is not so farfetched as it appears at first. We shall see furthermore that the imagery connected with *games* has become a very effective means of describing aspects of human activity. But let us remember: our thinking, although it is a natural yet unusually manysided activity of man, differs markedly from other activities like breathing, walking, eating, digesting etc.

Many philosophers and psychologists, to this very day, seem to have had the idea of constructing a thought model, to dream up a mechanism which would explain our thinking in a similar way to that of digesting or breathing. This dream has so far not come true and many people will surely be pleased about this.

Is the image of the thought-game of any further use to us? Do we let 'thought-players' act, 'thought-trainers' look after 'mental gymnastics' and finally do we let 'thought-umpires' look after observing the 'rule of the thought-game'? One could object that in the end thinking is more than just a clever game. Something does occur in our brains. A process takes place, a subtle mechanism, which throughout may perhaps be comparable to, but infinitely more complicated than, digestion. This must be a natural process, a thought process. Ryle comments:

'Notice that I am not saying that stretches of thinking and games of cricket are not processes. Of course they are. Nor am I saying that thinking and cricketing are unnatural, in any frightening sense of the word. It is quite natural for people to multiply, translate, and theorise, just as it is quite natural for them to play cricket. All that I am saying is, that people, like dogs and lizards, can digest without knowing anything about digestion; they can digest whether awake or asleep, infantile or adult, lunatic or sane; but multiplying, translating and theorising, like cricket, have to be learnt, and practised; people have to acquire a liking for doing them, and to attend to what they are doing when doing them. To be able to do them is to know what they consist of. Notice, too, that not all the things we class as thinking are subject to the epithets of coaches or umpires.'

Thinking, in Ryle's sense taken as a thought-game, is closely linked with another human activity, speaking. When people exchange thoughts they use language as the most useful means. Realizing this, Wittgenstein named primitive languages 'language-games'. By this he wanted to convey that language, like thinking, possesses a 'gamelike character'. This image leads to quite useful results. In his *Philosophical Investigations* Wittgenstein wrote: 'Here the term "language-game" is meant to bring into prominence the fact that the *speaking* of language is part of an activity, or of a form of life.'

In contrast with most philosophers, Wittgenstein does not consider language as an etherial structure, an ivory tower which, divorced from speaking man, floats somewhere in esoteric clouds. It is simply part of an activity which enables us to observe things. A market woman who chats with her customers uses a different language from the officer who commands his soldiers. A teacher speaks to his pupils in a different way from two mathematicians discussing algebraic problems. Politicians, footballers, waitresses, lawyers, nursemaids, journalists, etc., they all use a different type of language. Wittgenstein wrote:

'Review the multiplicity of language-games in the following examples, and in others:
Giving orders, and obeying them—
Describing the appearance of an object,

or giving its measurements—
Constructing an object from a description (or drawing)—
Reporting an event—
Forming and testing a hypothesis—
Presenting the results of an experiment in tables and diagrams—
Making up a story and reading it—
Playacting—
Singing rounds—
Solving riddles—
Making a joke; telling it—
Solving a problem in practical arithmetic—
Translating from one language into another—
Asking, thanking, cursing, greeting, praying.
It is interesting to compare the multiplicity of tools in language and of the ways they are used, the multiplicity of kinds of word and sentence, with what logicians have said about the structure of language.'

Many philosophers, before Wittgenstein wrote his *Investigations*, and indeed Wittgenstein himself in his *Tractatus Logico-Philosophicus*, tried to condense this immensely complex landscape of language into a single image of supposedly general validity. They often spoke of *ideas,* or *concepts, mental images, meanings,* of *consciousness,* of *truth* and of *falsehood.* These *esoteric subjects* were and still are bandied about, particularly in logic.

Such expressions form the component parts of a language which is not spoken every day. This is the language of *Metaphysics,* an artificial jargon, which speaks of an abstract, ideal landscape, the way to which was paved by Descartes' *Meditations.* Wittgenstein, who saw the purpose of philosophy as 'a battle against the bewitchment of our intelligence by means of language' admitted, however: 'What *we* do is to bring words back from their metaphysical to their everyday use'.

It is important in the light of this statement to note that Wittgenstein spoke of the 'use' of words and not, as is usual of their 'meaning'. After all we use the phraseology of language to make ourselves understood. Why should we merely consider language as a formulation of our thinking? Why are the tools of sound structures and written symbols nothing but materializations, the end-products, which make audible or visible what takes place in ethereal regions? Are linguistic expressions nothing but chance images, some more successful than others, of something abstract and incomprehensible to our senses?

We might consider the language-game, which our senses can perceive, as the direct means of thinking, or, in the words of Wittgenstein, as the 'vehicle of thinking'. This is just as valid a picture of language and of thinking as the many metaphysical images. Wittgenstein found that: 'When I think in language, there aren't "meanings" going through my mind in addition to the verbal expressions; the language is itself the vehicle of thinking.'

Anybody who is not yet philosophically 'loaded', or to use a more forcible expression 'indoctrinated', will probably not find this statement particularly unusual. But the person who is already more or less strongly involved with philosophy will at least raise his eyebrows, and then frequently bandy about metaphysical expressions, speak of *conceptions,* of *con-*

sciousness, eidos, logos, etc. But this is just the 'bewitching of our intelligence by means of language' that Wittgenstein referred to.

Consequently in his *Investigations* he used a language which comes very near to our everyday language; a language which is not usually spoken by his colleagues. His terminology is not that of metaphysics. Wittgenstein's thoughts will fully occupy us in this book; his goal was sincerity.

'I should not like to spare other people the trouble of thinking. But, if possible, to stimulate someone to thoughts of his own.'

His goal shall also be ours. And if some reader, in his deliberations, arrives at quite different conclusions so much the better.

1.2 Words from the tool-box
On the functioning of language

Wittgenstein's misgivings were about the *meanings* of verbal expressions. Before elucidating his ideas, we will briefly consider these abstract subjects and sketch the corresponding traditional concept of language. In doing this we shall deliberately confine ourselves to a few, rough outlines of this concept. The accusation that it is too schematic, too simple, too naive we will allow, since we believe that crucial new ideas should be simple. (This is particularly so in scholarship.) Even in Mathematics, the most exact of all exact sciences, this point of view has proved to be most appropriate. We shall come across this idea of purposeful simplicity over and over again.

To begin with, let us look up one of the standard philosophical dictionaries and read what it says under the keyword *meaning*: 'Word and concept are not the same. A word is a sound-complex or a written symbol for something super-sensory. This super-sensoryness is the meaning of the word and makes the word the representation of a concept'. In this sense meaning is interpreted as something super-sensory, as an ethereal structure in an ideal land. The verbal expression, the word, is the name for this structure. Each word is the name for a concept. From this point of view, language, works only in one sense: by means of words it names objects whether they be tangible to our senses or abstract.

We could imagine, in this connection, an ideal language which exists independently of speaking man. The fact that man would have to use a language to describe such a language is practically beside the point. Every word denotes something quite specific, possesses a definite meaning irrespective of whether it is pronounced or not. All these words are linked to form sentences or at least can be combined to form sentences. Thus, sentences form relations between more or less distinct terms which refer to concepts. In a certain philosophical work we find: 'The concept is an image of definite, clear

In his *Philosophical Investigations* Ludwig Wittgenstein tries to outline an image of the language for 'the multiplicity of the tools in language and of the ways they are used, and the multiplicity of kinds of word and sentence'. This is the theory of 'language-games'.

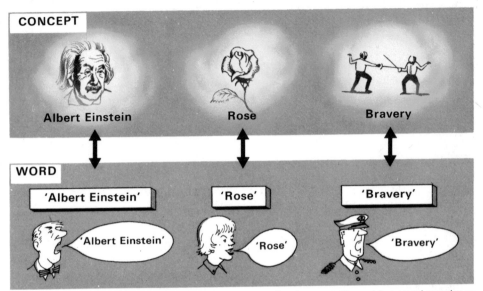

CONCEPT

Albert Einstein   Rose   Bravery

WORD

'Albert Einstein'   'Rose'   'Bravery'

'Albert Einstein'   'Rose'   'Bravery'

In classical philosophy one usually distinguishes between word and concept: 'A word is a sound-complex or a written symbol for something super-sensory. This super-sensoryness is the meaning of the word and renders the word the representation of a concept.'

unchanging, jointly established meaning'. This statement raises many questions. Everybody can, for himself, think about it: What, for instance is an unchanging meaning? How can a meaning be jointly established? Unfortunately this is formulated in such a vague and anaemic manner that it is best to forget this woolly sentence as quickly as possible.

But the obvious question does arise. Must this concept of language, containing the golden rule 'meaning → word → sentence', unquestioningly be accepted as gospel truth? It certainly cannot be said that this picture is completely false! It is true that it is still valid in certain, very primitive verbal situations. Yet it does not hold good for the whole language. It does not apply in the description of an object, nor in the telling of a joke, nor for translating, nor in the recording of pro-

ceedings, nor in swearing, etc. But Wittgenstein did find an example in classical philosophy where this picture of language could be applied. At the beginning of his *Investigations* he quoted the *Confessions of St Augustine* who lived from 354 to 430 AD. St Augustine, the most important elder of the Catholic Church, elucidated here a very simple verbal situation.

'When they (my elders) named some object, and accordingly moved towards something, I saw this and I grasped that the thing was called by the sound they uttered when they meant to point it out. Their intention was shown by their bodily movements, which is the natural language of all peoples; the expression of the face, the play of the eyes, the movement of other parts of the body, and the tone of voice which expresses our state of mind

29

in seeking, having, rejecting or avoiding something. Thus, as I heard words repeatedly used in their proper places in various sentences, I gradually learnt to understand what objects they signified; and after I had trained my mouth to form these signs I used them to express my own desires.'

Everybody, who has already been in a foreign country, the language of which he either hardly speaks or not at all, will be familiar with this way of communicating. A German tradesman might point to a fruit which we know as 'apple' and call it 'Apfel', his French counterpart says 'pomme' and the Spaniard 'manzana' etc. But in equally straightforward language games we find this relation 'word → meaning' no longer so simple. This prompted Wittgenstein to remark in connection with this example from the *Confessions*:

'These words, it seems to me, give us a particular picture of the essence of human language. It is this: the individual words in a language name objects—sentences are combinations of such names. In this picture of language we find the roots of the following idea: Every word has a meaning. This meaning is correlated with the word. It is the object for which the word stands.'

We have already become acquainted with the general facts of the traditional theory of images of languages. Further Wittgenstein observes:

'Augustine does not speak of there being a difference between kinds of words. If you describe the learning of language in this way you are, I believe, thinking primarily of nouns like "table", "chair", "bread" and of people's names, and only secondarily of the names of certain actions and properties; and of the remaining kinds of word as something that will take care of itself.'

But it is just such names for actions and properties of which there is an abundance in our every-day language. Also, language is connected mostly with a variety of actions. Thus, the understanding of the sentence 'make me some coffee' shows itself only in the execution of the corresponding action. The description of this language-game can be completely achieved without the need to speak of the 'meaning' of words. The important thing here is only how the words are being used. The person spoken to has to act and if he acts correctly, that is if he does make coffee and does not, instead, switch on the television-set, then he has understood the sentence. 'The explanations come to an end somewhere' wrote Wittgenstein and another Viennese philosopher Moritz Schlick, strongly influenced by him, takes this idea even further:

'It can easily be understood that the work of the philosopher lies not in the formation of sentences and also that the interpretation of sentences cannot in turn be given by other sentences. Because if I were perhaps to give the meaning of my words by explanations and definitions (that is with the help of new words), you would have to ask me for the meaning of these other words, and so we would go on and on. This process cannot continue ad infinitum; it is only sure to come to an end in an actual physical demonstration. This alone does not render further explanation possible nor does it require it. It is through demonstration then that the ultimate philosophical means of explanation is to be found; this forms the philosophical activity.'

Wittgenstein considered then as superfluous the use of 'meanings' which lie behind every verbal expression. 'The philosophical concept of meaning has its place in a primitive idea of the way language functions. But one can also say that it is the idea of a language more primitive than ours.' The classical image of language is thus not entirely wrong but, continues Wittgenstein:

'Augustine, we might say, does describe a system of communication; only not everything that we call language is this system. And one has to say this in many cases where the question arises "Is this an appropriate description or not?" The answer is: "Yes, it is appropriate, but only for this narrowly circumscribed region, not for the whole of what you were claiming to describe."'

If a generalization is taken too far—this is mostly done in the interest of achieving a general truth—then it can happen that the notion of the meaning of words 'surrounds the working of language with a haze which makes clear vision impossible'. Similarities in descriptions of the use of words, Wittgenstein thought, must not mislead one into haphazard generalizations. The technique of generalization presupposes considerable caution and is always associated with great risks.

'Assimilating the descriptions of the uses of words in this way cannot make the uses themselves any more like one another.'

The rich storehouse of words, which somehow or other have similar effects when we hear or see them, shows up in use: Words used in language-games are in most cases entirely dissimilar. Now and then they operate as differently as do a drill and a spirit level out of the same tool-kit. If we observe things closely we can establish that in their functions words resemble tools, each completely different from the next. (Although now and then there are similarities.)

'Of course the thing which confuses us is

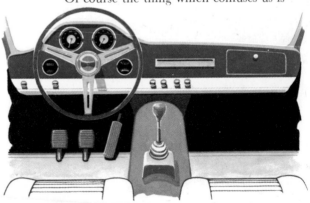

The dash-board of a motor car carries knobs which are similar to the point of confusion. And yet they can trigger off the most diverse actions; windscreen wipers, lighting, heating, cigarette lighter, etc. can be put into operation by a simple pressure on the corresponding knob.

1. The 'vehicle' of thinking

In his *Philosophical Investigations* Ludwig Wittgenstein quotes a simple system of communication which Augustine describes in his *Confessions*. The question of the usefulness of this description is discussed in detail by Wittgenstein.

their apparent indistinguishability when they are presented to us in speech or in writing and in print. For their application is not quite so clear to us; especially not when we philosophize.

'It is like looking at the footplate of a locomotive. We see handles all looking more or less alike. (Naturally since they are all supposed to be handled.) But one is the handle of a crank which can be moved continuously (it regulates the opening of a valve); another is the handle of a switch, which has only two effective positions, it is either off or on; the third is the handle of a brake-lever, the harder one pulls on it the harder it brakes; a fourth, the handle of a pump, it has an effect only so long as it is moved to and fro.

'When we say: "Every word in language signifies something" we have so far said *nothing whatever*; ...

'Imagine someone's saying "*All* tools serve to modify something. Thus the hammer modifies the position of the nail, the saw the shape of the board, and so on."—

'And what is modified by the rule, the glue-pot, the nails?—"Our knowledge of a thing's length, the temperature of the

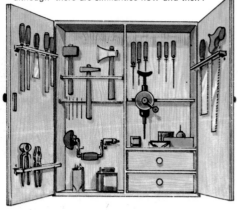

Ludwig Wittgenstein compared the functioning of the words of our everyday language with that of objects from a tool box. They can be completely different although 'there are similarities now and then'.

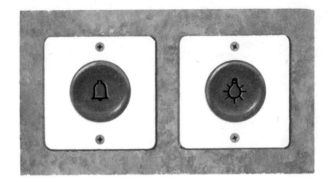

One often finds press buttons fixed to the walls of corridors in blocks of flats which are confusingly similar to one another. The frequently quoted 'press the button' causes the ringing of a bell in one case, and switches on the light in the other. Similar knobs can operate the electric door-opener, the lift, or call the porter.

glue, and the solidity of the box". Would anything be gained by this assimilation of expressions?'

Hardly, because in fact the question has been phrased in an unsuitable way; and good answers can just not be given to bad questions. This is true in everyday life just as in more learned fields. The verbal expression in this example unfortunately only becomes assimilated, becomes an approximation. Simply to assimilate descriptions of the use of words unfortunately

does not lead us any further. 'An inappropriate expression is a sure way of becoming bogged down in confusion', Wittgenstein warns, 'and so bars any escape from this'.

The inappropriate expression is just an approximation, it creates the illusion of an apparent uniformity where in fact real differences exist. If we say: Nails can also be hammered in with a glue-pot (if necessary) then we shall approach a general definition of the tool-concept in a most unsatisfactory and forced kind of

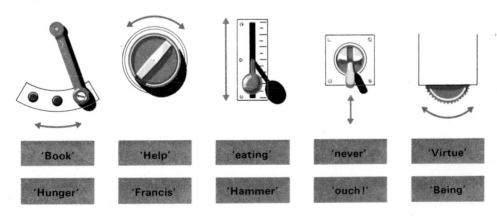

'Book'   'Help'   'eating'   'never'   'Virtue'

'Hunger'   'Francis'   'Hammer'   'ouch!'   'Being'

In the uniformity of their appearance words are like knobs which also look more or less alike. If however words are used in the language-game they function as differently as the knobs where one, say, switches on a tv set, the other turns on a gaslight, another reduces the speed of an electric motor, turns on a water tap, etc.

way. The absurdity of this is much more obvious in the case of the corresponding verbal problem.

We have just spoken of the tool-concept. According to our discussions we should not really do this. Wittgenstein was right when he said: '"Concept" is a vague term. "Concept" is something like an image which is used to compare objects.'

Roughly speaking, many philosophers in the classical tradition were and are of the opinion that the concept is a mental representation and has a meaning. This above all sounds very simple in principle, but is not easily digested when read in textbooks and is ultimately far too simple to allow one to draw conclusions about thinking and language. Similarly this applies to the following statement made by a modern philosopher, who uses these linguistic components: 'The most general definition of thinking is: a movement of mental representations and concepts'. With such definitions one can do very little as we have seen. They merely serve to bewitch our minds.

1.3 Language as 'vehicle of thinking'
Relations between thinking and speaking

Our object was to consider the territory of thinking and language. We have already learnt something about language, which makes us sit down and think. According to Wittgenstein 'One cannot guess how a word operates; one has to look how it is used and learn from this'. But what about language as the 'vehicle of thinking'? Up to now we have mainly tried to confirm Wittgenstein's assertion: 'When I think in language, there are no "meanings" going through my mind in addition to the verbal expression'.

We have, however, barely spoken of the actual activity of thinking or of the process of thinking. Now that we have gained some insight into the way a language works we shall again turn towards thinking. For this the landscape of language is particularly well suited because we can see it relatively clearly and all we need to do is to watch it closely. If we watch ourselves while we think we have to remember not to probe for the 'meaning' of the word 'think'. Wittgenstein, by making a comparison between a chess-game and a language-game, explained: 'It would be as if without knowing how to play chess, I were to try and make out what the word "to mate" means from the close observation of the last move in a game'. A person does not need to understand chess to realize that this method leads nowhere. What then is the most suitable image to represent a link between thinking and language? Wittgenstein began his reflections with the negative example:

'Misleading parallel: The cry is an expression of pain—the sentence is an expression of thought. As if it were the purpose of the sentence to let one person know how the other one feels, but only mentally and not physically so to speak.'

This is, of course, again a brilliant

innuendo directed against the 'meaning-ful' sentence, and the linking of words. Wittgenstein exhibits here a certain amount of spitefulness although up till now he wrote in a rather witty and lively manner which makes his writing a pleasure to read. What is so interesting about Wittgenstein's observations are the seemingly leading questions, the analyses of day-to-day situations. And he made no exception concerning his own explanations on the theme 'thinking'.

'Suppose we think while we talk or write—I mean, as we normally do—we shall not generally say that we think quicker than we speak: the thought seems not to be *separate* from the expression.'

That is all very well, we could say, as long as we don't have to think it out. The situation which Wittgenstein described here is more or less an automatic side-by-side of thought and word as happens in the case of the kind of chat which may be inconsequential but not necessarily thoughtless, or the exchange of polite nothings, or perhaps childish patter; just like a clockwork running down.

Wittgenstein continues:

'On the other hand one does speak of the speed of thought; of how a thought goes through one's head like lightning; how problems become clear to us in a flash and so on. So it is natural to ask if the same thing happens in lightning—like thought—only extremely accelerated—as when we talk and "think while we talk". So that in the first case the clock-work runs down all at once, whereas in the second case it runs down only gradually as if it were slowed down by the words.'

Wittgenstein often answered in this way—with questions. Thus he unmasked images or models which are hidden by day-to-day formulations and which control our thinking without being noticed themselves. Is thinking in his image then 'a kind of speaking'?

'I would like to say that it is what distinguishes speaking with thinking from speaking without thinking—it thus appears to accompany something else or can go on by itself.'

As an illustration of this thought Wittgenstein referred to a situation in which he often found himself when writing. His pen would not write. And this is what he thought:

'Say the following line: "No doubt, the pen is blunt. Oh, I suppose, it will do." First say it with thinking then without thinking then think it only without the words.—Well, in the course of writing I could test the tip of my nib, make a face, —and then with a gesture of resignation, continue with writing.—Whilst making some kinds of measurements, I could also behave in such a way that any one watching me would say I had thought (not using any words): If two quantities are equal to a third, they are equal to one another.—But what constitutes thinking here is not a process which has to accompany the words, if they are not to be uttered thoughtlessly.'

The following rider will be helpful: 'Imagine people who could only think aloud (as there are people who can only read aloud).'

But how do we recognize the difference between the two types of speaking? What is thoughtless speaking? The difference is simpler than one might assume. 'Thoughtless and not thoughtless speaking should be compared with thoughtless and not thoughtless playing of a piece of music.' The whistling of a pop-song will be just as good an example for comparison as the rendering of a Beethoven piano sonata. This picture helps to explain another situation: '"Only someone who is convinced of it can say that."—How does the conviction help him when he says it?—Is it somewhere at hand by the side of the spoken expression? (Or is it masked by it, as a soft sound by a loud one, so that it can, as it were, no longer be heard when one expresses it aloud?)'

This image could also explain the situation of someone saying things which are quite different from what he is thinking. One speaks but 'keeps one's thoughts to oneself'.

One also says that one is looking for a suitable expression in order to formulate a thought clearly and unambiguously. 'Did I make myself clearly understood?' many people would ask; or: 'You know what I mean?' Sometimes they would even have to admit: 'I simply can't find words for it.' How does the instrument of thinking, the language, operate? Wittgenstein explains:

'What happens when we endeavour—say when writing a letter—to find the right expression for our thoughts? This phrase compares the process with a translation or description: the thoughts are there (perhaps were there for some time) and we merely look for their expression. This picture is more or less appropriate for different cases. But can't all sorts of things happen here? I surrender to a mood and the expression comes. Or: I see a picture before my eyes and I try to describe it. Or a German expression came into my head and I am trying to think of the corresponding English one. Or: I make a gesture and ask myself: "What words correspond to this gesture?" And so on.

'Now if one were to ask: "Do you have the thought before finding the expression?" what would one have to reply? And what to the question: "What did the thought consist of as it existed before the expression?"

'This case is similar to the one in which someone imagines that, with the peculiar word order of German or Latin, one could not simply think a sentence as it stands. One would first have to think it out and then bring the words into this strange order. (A French politician wrote once that it was a characteristic of the French language that the words occur in the order in which one thinks them.)'

Such thoughts must seem strange to anyone who is not willing to follow the previously mentioned statement by Wittgenstein: 'One cannot guess how a word functions. One has to look at its use and learn from that.' There are considerable prejudices which one has to overcome. 'But the difficulty is to remove the prejudice which stands in the way of this learning. It is in fact no silly prejudice.' That it is in fact no silly prejudice is explained by the American linguist Benjamin L. Whorf (1897–1941) in his investigation *Language, Mind and Reality* in which he took a stand against the 'misconception of the independence of language from thinking':

Ludwig Wittgenstein's image of thinking and speaking could be called a 'chess-game theory' of language. To Wittgenstein the naming is only a 'preparation to the use of a word'. He explains this in his *Philosophical Investigations* by means of a simple situation.

'Every normal person in the world, past infancy in years, can and does talk. By virtue of that fact, every person—civilized or uncivilized—carries through life certain naive but deeply rooted ideas about talking and its relation to thinking. Because of their firm connection with speech habits that have become unconscious and automatic, these notions tend to be rather intolerant of opposition.'

Thus, the prejudice of which Wittgenstein spoke is by no means accidental and is not restricted to different individuals. Even linguistic habits often tempt us not to abandon images and pictures which we have become used to. This can be seen in the case of a picture referred to by Whorf:

'Talking, or the use of language, is supposed only to "express" what is essentially already formulated non-linguistically. Formulation is an independent process, called thought or thinking, and is supposed to be largely indifferent to the nature of particular languages.'

But Wittgenstein helped us to recognize this picture as being far too narrow and by no means as generally valid. Between thoughts and words, between ideal, ethereal structures on the one hand, and material objects which we can feel, hear or see on the other hand, there is more than just the rigid relation between pictures. The picture of language and thinking is not only more complex but it is also far more complicated. Was then the French politician right in saying that in his mother tongue words stand in the order in which they are thought? If this applies to French why not also to English, German, Russian, Chinese? Wittgenstein hit the nail on the head by asking:

'Does the beginning of a sentence, before it is even spoken, not imply that the form of the whole sentence is already in my mind? If it was in my mind then it would normally not have been there with a different order of words. But here again we arrive at a misleading picture of the use of the word "planned". The planning is embedded in the situation, in human customs and institutions. Were it not for the technique of chess I could not plan to play a game. The planning of the sentence in advance is made possible by the fact that I can speak the language in question.'

Every language, be it English, Russian or Chinese, demarcates a more or less complicated language-game which has to be learned. Perhaps Wittgenstein's central theme could be highlighted by modifying it: Were it not for the technique of the language-game I could not plan to play such a game, in other words, to speak. This he explains: 'After all one can only

say something if one has learnt to talk. Therefore in order to *want* to say something one must also have mastered a language; and yet it is clear that one can want to speak without speaking. Just as one can want to dance without dancing.'

One could refer to Wittgenstein's image of thinking and speaking as a 'theory of the chess-game'. Does not the expression 'language-game' suggest this simile? In his *Investigations* he often refers to the image of the chess-game. And in doing so he draws attention to the difference between 'naming' and 'meaning': 'Naming is something like attaching a label to a thing'. But this is in effect only 'a preparation for the use of the word'. In order to ask for the name of a thing we must know, or be able to do, something. Wittgenstein illustrates this situation with the help of chess:

'When one shows someone the king in chess and says "This is the king" one does not tell him the use of this piece— unless he already knows the rules of the game except for this one thing: what the king looks like. One could imagine that he learnt the rules of the game without ever having been shown an actual piece. The shape of the chess-piece corresponds here to the sound or form of a word.

'One could also imagine that someone has learnt the game without ever having learnt or formulated rules. Say, he could have learnt simple games, as played on a board, just by watching and then progressed to more and more complicated ones. He too might be given the explanation "this is the king"—if, for example, he were shown chess-pieces of a shape he had never seen. This explanation teaches him the use of the piece only because, as we might say, the plot on which it was placed had already been prepared. On the other hand we could also say the explanation teaches him the use only when the plot has already been prepared. And he has come so far not because he, to whom we are giving the explanation already knows the rules, but because in another sense he can master a game.

'Consider this further case: I explain to somebody how to play chess and begin by pointing to a chess-piece and say: "This is the king; it can move like this, and this..." In this case we shall say: the words "this is the king" (or "this is called the king") are only then a definition when the learner already "knows what a chessman is"; that is, if he has already played other games or has shown "understanding" when watching other people play. Only then will he be able to ask the relevant question in the course of learning the game: "What is this called?" —referring to the chessman.

'We can say: having given something a name, only the person who knows what to do with it will be able to ask significant questions.'

Summarizing we can say that Wittgenstein's *Philosophical Investigations* have shown us that language is a far more complicated landscape than is usually believed. The popular concept that we can simply 'name' physical and spiritual things and then, knowing the names, that we can talk about these objects, has been found to be misleading on closer examination. Our language works rather like a not exactly simple game of chess.

It is for this reason that Wittgenstein spoke of language-games.

Thinking, in his theory, is very closely connected with these language-games and would not be possible without them. This contradicts not only common sense and also certain philosophical ideas but agrees with modern linguistic research. We all, as Whorf found, from the wildest savage to the scholar, are relatively helpless when it comes to matters of language. Only linguistics has now begun to penetrate somewhat into this landscape. Its most remarkable discovery is that thinking is done in the language; we shall deal with this in the following chapter.

2. SPEAKING ABOUT LANGUAGES

2.1 Of 'language engineers' and 'egg-heads'
Language and precise thinking

'Were it not for the technique of chess I could not plan to play a game'. We have used this thought of Wittgenstein to elucidate his own image of language. Were it not for the technique of the language-game we could not plan to play such a game, in other words, to speak. This simple, apparently trite sentence says far more than it appears to at first. We have already learnt that language can be regarded as the 'vehicle of thinking'. But also in the writings of the linguist Benjamin L. Whorf we find quite a similar formulation of this significant fact:

'...thinking itself is in a language—in English, in Sanskrit, in Chinese. And every language is a vast pattern-system, different from others, in which are culturally ordained the forms and categories by which the personality not only communicates, but also analyses Nature, notices or neglects types of relationship and phenomena, channels his reasoning, and builds the house of his consciousness.'

We have already met this indivisibility of speaking and thinking in Wittgenstein's writings. It was pointed out how reasoning is channelled by the language. Whorf speaks of a pattern-system, of patterns in the language which determine thinking. Accordingly, our thoughts are cast into

The genius, Albert Einstein (1879–1955), has given the physics of our century a new 'dialect'.

linguistic moulds which vary from language to language.

Our thinking works like a 'trial action' in the particular language. To use the formulation of Sigmund Freud we can say that to begin with the 'trial-acting' man establishes 'stations', 'connections' and 'links' for his trains of thought in the 'railway guide' of his mother tongue. As we shall see the differences between the various 'timetables' do not have to be overemphasized; the German timetable is similar to the English one, the Russian to the Spanish etc. (see page 50).

We can again establish a pattern of similarities, similarities which can also be seen in coins minted from different dies. That language 'builds the house of our consciousness', that it has a decisive influence on our understanding is something we shall consider in some detail. Whorf's teacher and colleague Edward Sapir (1884–1939), another exponent of early American linguistics, came to the following conclusion which is perhaps not quite so unusual to us:

'Human beings do not live in the objective world alone, nor alone in the world of social activity as ordinarily understood, but they are very much at the mercy of the particular language which has become the medium of expression for their society.'

An Eskimo sees his world with different eyes as compared with the physicist Werner Heisenberg. A trained astronomer has a different relationship to the sky from a miner. This is mainly due to the different languages which they speak. Sapir continues:

'It is quite an illusion to imagine that one adjusts to reality essentially without the use of language and that language is merely an incidental means of solving specific problems of communication or reflection. The fact of the matter is that the "real world" is to a large extent unconsciously built up on the language habits of the group.'

We can also find a very decisive sentence in Wittgenstein's *Tractatus Logico-Philosophicus*: 'The limits of my language mean the limits of my world.'

Certain thoughts which are reflected in the writings of Wittgenstein, Whorf and Sapir are already indicated in the works of the German linguist Wilhelm von Humboldt (1767–1835). What Wittgenstein called language-game, by which he characterized the speaking of language as part of a way of life, is described by Humboldt as: 'Languages and life are indivisible concepts'. The following sentence points clearly to the field which Whorf describes by channelled reasoning: 'In this field learning is never anything but reproduction.'

Friedrich Nietzsche, the well-known nineteenth century philosopher, also noted some tempting thoughts in his essay *Basic Solution (Grundlösung)*: 'We cease to think if we don't wish to do it within the linguistic constraint. Rational thinking is an interpretation based on a scheme of which we cannot rid ourselves.' But hardly ever has the momentous force of the language been expressed so con-

vincingly and briefly as was done in this century by Karl Kraus the Austrian writer:

'I don't master the language but the language completely masters me. It is not the servant of my thoughts. I live in a relation with it from which I derive thoughts, and it can do with me what it likes. Because the not-yet-formed thought leaps at me from the word and by some feedback mechanism forms the language which created it.'

Another of Kraus' aphorisms is the somewhat aggressive and mocking 'negative' statement: 'Not only should one have no thoughts one must also be unable to express them'.

It pays to think about such sentences. Perhaps we will then arrive at the conclusion that to occupy ourselves with the grammar of language is not quite so unnecessary as we believed during our schooldays. Even the early linguists recognized the great importance of grammar. As Whorf says:
'It was found that the background linguistic system (in other words, the grammar) of each language is not merely a reproduction instrument for voicing ideas but rather is itself the shaper of ideas, the program and guide for the individual's mental activity, for his analysis of impressions, for his synthesis of his mental stock in trade. Formulation of ideas is not an independent process, strictly rational in the old sense, but is part of a particular grammar, and differs, from slightly to greatly, between different grammars. We dissect nature along lines laid down by our native languages. The

categories and types that we isolate from the world of phenomena we do not find there because they stare every observer in the face; on the contrary, the world is presented in a kaleidoscopic flux of impressions which has to be organized by our minds—and this means largely by the linguistic systems in our minds. We cut Nature up, organize it into concepts, and ascribe significances as we do, largely because we are parties to an agreement to organize it in this way—an agreement that holds throughout our speech community and is codified in the patterns of our language.'

However modern these ideas may seem to us they are not really. Some ancient Greek philosophers already recognized this very close link between language and thinking. In the history of philosophy they are referred to as 'presocratic philosophers'. Their writings, often only surviving as fragments, are dominated by the ambiguous classical Greek word *logos*. It often describes in an amazing manner this unity of language and thinking. In the writings of the obscure thinker Heraclitus (544–483 BC in Asia Minor), whom we shall meet again in a different context later on, the 'logos' of an all-embracing universal intellect controls the events of reality. Man also has to conform and bow down before the logos.

Thinking, reason, language: these three landscapes, which cannot be separated from one another were described within the framework of the philosophical language-game of ancient times by different shades of meaning of the word logos. The best example can be found in the writings of Aristotle (384–322 BC), the gifted pupil of Plato and the tutor of Alexander the Great. He gave the classical definition of man as a living being which possesses logos. By this is not only meant that man differs from other living creatures by his power of thought, his reasoning; it is the characteristic use of his language which makes him what he is: man.

We are quite well aware nowadays that the accent on a purely linguistic talent is no longer sufficient to distinguish man from other living creatures. It is not possible to make a clear-cut distinction in this field. Animals too have their sign language or are in communication but only man is in the position to speak about his language and to think about his thoughts; he thus becomes a 'philosophizer' in the broadest sense.

Many scholars these days consider rational philosophizing as thinking about language which is done in strict and methodical manner. The novel speculations of philosophizers like Wittgenstein and Ryle, however, no longer lead into the field of metaphysics; they observe accurately and work with common sense.

Similar thoughts about language and thinking were expressed by John Wisdom, Alfred J. Ayer and Max Black in straightforward and clear statements. As far back as the nineteen-thirties a movement set in, which made the theoretical aspects of language also interesting to philosophers. Polish logicians like K. Ajdukiewicz, S. Lesniewski or Alfred Tarski began to cut up language in unemotional, penetrating analyses.

Eventually Rudolf Carnap (b. 1891), Willard van Orman Quine (b. 1908) and Yehoshua Bar-Hillel (b. 1915) produced clear-cut insights into the mechanisms of language. Carnap may well be considered to be one of the most important philosophers of our century. His book *The Logical Syntax of Language* (Vienna, 1934; translated into English: London, 1937) is a 'classic' about modern linguistic philosophizing. Carnap and Bar-Hillel investigated the wide landscape of the language with the thoroughness of surveyors.

In philosophy and in poetry where language is used over and over again as material for language men have come up against the enormous problems which are connected with language, the top priority in human affairs. Particularly in philosophy one has to formulate sentences about sentences. One could express this more effectively: language is being talked about by means of language. But language-material is also being used in poetry. The writer Helmut Heissenbüttel says quite rightly: 'It seems to have been forgotten these days that literature does not consist of pictures, images, sense perceptions, meanings, assertions, controversial points, spiritual objects, etc. but of language and that it has nothing to do with anything but language.'

Thus, particularly in modern literature, language has often become a scalpel for language. One might refer to the adherents of this literary movement of our time in the somewhat derogatory manner as 'language engineers'. But if one of Heissenbüttel's poems contains the lines: 'And the questions are the sentences which I can't pronounce; and the thoughts are the birds which fly away and never return' then in our time such lyric has to be assessed and commented on in different ways as was done in a previous age when the poet Marie von Ebner-Eschen-

bach considered that the ingredients of a poem should be '...A little bit of sound, a little bit of harmony and song, and a complete soul'. Even before the second world war the American poet Ezra Pound suggested to his fellow poets: 'Use no superfluous word, no adjective which does not reveal something. Don't use such an expression as "dim lands of *peace*". It dulls the image. It mixes an abstraction with the concrete. It comes from the writer's not realizing that the natural object is always the *adequate* symbol.'

As mentioned already, Heissenbüttel wrote that literature consists of language and that it has nothing to do with anything but language. Poems, therefore, are also language—language in which the thinking of the poet occurs. Looked at in this way we do not need to regard poets as either versatile word painters or as thorough consolers of souls. Ezra Pound continues:

'Don't be "viewy"—leave that to the writers of pretty little philosophic essays. Don't be descriptive; remember that the painter can describe a landscape much better than you can, and that he has to know a deal more about it....Consider the way of the scientists rather than the way of an advertising agent for a new soap.'

These literary 'language engineers' among the poets and philosophers of our century have come up against big problems which are connected with the language and consequently also with thinking. A fascinating landscape is conjured up when speaking about language but this also has its dangerous paths and cul-de-sacs.

This landscape is part of the region of the pure intellect and is referred to by the Spanish philosopher Ortega y Gasset:

'The so-called "intellect" is an extraordinary ethereal power which loses itself in its own labyrinth, in the labyrinth of its own infinite possibilities. Thinking is far too easy. The intellect hardly meets any resistance in its flight. It is, therefore, important for intellectual man to grasp material objects with his hands and through knowing something about them to learn the discipline of battle. The bodies taught the intellect what to do. Without the things which one sees and touches the conceited "intellect" would be no more than madness. The body is the policeman and teacher of the intellect.'

Therefore our discussions about thinking and language will be directed primarily towards the *body of thinking* and the *body of language*. It is constructed from the material symbols of the language which are real, perceptible structures. Should it happen that one talks about language without taking such precautions then simple, comprehensible language-games dissolve into a very confusing, indistinct criss-cross of languages. An aphorism of Karl Kraus again helps to give us an idea of the entanglement this huge criss-cross of languages poses for the inquiring man: 'If I cannot make progress I have hit the language barrier. Then I withdraw with a bleeding head. And I want to go on.' This powerful, only apparently poetic image is remarkably similar to a note by the Prague poet Franz Kafka who achieved world fame with his novels *The Trial* and *The Castle*: 'Sein eigener Stirn-

The French poet Paul Valéry (1871–1945) created in *M. Teste* a key figure for the precisely thinking type of man of our time. 'All in all it is a matter of making use of what could possibly be conceived.'

knochen verlegt ihm den Weg. An seiner eigener Stirn schlägt er sich die Stirn blutig.'* How can one then be surprised to read in Wittgenstein's work:

'The results of philosophy are the uncovering of one or another piece of plain nonsense and of bumps which the understanding acquired by running its head up against the limits of language.'

Speaking about language, thinking about thinking can at times become a painful, indeed tortuous, activity for men who think profoundly and precisely. Around the turn of the century the French poet Paul Valéry created his *Monsieur*

*Translator's note: One would not do justice to this passage by translating it. In essence it means: His mind is restricted by his body. The more he fights this the more he realizes his own shortcomings.

Teste, a key figure for the precisely thinking type of man of our century. Valéry admitted that during the writing of his thoughts he 'suffered from the acute pain of precision'. In *The Extracts from the Logbook of M. Teste* Valéry wrote: 'What did I suffer most from? Perhaps being used to developing all my thinking—going to the limit within myself.' This attitude of Valéry's to thinking will certainly become clear to us from his notes: 'All in all it is a matter of making use of what could possibly be conceived.' This naturally demands certain efforts; Valéry, therefore, remarks ironically: 'Silliness is not my forte'.

Are such efforts in thinking not just exaggerations? Is it worth while for the average man to mess around with this thought-business of superclever intellectuals? This question has to be answered in the affirmative.

We have learnt from Edward Sapir that we humans also live in the world of the particular language. And people who think precisely in fact speak a language which is different from the one used day-by-day. But he who finds the language of the other person no longer quite so strange will find it easier to make contact and to understand his 'world of the particular language'.

This applies to all walks of life. There would be far fewer prejudices and misunderstandings among men of different occupations if they would only 'more often look into the workshops of others' to see their world of the particular language. After all not only politicians and economists, physicists and biologists mathematicians and engineers but also philosophers and poets all contribute towards the type of society of the coming decades. The interlinking of different subjects in the age of cybernetics will be manifold: at the moment we are only standing on its threshold. A physicist, who believes that the reasoning in the theory of cognition—a philosophic discipline—is of no importance to him, will come to the conclusion one day that he can no longer follow certain discussions within his own science, physics. He runs the danger of being isolated or ignored as happened to Johan Wolfgang Goethe, the originator of the theory of colours, who believed that in natural science one can do without the very refined tools of mathematics. A similar fate awaits the philosopher who ignores the results of modern mathematics, the poet who by-passes the discoveries of research into behaviourism etc. The *thought engineer*, the intellectual *egg-head*, belongs nowadays to our society as does the motor mechanic or the shorthand typist. But he must not be just respected and placed on a pedestal as used to be the case with the (absent-minded) professor or scholar. The reason is very simple: Men with power—in this case intellectual power—must never be isolated in a well-ordered society.

How does one recognize such an egg-head or intellectual, the man who is dedicated to precise thinking? Malicious tongues will maintain that it is by his arrogance, less prejudiced critics will say by his eccentricity. Although these are extreme opinions one does, however, hear them over and over again; but they are not typical of this type of man. The mathematician and theologian Heinrich Scholz gave a very appropriate explanation:

'There are people who think in a way which I would simply call "accurate" thinking. They are people with persistent, highly controlled intellectual habits. These people can be recognized by four characteristics:

1. They remain inexorably silent if they have nothing to say which is at least formulated in such a way that it could be tested.

2. They only make assertions about something when whatever this may be will stand up to a possible subsequent test; with the reservation, however, that some time in the distant future something could be discovered that might lead to a revaluation of their statement.

3. They distinguish precisely in what they say between that which they can prove and that which they cannot prove.

4. They object relentlessly to something being said in such a way that it cannot be tested, or if it can be tested it will not stand up to a rigorous repeat-test.'

This accurate thinking, in the way Scholz defined it, is essential in the exact sciences. People who think accurately, and therefore speak accurately, Scholz called 'intellectual characters'. Mathematicians, physicists, chemists, biologists etc., they all must possess these characteristics. No doubt, to begin with, this applies only to their immediate research work. In everyday situations we find that these relatively rigorous characteristics more or less fade away. We do not necessarily need to feel sorry about this; those who work in the exact sciences are after all *human beings* and they do not have to think precisely and do not have to progress methodically in all day-to-day situations. The consequent, inflexible application of the 'persistent, highly controlled intellectual habits' often don't make sense; they are specialized rather than universal tools. At times the egg-heads lack the feeling for the realities of others, for their 'world of the particular language'. One accuses them at times of possessing intelligence without good sense. This also shows up clearly in 'perturbed' language-games. The deficiency becomes evident in the language. A mathematician who talks to his charlady about a scientific problem in the same manner as to one of his mathematical colleagues deserves our sympathy rather than admiration. It is entirely his fault if the language-game does not function.

From our point of view it is important that this strictly disciplined, well-thought-out, accurate thinking is done *in the language* (thereby creating a world of the particular language) just as are the simple thought processes which we learnt in Wittgenstein's *Philosophical Investigations*. But, similarly, another situation exists if we recall Wittgenstein's differentiation: 'Thoughtless and not thoughtless speaking should be compared with thoughtless and not thoughtless playing of a piece of music' (see page 35). This also applies to precise thinking and speaking. It can easily be seen that much more skill is required to thoughtlessly rattle off one of Chopin's *Studies* on the piano than a simple children's song like *Baa Baa Blacksheep*. Teachers of music will, however, agree that this is not always so.

2.2 The dialect of Physicists
Linguistic relations of the exact sciences

So far our excursion through small areas of the vast landscape of thinking and speaking has perhaps succeeded in giving some impression to the interested outsider of the almost complete incomprehensibility of this field. This applies even to the learned scientist who is an expert in one particular field only. In this cybernetic age we find that the various branches of research are somehow connected with the most exciting findings about human thinking and speaking. It is hardly possible these days for the economist, for example, to have a clear idea of what goes on in research about the fundamentals of mathematics. The same of course can be said about the mathematician and his knowledge of economics literature. Such examples are numerous and this is by no means surprising. For, to all people, the language represents such a well-equipped toolbox that, whether they are ordering beer in the pub or formulating a law of physics, the required tools are available. The army lieutenant takes his vocabulary from it in the same way as does the ice-cream salesman, the lawyer or the bus conductor. Language is as indispensable to the gossip over a cup of tea as it is to a philosophical discussion, to the theatre as to the boardroom meeting. But for a scientific analysis of language this means that the psychologist must be concerned just as much as the sociologist, the biologist as the philologist, the physicist as the theologian, etc.

We have already mentioned that nowadays it is most important, even indispensible, that philosophers should interest themselves in language. As grandmaster of this craft we have already met Rudolf Carnap. We have also spoken of the exponents of the early American linguistics, B. L. Whorf and E. Sapir. Although their thoughts were useful stimuli to us, they were just stimuli. In the USA the modern science of languages, let us call it *theoretical linguistics*, has been created and worked out by other linguists like Roman Jakobson, Zellig Harris and A. Noam Chomsky. Chomsky's work on *Syntactic Structures*, written in 1957, will probably turn out to be a milestone in the development of theoretical linguistics as Carnap's *The Logical Syntax of the Language* was for theoretical philosophy (see page 43). In the words of Y. Bar-Hillel, Chomsky turned linguistics into a 'rigorous theoretical discipline which can be compared with theoretical physics or genetics'. But the developments in the field of the exact sciences have shown that the interactions between theoretical linguistics and cybernetics were far less significant than was assumed at first. This must be stated to the regret of many scientists all over the world. For this reason, in the development of our arguments in this book, we shall by-pass this fascinating new field of activity of the exact sciences. The theoretical linguistics of Harris and Chomsky did not require cybernetics, either as midwife or wet-nurse, in order to develop as a science.

For our discussion we shall first consider the interesting linguistic references in the modern natural sciences about which the mathematician and logician Paul Lorenzen writes: 'The findings of an exact science do not necessarily have to consist of numbers only but they must be freed from the inexactness of the natural language to such an extent that they can be formulated with a standard vocabulary. In brief: an exact science must not only want to, but also be able to, speak in an artificial language.' These artificial languages, which channel precise thinking, will be discussed in more detail later.

For instance in modern physics, which is surely the purest expression of the exact natural sciences, the theoretician finds it expedient to distinguish two languages, a language of observation and a theoretical language. The language in which the physicist notes his observations and descriptions of experiments is fairly similar to our every-day language; it has not yet become an artificial language.

We will not use the expression *language of observation* in such a clearly marked way as was done by R. Carnap in 1956 in his penetrating investigation of the theoretical concepts (*The Methodological Character of Theoretical Concepts*). In this work Carnap considered the entire scientific language as being made up from a language of observation L_o and a theoretical language L_t. He attempts there, as also in his other publications, to give an exact definition of the basic scientific concepts within the framework of a rigorously formalized language. According to him the theoretical language L_t contains the scientific theory T as an undefined calculus (see *Modern Mathematics*, in this series, Ch. 1). The language of observation L_o can be built up in a similar manner to L_t.

The American A. Noam Chomsky (born 1928) is the 'young father of a young science', the modern theoretical linguistics.

The meanings are clear only here; the *variables* of L_o refer to observable events. (We shall learn later of the meaning of *variables*.) Observable properties and relations are the verbs of this language.

Our reflections about the language of observation of physicists will be of a more pragmatic nature, that is they should not be directed towards the theoretically constructed language but towards the grammar of the language actually used in observations (see also page 61). On this basis we shall again remain outside the regions of theoretical linguistics and of philosophy.

This language of observation contains

numerous specialized terms like *beam balance, dynamometer, Voltmeter, Geiger counter, bubble chamber*, etc. These words describe instruments used in experiments; with these instruments one can make measurements which in turn yield numerical values. This method has been used since the days of Galileo.

Statements about properties like warm or cold, bright or dark, light or heavy can then be made plainly and unambiguously by numbers, or numbers and units, as for example 36·8 degrees Celsius, 0·1 lux, 5 Amperes etc. Thus qualitative statements have been changed into quantitative ones. Of course quantitative descriptions can also frequently be found in every-day language but in the language of observation of the physicist this process of simple mathematization is more pronounced. In addition this language contains expressions like scale reading a, position b of the pointer on the dial, reading c, result of the measurement d, etc. In this context a, b, c, d simply indicate blank spaces into which one places numbers. These place indicators are called variables (see page 129). We have already pointed out that the language of observation is not an artificial language; it merely contains some artificial components. This language is richer in mathematical expressions and numerical values; it contains mainly quantitative statements.

Let us recall what B. L. Whorf said (page 42). The world of phenomena is organized by our minds, placed in order, and is thus formed by the linguistic systems in our minds. The enormous variety of phenomena which we perceive is being observed by us as pre-fabricated, mentally categorized material. To a large extent this process is determined by the language; for the physicist by his language of observation. This means that, from the outset, the physicist sees natural phenomena in a different light compared with the man in the street. In this respect the latter will speak, think and see in everyday language.

'This fact is very significant to modern science, for it means that no individual is free to describe Nature with absolute impartiality, but is constrained to certain modes of interpretation even while he thinks himself almost free.' (B. L. Whorf).

And this is confirmed by the French mathematician and astronomer Henri Poincaré: 'All that the investigator manages to extract from a fact is the language in which it is expressed.'

Taking this to the extreme it would mean that the observation is influenced, from the outset, by the mother tongue of the physicist whether this be English, German or French. This is contradicted by the fact that in the whole world there is only one physics. After all we do not distinguish between American, Russian or Chinese physics. Or is it conceivable that the disastrous idea of a 'German physics', which was concocted during the time of the Nazis, could be right?

Fortunately, we don't have to go to such lengths. There is no doubt that physics is a typically western cultural achievement. This explains also its relations to language. The development of the natural sciences, particularly physics, is largely due to investigators who spoke Ancient Greek, Latin, Italian, English, French and German. It was only during this century that the situation changed slightly but so far without any considerable shift of ideas. There is no doubt that the men responsible for the development of the exact science physics were investigators such as Aristotle and Copernicus and particularly Galileo, Newton, Laplace, Maxwell, Einstein and Born. They all spoke and thought in Indo-European languages which sometimes are referred to by the misnomer Indo-Germanic. Especially in this connection the word Indo-Germanic gives the wrong impression. It is not altogether irrelevant that the part of the exact sciences which we nowadays call physics originated with Galileo who thought, spoke and even wrote in Italian. It was in this romance language that he founded modern physics which he called 'la nuova scienza', the new science. In his penetrating analysis of the phenomena of motion he stated: 'We develop a new science about a very old subject.'

With this guiding principle today's physics still remains Galileo's *nuova scienza*. This has always been the unspoken motto of all fundamental works in physics no matter whether they came from the pens of Isaac Newton, James Clerk Maxwell, Max Planck, Albert Einstein or Niels Bohr. These theoreticians have formed the 'Weltbild' (world picture) of physics and the dissemination of their thoughts has changed the layman's awareness of Nature and natural phenomena. The fact that in the course of time a new discovery in physics becomes less and less strange to us is due to our having become accustomed to certain formulations of the physicists. In other words we have grown accustomed to their language. Quite rightly Whorf said:

'Science has adopted new linguistic formulations of the old facts, and, now that we have become at home in the new dialect, certain traits of the old one are no longer binding upon us.'

It was mainly due to Albert Einstein that the physics of our century has been given a new dialect. His relativistic ideas of space and time are mainly refinements of the classical dialect of Isaac Newton. Einstein was by no means a revolutionary but rather a reformer who extended and re-interpreted more precisely Newton's language-game of classical physics. His theories of relativity are fundamentally no less intuitive than is Newton's physics. Whorf remarks to this:

'It is sometimes stated that Newtonian space, time, and matter are sensed by everyone intuitively, whereupon relativity is cited as showing how mathematical analysis can prove intuition wrong. The offhand answer, laying the blame upon intuition for our slowness in discovering mysteries of the Cosmos, such as relativity, is the wrong one. The right answer is: Newtonian space, time, and matter are no intuitions. They are receipts from culture and language.'

In fact Newton's ideas about space, time and matter can be formulated in a relatively simple and clear language. Anyone with common sense will find nothing wrong with them. But what about Einstein's relativistic view of Nature? It hardly appeals to the common sense of the average man 'not because Nature herself refutes it, but because it must be talked about in what amounts to a new language'. Today, however, more than half a century since Einstein conceived his ingenious theories, the A B C of this new language of physics is available to the interested layman. This is mainly due to the popular science writing of the Anglo-American world. We only need to point to the work of Bertrand Russell, James Jeans and Hermann Bondi. (The very important changes which Einstein's *special theory of relativity* brought about in the meaning of the classical mechanics of Newton and Galileo are described in detail in the book *Modern Physics* in this series.)

Let us recall the starting point of our discourse; we have said that throughout the history of physics all thinkers of significance belonged to the family of Indo-European languages. The fact that the precise linguistic references of physics do not indicate the existence of an Italian, German or English physics is due to the close grammatical link between these languages. Whorf said:

'Among these tongues there is a unanimity of major pattern which at first seem to bear out natural logic. But this unanimity exists only because these tongues are all Indo-European dialects cut to the same basic plan, being historically transmitted from what was long ago one speech community; because the modern dialects have long shared in building up a common culture.'

It is just these circumstances which help to explain the remarkable fact that the description of physics is uniform, that scientists all over the world speak a common language. Concerning the

equally important standard vocabulary of what Lorenzen called the *artificial language*, and which the exact sciences have to use, we shall discuss this later. This artificial language is also responsible, to a very great extent, for the fact that American and Russian, Indian and Chinese physicists don't misunderstand one another.

We have already referred to physicists who do not speak in an Indo-European dialect. (It should be noted that Russian scientists also speak in an Indo-European dialect; one can so easily be deceived by the cyrillic script which looks very strange to us.) There are distinguished physicists in Japan, in China, in Turkey and in the African countries. Whorf explains how they fit in; and he arrives at the explanation by simply restricting himself to the language of observation of the physicist which, as we know, is distinctly coloured by the particular mother tongue (see page 42).

'It must be emphasised that "all modern Indo-European-speaking observers" is not the same thing as "all observers". That modern Chinese or Turkish scientists describe the world in the same terms as Western scientists means, of course, only that they have taken over bodily the entire Western system of rationalizations, not that they have corroborated that system from their native posts of observation.'

Well into the nineteen-thirties physicists from all over the world have either studied in Indo-European (or western) Universities like Cambridge, Göttingen, Copenhagen, Princeton, or they had to study intensively the scientific literature written in Indo-European dialects. But this situation has considerably changed especially since the middle of this century although, as already mentioned, this was not accompanied by any shift of ideas. That such a thing could happen one day was quite probable. The Galileo or Einstein of the late twentieth century could well be an Asian or an African. Perhaps here is the chance of a theoretical renewal of science.

But let us not follow the devious routes of speculation. It is good to know that natural science owes a great deal to the human effort which is put into the experiment, as well as to the language in recording and noting experimental facts. Physics and grammar are very closely related to each other. It is not without significance that the classical scientific languages Italian, French, and German are cut to the same pattern as are the new dialects of the physicists, English and Russian. (The *new* English refers especially to the English of the American scientists. The English of Great Britain is of course a classical dialect of physics.)

Our observations refer exclusively to languages and their structures. In order to avoid misunderstandings it is necessary to take up the stupid catchword 'German physics' which we came across earlier. This term, which first appeared after the First World War and which reached its questionable climax in Germany during the Nazi regime, touches upon quite a different aspect. It was directed at racial, religious and political prejudices and was used in particular to denigrate Einstein's theory of relativity. Such racial 'leitmotifs' have never been of any use in the exact sciences; they have led to nothing but immense harm and created a lot of confusion.

A few words about German physics will, therefore, not be out of place. This embarrassing outcome of national and racial ignorance was due to the leadership of two distinguished Nobel-prize winners Philipp Lenard and Johannes Stark. Both were good experimental physicists but incapable of comprehending the brilliant theoretical high-level flights of Einstein's thoughts on relativity.

The blood-and-soil ideology which the Nazis rejoiced in preaching also penetrated into science. The laboratory bench of the 'Aryan' investigator was placed so to speak, upon German soil. One spoke of the 'Faust-like craving' of the 'nordic' scientist who pined for the knowledge of 'what makes the world go round'.

If men like 'Einstein the Jew' only sit at their desks and 'frivolously and playfully' invent their theoretical thought games, devote themselves to the disintegration of what the Aryans had built up, then they ignore the 'upright, honest, and faithful' observation of Nature, which only the nordic researcher is capable of. Close to Nature, clear and full of common sense—this is how the Aryan saw the 'true depth' of Nature in this embarrassingly naive picture. Abstract, highfaluting, 'formalistic', incomprehensible —this, on the other hand, is how 'Jews' and 'Bolsheviks' see only the surface of Nature.

With this cheap cliché of denigration German physics had a truly tremendous 'success'. Many eminent scientists of German origin who could not prove their Aryan descent, had to go into exile during those years. Einstein sought asylum in the USA. Physicists who were 'influenced by Jews' were accused of ignoring the 'nordic' concept of 'force'. The expulsion of the *ether* from physics, for which Einstein was responsible, was compared so to speak to the killing of a noble animal. An extract from an inflammatory article which appeared in the *Zeitschrift für die gesamte Naturwissenschaft* may serve as an example of a prostituted language:

'The ether was done away with. With this fell a spiritual weapon of Aryan science which in the hands of great scientists has, over the centuries, produced the richest fruits in the understanding of Nature. In fact the consequences of the abolition of the ether by Einstein and his Jewish henchmen have been taken with a frivolity and brutality which only a conqueror is capable of in the country which he has occupied.'

In those depraved days symptoms of racialism could be found even in the mathematics literature. Here too non-nordic mathematicians were censured because they abandoned 'clarity'; and 'Jewish thinking' was insulted because it 'never came from Nature or human experience'. The ignorant chatter concerning racial superiority in mathematics and physics did not exempt even distinguished experts.

By sketching the unique position of language in the modern sciences we have moved into a region which has a dangerous neighbourhood; yet it would be wrong to exclude this region from our way of thinking. The Indo-European dialects are important to the shaping of the exact sciences which has nothing whatever to do with racial or national ideas. Each crossing of the frontier in this direction should be condemned or else it could have dire consequences. To speak of a western physics is just as silly as the contemptible talk about German physics.

Let us keep this in mind: the *nuova scienza*, physics, is a cultural achievement of people who belong to the Indo-European family of languages. By this we do not mean that common basic structures, the grammars of the Indo-European dialects, have triggered off, or even produced, by themselves the modern natural sciences. They did not form a sufficient criterion for these important researches which, by way of technology, have so decisively shaped our civilization. But this unique position of the language has left its mark on modern science; it has definitely coloured it. The grammars of the Indo-European dialects have up to now shaped the thoughts of the scientists.

It was a great mistake to infer from this situation, and the undisputed dominance of modern science in our civilization, a superiority of these modern dialects (English, Russian, French, German) over other languages. Just the investigations of Whorf have shown that some languages which we consider primitive, as for example the American Indian languages, are in many situations remarkably precise and expressive and that they are often superior to the Indo-European languages. Let us illustrate this by two small examples from Whorf's writings:

'We say "see that wave"—the same

pattern as "see that house". But without the projection of language no one ever saw a single wave. We see a surface in everchanging undulating motions. Some languages cannot say "a wave"; they are closer to reality in this respect. Hopi say *walalata*, "plural waving occurs", and can call attention to one place in the waving just as we can. But, since actually a wave cannot exist by itself, the form that corresponds to our singular, *wala*, is not the equivalent of English "a wave", but means "a slosh occurs", as when a vessel of liquid is suddenly jarred.'

The physicist, who is so familiar with the mechanics of wave motion, will not be the only one to establish with amazement how precise and useful the tool of the Hopi-language is in this situation.

The second example again shows clearly the superiority of this supposedly primitive Indian dialect. Certain sentences in the Indo-European dialects are formed by connecting a substantive noun with a verb. This corresponds to the situation of somebody doing something, such as Walter eats, Mr Miller works, the sun shines, it rains. Whorf comments:

'We are constantly reading into nature fictional entities, simply because our verbs must have substantives in front of them. We have to say "It flashed" or "A light flashed", setting up an actor, "it" or "light", to perform what we call an action, "to flash". Yet the flashing and the light are one and the same! The Hopi language reports the flash with a simple verb, *rehpi*: flash (occurred)". There is no division into subject and predicate...Hopi can and does have verbs without subjects, a fact which may give that tongue potentialities...as a logical system for understanding some aspects of the universe.'

All our knowledge, not only the scientific one, depends on such linguistic points of view, which today are largely still unknown. It would, therefore, pay our scholars to investigate intensively this manysided tool *language*. The understanding of this dependence should, according to Whorf, 'foster that humility which accompanies the true scientific spirit, and thus forbid that arrogance of the mind which hinders real scientific curiosity and detachment.'

3. 'SUPERFLUOUS' SUPERFLUOUSNESS IN LANGUAGES

3.1 Should one count words?
First thoughts about an 'information theory'

Up to now our path has led from thinking to the language in which thinking takes place. No doubt it was only one of many which traverse this immensely rich landscape. There are many twisted, dark lanes but also straight roads and these are usually the ones which are preferred by the casual tourist. It is not easy here to choose a golden mean, that is to point out what is worth knowing, not to get lost in details which are of interest only to the specialist, and also not to run past certain regions in this over-hurried excursion. One thing is important: thinking and speaking are such important human activities that it is certainly worth-while to rack one's brain a little about them—if only because they appear so obvious to us.

Let us emphasize once more: the goal of our journey is cybernetic machines, 'machines that think'. In this sense cybernetics is to be regarded as the mathematization of information and its technical realization. For obvious reasons, however, we have moved earlier on from the field of thinking into the field of language. Yet it was not considered advisable to proceed through the most precise field in this context, theoretical linguistics (see page 48). This is perhaps worthy of further consideration elsewhere.

No doubt there are readers who have read Goethe with respect and know that he once said: 'My child, I have been wise, I have never thought about thinking.' Many people will certainly agree with the prince of poets, and all philosophers, poets and linguists will, at least, regret that so much valuable time has been wasted on a natural, obvious subject. Perhaps one may make just one little remark: not everybody commands the tools of thinking, and consequently those of language, so magnificently and confidently as Goethe did. Not everybody can use those tools so brilliantly in order to create *his* reality.

This applies to the poet Johann Wolfgang von Goethe who could say with clear conscience about himself: 'Ever since my childhood whenever I heard or read a verse I could continue in speech or in writing in whatever metre this verse was written. The mould was obviously in my head if only the mixture which I had to pour in had been of some use.' It is this very mould, which forms the thoughts and channels the flow of language, that matters to the poet. It is a pattern and defines a model, a structure, a system of structures, of the type which Whorf referred to (see page 41). The problem of structures is decisive in all exact sciences. We shall return to it at times; it has been discussed in detail in the book on *Modern Mathematics*.

What in the case of Goethe, who never managed to establish a proper relation to the mathematics of his time, functioned instinctively and confidently was estab-

The word 'information' appears often in texts written in everyday language. Can it also be used in this sense in 'information theory'?

lished methodically by more recent poets. Paul Valéry, whom we mentioned earlier, wrote about the French poet Stéphane Mallarmé (1842–89): 'The literature as he saw it seems to me to correspond to algebra.' But algebra is an abstract mathematical discipline which deals with structures, with structures of laws of arithmetic. And Walter Benjamin wrote about the famous poet Charles Baudelaire (1821–67): 'His poetic production goes hand-in-hand with a conscious responsibility; there seemed to him to be (cultural) vacancies into which he inserted his poems.' The close connection of this thought with the basic ideas of mathematical activity will become apparent to us later on (see page 133).

Let us once more return to Goethe whom so far we have mentioned only as a poet. Justifiably he recognized also his own importance as a scientist. Although Goethe's science is quite different from the modern exact sciences it would be more than arrogant to dismiss it as being wrong or useless. Goethe's scientific work mirrors the world of his particular language (see page 41). The impression that some physicists may have of out-of-date relics covered in dust could perhaps one day again assume great importance. Goethe was a very thorough investigator. He always admitted openly to his often considerable methodical limitations. He once wrote: 'It is not the first time in my life that I find it impossible to comprehend that which is plausible to others.' Although this is a personal confession it is nevertheless disarmingly honest. How different is the type of scientist of our time who, in the words of Paul Valéry's M. Teste, would admit: 'All in all it is a matter of making use of what could possibly be conceived' (see page 46). According to where the boundary is marked out in the landscape of thought and language we also define the region which is called reality.

Compared with Goethe many research workers nowadays think differently about thinking and language. This of course is not surprising. 'Who can take it from me that I was born in 1749?' Goethe once asked. Well, B. L. Whorf was born in 1897, L. Wittgenstein in 1889, N. Wiener in 1894, and R. Carnap in 1891, to name but a few of this important generation of scholars. These scholars handled language much more severely; they often took it inexorably at its word. They showed the way to handle language in a critical and sober manner. Even Norbert Wiener, by training a rationally thinking mathematician, had to admit that to man *speaking* was the most important thing and his most prominent achievement.

Our era is governed by the exact sciences. It is therefore not to be wondered at that, when concerned with language, many research workers nowadays ask questions which are quite different from those Goethe would have asked. But how is it possible to investigate our natural tool the language with the artificial, even technical tools of the exact sciences? Are we not running into difficulties similar to those which we indicated when discussing the subject *speaking about languages*? Let us recall in particular the poignant sentences of Kraus, Kafka and Wittgenstein.

An important characteristic of all scientific activity is the measurement. Galileo, the father of modern science, already suggested: 'Measure everything that can be measured'. But is it possible to measure everything? Although such a question is spontaneous and natural it is very vague; particularly since it has been established that in our surroundings there are many more phenomena that can be measured than one had imagined. Galileo therefore makes the encouraging remark: 'Render measurable what is not yet measurable'. Yet how can language be rendered measurable? What is this measurable something in language? The ineffectual necromancy in this question, which is formulated in colloquial language and which forces us to use the word something, shows us that such a problem does not exist in everyday language (see page 55).

Some people often pronounce weighty words or carefully weigh up what they are saying. They consider many a sentence as ponderous. Though what exactly they are supposed to be weighing or measuring they do not say. There is no doubt that no weight is attached to this problem; at least no comment of substance has been voiced in this connection. But enough of this sarcasm. Our everyday use of language contains no precise suggestion how the language could be rendered measurable. This is the special situation from which information theory, a new and most important branch of the exact sciences, has developed.

Before turning towards this new field which is defined by the words 'information theory' let us dwell a little on this special situation. Such a situation is by no means unusual in the exact sciences. Most of the new branches of research have developed from unusual, seemingly artificial questions which are foreign to everyday thought and speech. Let us recall what we said about Galileo's *nuova scienza* (see page 13). It was mainly because he asked new questions that the Italian scholar became the founder of the modern exact sciences. These questions were unusual, revolutionary even, to the life and science of his day. It was these new questions which, together with the new answers, opened up the new science of which Galileo spoke. And something similar applies to the reforms which Albert Einstein brought about in the language of physics (see page 51).

Mathematics too has progressed by constantly asking new questions. For example, in the theory of sets, an important branch of pure mathematics, one might ask the characteristic question: What *is* a set? The answers to this question, which are called definitions of sets, were altogether most unsatisfactory. But when asked in what way sets or classes could be introduced into science it became possible to give sensible answers.

And now to information theory. To begin with the following simple question seems relevant: What is information? The word comes from the Latin 'informatio' and Old French 'une information' and can have different shades of meaning. It can, for instance, convey communication or exchange of knowledge, it can convey a warning or advice or a notice or a hint, it can refer to documentation and records, intelligence and news, messages and reports, and so forth. If we were to substitute, for instance, theory of communication of knowledge, or theory of documentation, etc. for information theory we would not get very far. Even an examination of the day-to-day use of language, which is almost extravagant in the use of words like information, informative, informatory, does not get us anywhere. The many shades of meaning which the word information conveys indicate that language plays a major part in this context. Informations in the widest sense, must be formulated; they have to speak to us if they are to be of any use to us. Thus the main carrier of information is the language.

Our discussions about language were a good preparation for the understanding of the problems with which information theory is concerned. We are all familiar with the use of language—and speaking it is a thoroughly natural activity. But, as we have seen, the linguistic image which one normally uses is too simple. It would pay to carry out intensive linguistic research for each branch of science, but definitely for the one that carries the adjective exact.

Some way back we have briefly referred to the body of language (see page 45). It is constructed from real structures which can be perceived by our senses. This body of the language can be recognized most clearly by the carved, written or printed word. Such recorded words are the building stones of all advanced languages. The 'picture of the written word' enables us to obtain a visible and relatively permanent impression of the language. Without philosophizing too much we can say that here language materializes. Whether there is something spiritual, ethereal or metaphysical behind all this does not interest us here. Real symbols are of course very clear signals once one has become familiar with them and knows how to use them. It is for this reason that for the recording of the language writing is far more suitable than its natural sound. Spoken words pass or fade away; the audible body of language is ephemeral. On the other hand the simple experience of speaking is more gripping, more impressive, more natural than the writing and reading of a script. We shall, however, see that even the written word contains this basic experience of speaking. Language and the speaking man, and therefore language and life, are inseparable. Wilhelm von Humboldt once wrote: 'The inseparable link between thought, vocal organs and hearing on the one hand and language on the other lies irrevocably in the original and inexplicable equipment of human nature.'

And a well-known philosopher of our time, Martin Heidegger, who acknowledged Humboldt's 'profound and penetrating views on the nature of language' explained this significant relation very clearly:

'Part and parcel of speaking is the making of articulate sounds whether we accomplish them—in speech, or omit them—in silence, or are incapable of them—in dumbness. Part and parcel of speech is the making of articulate vocal sounds. Language appears in speech as the activation of vocal organs such as the mouth, the lips, the teeth, the tongue, the throat. The fact that, since the days of yore, the language is represented as being due to these activities is shown by the names which the western languages have given themselves: glossa, lingua, langue, language. The language is the tongue.'

When Heidegger says that 'the language shows itself in the speaking' then it has to be pointed out that it can be dangerous, when, in the exact sciences, language and speaking become mixed up. This danger exists even when one looks at linguistic problems exclusively in Wittgenstein's manner. For a scientific treatment Wittgenstein's ideas may be considered nowadays to be a kind of fruitful introduction. Every scientist who works systematically around this problem must go beyond Wittgenstein. (One could advise him, especially, to consult Carnap!). The reason why we went deeply into Wittgenstein's *Philosophical Investigations* is that in our discussions we are not actively engaged in doing advanced science but that we shall lead up to it. This book is not a contribution to science; it is not written for experts.

The disagreeable mix-up between language and speaking is particularly obvious in German. The two words 'Sprache' and 'sprechen' (language and speaking) sound confusingly similar to one another. Other languages show the distinction between them far better, e.g. in English (language—speech) or in French (langue—parole). This separation was clearly emphasized by A. N. Chomsky (see page 49). He distinguishes between the language as a theoretical structure and the grammar as the theory of a language. In his terminology, which he developed in association with the American psychologist George Miller, he speaks of linguistic competence on the one hand and linguistic performance on the other. This is just mentioned by the way.

These dangerous connections are particularly obvious in writing but not in such a simple way as some might have suspected. The words 'picture of the written word', which we used previously, might indicate that a close link exists between writing and picture. Although amongst the oldest known writings we find inscriptions in pictorial form, 'picture-writing', they are no longer typical today. Among the major languages the Chinese script is the only one which has remained a kind of picture-writing. This no doubt has been overemphasized by some western scholars especially by some philosophers and poets. The Chinese script is not pure picture-writing. More than eighty per cent of the Chinese signs contain elements which indicate definite sounds and pitch. We shall become better acquainted with this process, which is very widespread nowadays, when discussing letter-writing.

In addition to the sign system of the Chinese, which one cannot exclusively refer to as picture-writing, one also uses the ancient Egyptian hieroglyphic writing, no longer in use today, as a typical example. In the illustrations of both scripts one can see some signs indicating pictorial origins. We can definitely recognize the effects of certain abstracting processes; but the abstraction does not go so far as to render the root of this simple pictorialization no longer recognizable (see page 65).

In comparison with picture-writing the syllabic-writing and the letter-writing are of more practical use and more manifest in the abstraction. Naturally also this book, like all printing in the Indo-European languages, is written in letter-writing. Letter-writing is nowadays the most useful abstraction for the recording of language. It is a record of sounds,

sounds of spoken words, which are constructed from building stones called syllables. Thus *beer* is a monosyllabic word, gen-tian a two-syllable, and stone-ma-son a three-syllable word. Do these building stones of sound confer a superiority upon letter-writing?

This, in fact, is the case. It is no longer necessary to make the pictorial meaning of a word the decisive thing, to take the roundabout route via a super-linguistic structure, whose limited capability we have already discussed (see page 27f). What matters is only the sound of the spoken word about which Heidegger said: 'The speaking man and his linguistic utterances are not surrendered in favour of a metaphysical substance' (see page 26). We must never disregard this important fact; in the words of Wittgenstein: 'The speaking of language is part of an activity or of a way of life.' He consequently spoke of language-games.

If language is being spoken as part of a human activity then the building bricks of this game are the spoken words, words which are composed of syllables and syllables which are composed of natural sounds. These sounds are indicated by letters in the letter-writing.

Let us first have a look at the letters.

We are all familiar with the Latin letters which can be ordered into the alphabet: A, B, C, D, etc., or a, b, c, d, etc. We are quite familiar with the distinction between capital and small letters but in order to indicate a sound this distinction is quite unnecessary. This book could have been printed in small letters only without making it more difficult for the reader to follow. THE SAME APPLIES HAD WE USED ONLY CAPITAL LETTERS.

But let us stay with the picture of the writing that we are used to. Most of the Indo-European languages which make use of Latin letters to indicate sounds also employ additional symbols in order to denote sounds which are characteristic of a particular language. In German the symbols 'ä', 'ö', 'ü' denote certain Umlaute, in French there is 'é' and 'è', in Spanish the typical symbol 'ñ' and in Polish '†'. Lessons in classical language or geometry have made people familiar with the Greek letters α, β, γ, δ, etc. Some people may be acquainted with the Russian alphabet which uses cyrillic symbols, А, Б, В, Г, Д, etc. All these different kinds of writing are tailored to the needs of the particular language and its diverse daily usage. None of the

| LINING | HE THERE |

Symbols of Chinese writing are often composite: In addition to the picture sign there is a second one which is not pictorial but which indicates sounds. It is a 'sound component' or 'phonetic symbol'. One cannot refer to this writing as purely pictorial. The sound component by itself also has a meaning (in the first example the sign on the right means 'hamlet' and in the second 'skin'. What is important here are the pronunciations 'li' and 'pi' respectively of the two additions.

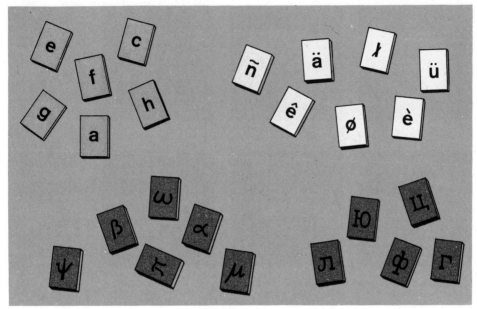

In alphabetical writing the sounds of the spoken words are indicated by letters. Most of the Indo-European languages use Latin letters but additional signs appear in the various languages (top centre). Quite apart from these, Indo-European languages also use cyrillic (bottom right) and Greek symbols (bottom left).

quoted systems is suitable for the formation of a comprehensive international phonetic alphabet which would indicate all sounds in human speech. (The reader who finds this natural situation somewhat unfortunate should re-read the second chapter of this book.) Incidentally, a linguistic society, the *Association Phonétique Internationale,* has introduced clear sound-symbols for an international phonetic writing. Some of these unusual symbols have been collected in the following illustration and have been used to form a few words from different languages. It is obvious that this phonetic writing is somewhat involved. If one considers that one has to use about eighty symbols in order to represent the linguistic sounds then one must admit that the different kinds of writing with letters (alphabetical writing), which use normally less than thirty symbols, are quite reasonable practical solutions to represent a language. Moreover, if we recall Wittgenstein's critical remarks on the meanings of linguistic expressions, the alphabetical writings gain additional points. Yet, let us carefully consider the following: We always say that the sounds are *indicated* by letters; but indicated has by no means the same meaning as represented. The real body of language, the embodiment of the sound of a word by the written symbol is not a representation in a strict

3. 'Superfluous' superfluousness in language

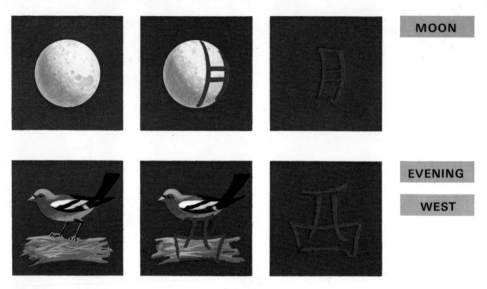

MOON

EVENING

WEST

The Chinese writing is based on the picture. Not all signs, however, can be so simply abstracted as the moon symbol or the meaning of 'evening' or 'west' (a bird descends to its nest).

An international phonetic script tries to represent the sounds of all languages with a repertoire of over eighty mostly unusual signs. When ordered these signs form an international phonetic alphabet.

mathematical sense. If it were, then clear and unequivocally reversible correspondences between the elements of sound and the written symbol would have to exist. Later on we shall return to this relation which is important to the exact sciences (see page 105). Thus alphabetical writing is a reliable, extremely practical instrument for indicating the spoken sounds of a particular language. It is useful for capturing our speech as a means of communication.

Perhaps some readers will find it out of place to regard the delicate structures of language and writing from the point of view of usefulness and expediency. It is true that this view is advantageous, even indispensible, to the methodology of the exact sciences. Every language, especially the scientific language, should be practical, not complicated and chatty, but clear and articulate. The physicist Ernst Mach (1838–1916) found that language is an altogether economical institution: 'Experience is more or less completely resolved into simpler, frequently recurring elements and, for the purposes of communication, is always symbolized by a sacrifice of precision.' Mach's expression 'economical' reiterates the point of view of usefulness which we have already explained and used.

In this way we have managed to track down one of the exact secrets which are hidden in the language. Is it then not a paradoxical situation that the consequent abstraction, which we have spoken of above, in the development of alphabetical writing should again lead to the most natural source of language, namely the activity of speaking? Or is this process of development which we have sketched out no abstraction whatsoever in the usual

Much clearer than Chinese writing, ancient Egyptian writing shows a certain pictorial relation. The process of abstraction is not taken to such lengths that the picture is no longer recognizable. The last element of the sign sequence is essentially decisive for the pictorial content.

sense of the word? It has indeed required lengthy and detailed reflections in order to highlight the limits of efficiency of the much quoted 'meaning', and that it is far more practical and comprehensive to start off directly with the language-game. A similar situation obtains with the advance towards the real, perceptible sound of a word. The physicist and philosopher Carl Friedrich von Weizsäcker gives a good answer to this: 'The reflection upon the fact that the word is not simply the thing for which it stands but, divorced from its meaning, possesses a body, a sound structure, that it is something different from what it means, this reflection may be called *abstracting* and its result may be called *abstract*.' We can therefore, state with conviction that only a bold abstraction in the development of writing has revealed again what language is all about.

This paradoxical situation mirrors one of the many secrets of language which only rigorous science could make intentionally precise and exact. But an exact science remains after all still a secret. Carl F. von Weizsäcker refers to a similar situation by the 'hardened tip of a not hardened mass'.

We shall always agree with Wilhelm von Humboldt that it is a magnificent secret 'how the thought connects with the word', that much about the language gives the impression that it is 'something special, incomprehensible, a spiritual breath of life'. An exact science must not, however, stop here; it certainly must not cultivate this reverence for the language. Linguists of our century, particularly if they use mathematical tools, are not lonely, great prophets who uncover, or

perhaps disguise even more, the nature of language with penetrating and mysterious views. They show interest principally for the structure and the capability of language as a tool.

Let us recall what Galileo said: 'Render measurable that which is not yet measurable' (see page 59). In the alphabetical writing it is quite natural to count the words, syllables and letters of a text. The sentence 'Peter is thirsty' is made up of three words, five syllables and fourteen letters. Most readers will have a rough idea of the complicated physiological situation in Peter's body which this short sentence expresses. It is surprising how few building stones of colloquial language suffice in this case to give such an important information.

What delightful and important results can be obtained by simply counting, arranging and comparing the building stones of the language! Let us consider a few examples. We begin with the most natural building stone, the word. What use is it to us to count the words of a text? The following thought is attributed to a very wise rabbi, a scholar of the Jewish religion: Every invention in modern technology teaches us something. From the invention of the telegraph for example we can learn that each word which we pronounce is being counted.—One can certainly meditate deeply and for a long time about this very profound statement. But let us consider only the surface of the statement. When sending a telegram it is important to count every word. The reason for this is quite simple; the more words one uses the more expensive is the telegram.

We now consider another example,

simple but instructive. Little Johnny who lives in Manchester is going to celebrate his tenth birthday next Thursday. He invited his grandmother to visit him on this day. As she lives far away from Manchester, in the neighbourhood of Glasgow, he wrote her a short letter on Sunday and posted it that evening. The letter arrived on Tuesday afternoon. Naturally the grandmother is very pleased about the invitation from her grandson. But how does she react to it? First of all she has to let Johnny know that she will be coming and when she will arrive. Since Grandmother does not own a fast sports car, and in any case does not drive, the problem arises what means of transport she should use. Most grandmothers don't like to fly, so she decides to go by train. She does not wish to take a night train, particularly since she read Agatha Christie's *Murder on the Orient Express*. Therefore, she decides to take a morning train to Manchester on the following day, Wednesday. Naturally she would like to be met at the station in Manchester; after all she knows that her son-in-law, Johnny's father, drives a comfortable large car. Of course she does not know anything about the parking difficulties in the centre of Manchester. Her first thought is to write a letter:

'My dearest Johnny, you can't imagine how pleased I was to receive your invitation. At last I shall be able to see you again and your dear mother and father. How are you all? I am sure, dear boy, that you have grown quite a bit again. So we are going to celebrate your tenth birthday. I shall arrive at the station in Manchester at half past six on Wednes-

day evening, on the same train that I took last year. Will you all come to meet me at the station with your nice car? I am sure it is going to be a marvellous birthday party on Thursday. All my love to you and best regards to your mother and father. In haste, your Granny.'

Whilst Grandmother wrote this letter in haste a few thoughts occurred to her. Will the letter arrive in time? A telegram would certainly be safer. But then Grandmother would have to pay for each word in the text. She has expressed her pleasure about the invitation and given the information about her arrival in Manchester in 125 words. To send this as a telegram would be terribly expensive, certainly so for an ordinary grandmother. Hence the text of her letter has to be shortened considerably so that the really necessary information to Johnny shall be sent with the minimum amount of words.

There is no doubt that Grandmother drew freely from lavish resources. She did something which always happens in the colloquial language-game and this is to formulate personally, to commit to paper the natural superfluousness of the colloquial language. Nobody will hold this against her. In the daily use of language the superfluousness of colloquial language is a good and natural thing. After all there is nothing that tells us more about man than the language he speaks. We know already that thinking is being done in terms of language; and the whole richness of human thinking is reflected in the various ways in which men speak. Out of purely financial, or generally speaking economic considerations it is understandable that people

67

would not telegraph in the same way as they would speak or write. Every superfluous word represents wasted money. It is for this reason that in every civilized society a telegraphic style has evolved, a concise manner of expression, which is by no means beautiful but is certainly very practical, in other words very economic.

Seen from the economic point of view the situation appears as follows: the many superfluous words in Grandmother's letter stem from the natural abundance of the everyday language, its lengthiness or, as the scientist calls it, its redundancy. Looking at her lengthy letter we can say that the redundancy in Grandmother's language is very high. Her highly redundant way of expression embroiders the simple information which she wishes to transmit to Johnny with expensive and thus superfluous adjunct. In fact the very same information has been repeated several times, e.g. ... I shall arrive at the station..., or meet me at the station... etc.

People who are talkative mostly talk redundantly; they are loquacious. Who has not come across someone among his acquaintances who would not begin a story in the following way: 'I hope you won't mind if I make so bold as to give you my own honest and considered opinion...' or 'I am sure you won't mind if, for once, I speak straight from the shoulder...'.

So far no information has come forth and yet at times it is great fun to listen to such tales. The linguistic extravagance of these people is so enormous that one would still know what they mean if one only understood every fifth or tenth word. At times this could be an advantage which should not be underestimated. We shall come back to this later. Such people paint or make music with words, dress the bare information in rich clothes. Those who have had occasion to shop in an Italian or Greek market will have a vivid idea of good and natural redundancy of colloquial language. In this context the language-game is played with great gusto. Fiery sermons, appealing electioneering speeches of politicians, stories invented by writers, these are further examples of an amusing redundancy in the language. On the other hand texts from the world of pop songs and advertising do not always represent pure amusement. When one hears of 'greatest washing power' or 'whiter than white' then in most cases one can be certain of highest redundancy; similarly when one hears songs about 'red roses' or about 'parting, which, alas, makes the heart grow so heavy'. In order to drive redundancy still higher one embroiders the text with 'dibidibidib' or 'umba-umba-tatarata'.

There is no doubt that redundancy represents ballast; but a natural, living language requires it. How poor would be our literary life, how dull would be human conversation if the telegraphic style were our ideal of language. Con-

The unusual signs of the International Phonetic Script help to 'fix' the words of all languages. Since the phonetic script, in contrast to the usual alphabetical writings, is not tailored to the requirements of a particular language it forms a very cumbersome tool which is of interest only to the expert. Here, too, no reversibly unique correspondence between the written sign and the sound is possible.

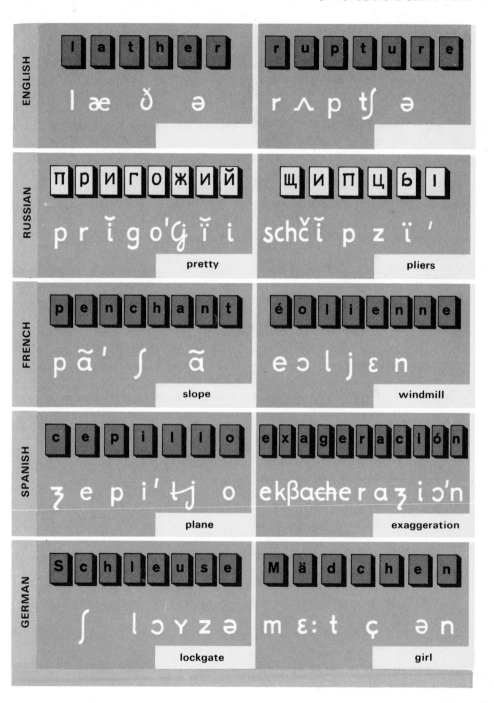

ENGLISH

l a t h e r

l æ ð ə

r u p t u r e

r ʌ p tʃ ə

RUSSIAN

ПРИГОЖИЙ

p r ĭ g o'ǧ ĭ i

pretty

ЩИПЦЫ

s ch č ĭ p z ï '

pliers

FRENCH

p e n ch a n t

p ɑ̃ ' ʃ ɑ̃

slope

é o l i e n n e

e ɔ l j ɛ n

windmill

SPANISH

c e p i l l o

ʒ e p i ' t j o

plane

e x a g e r a c i ó n

e k βa e h e r a z i ɔ' n

exaggeration

GERMAN

S ch l e u s e

ʃ l ɔ ʏ z ə

lockgate

M ä d ch e n

m ɛ: t ç ə n

girl

versation and reading would be not only boring and colourless, they would also be extremely strenuous. Indeed our conversation would, more often than not, cease to function. One single misprint in the text, one misunderstood word could cause considerable confusion. We shall deal with this area of problems in more detail later.

First of all let us return to the example of the telegraphic style, to Johnny's grandmother who would like to transmit an information in a way that should not be too expensive. When sending a telegram we know that a high degree of redundancy, a high degree of linguistic superfluousness is an unwarranted luxury. Every word is counted and has to be paid for. Grandmother's letter consists of 125 words, and is therefore far too profuse to be used for a telegram as it stands. Let the old lady take the blue pencil. To begin with there is the heading: 'My dearest Johnny'. For a telegram this is completely superfluous. This is no new information and is completely unnecessary; as it is, the telegram is addressed to Johnny and nobody else is going to receive it. In the same way she can leave out the first sentence of the letter. It does not express an important information. Affection, love and politeness, these are virtues which should not be formulated in a telegram. The same argument applies to the subsequent remarks and to the question about the boy's well being.

The important information is contained in the sentence: 'I shall arrive at the station in Manchester at half past six on Wednesday evening, on the same train that I took last year.' Even the subordinate clause of this sentence is superfluous. The

actual information to Johnny and his parents is contained in the first part of the sentence; but even this is formulated with a high redundancy. The fact that Grandmother is going to arrive in Manchester is known to the addressee. Also that she will arrive at the station; unless there are two stations, or she were to arrive at the airport, or coach station. If the time of arrival could be expressed more concisely then all that would be left in the end is: 'Arrive Wednesday eighteen thirty. Granny.' All other words are superfluous for the formulation of a purely informative telegram. Naturally having received this information Grandmother will be fetched from the station. The loving communication consisting of 125 words has changed into a short impersonal text of five words which nevertheless fulfils its purpose satisfactorily. The required information has been transmitted. Johnny and his parents know what is going to happen—Grandmother is coming. It is also quite clear when and where she is going to arrive. About ninety-five per cent of the words used in the letter were superfluous for a telegraphic communication. Of course the text of the telegram consisting of five words still possesses a certain measure of redundancy even were we to restrict our discussion purely to the word material. (We shall consider the letters as building stones later on.)

Economically thinking people could continue to argue as follows:

'The word "arrive" can be left out because what else could Granny do than to arrive? From the text: "Wednesday eighteen thirty, Granny" it is quite clear that she is coming. Also the word "Granny" is superfluous because it is evident from the telegram that it was sent from the neighbourhood of Glasgow. Who else but Granny should be coming?'

Therefore 'Wednesday eighteen thirty'. One could argue that this is still far too long.

'Grandmother sends the telegram on Tuesday afternoon and Johnny receives it presumably on Tuesday evening. If, therefore, Grandmother sends a telegram then she will not arrive on Thursday evening because by then the birthday is almost over. It is therefore quite sufficient to wire "eighteen thirty". No doubt, giving the matter a little thought, Johnny will realize that this combination of figures refers to a time. A glance at the timetable will verify this.'

One can see that even the telegraphic style possesses redundancy. The meaningful saying 'Speech is silver, silence is golden' points to another boundary region between speaking and silence in the linguistic landscape. All readers who found our blue pencil tactics regarding Grandmother's letter too malicious, too cold, even too heartless, may take comfort from the fact that the technical process of *denaturing* our colloquial language cannot be taken too far. A charming parody about this process of removing linguistic superfluousness can be found in a little book *Der jüdische Witz (The Jewish joke)* by Salcia Landmann. We shall relate it here because it hits the nail on the head.

A proud young father wires to the parents of his wife: 'Rebecca happily delivered son.' This brief and yet very informative text is written in typical telegraphese. One certainly cannot consider this telegram as being full of linguistic superfluousness. Nevertheless the father-in-law reproaches the sender of the telegram with the following words: 'How can you be so rash and waste money on superfluous words in the telegram. Look—you write "Rebecca"—who else could it be? Would you have wired if a complete stranger had had children? And then "happily"—since when does one send a telegram if a birth is not successful? And what really beats everything "delivered"—what else could it have been? Were you afraid I might think that the stork brought the child? And finally "son"—surely had it been a daughter one would never be so pleased as to run to the telegraph office. I am sure we would have guessed!'

This little story points once more, and with emphasis, to the process of abstraction which characterizes the development of a telegram style. It parodies particularly the very bad distortion of the word-material from the well-equipped tool box of the natural language. But even the grammatical model is being trimmed in the telegram and turned into a thin, unimaginative manual. Where then lies the danger if we were to accept the telegram style unconditionaly?

A first thought: no intelligent person would wish that in the near or distant future we should converse in such an imagination-killing language which is so deficient in words. This unnatural way of speech communication would not only be tedious and devoid of feeling, trite and empty; what would be much worse, considering that our thinking would have been done in this language, that this would result in a terrifying curtailment of human thought processes. Don't let us forget that in the course of our discussions we have sketched out thinking mainly as a game; that is to say within the language-game it takes on an active role rather than becoming a passive illustration. Human action is the mainspring; the activity is not the ethereal idea. Who would not be perceptive enough to see that the telegraphic style can only mark out a narrow and bare region of the language-game?

Discriminate, manysided and imaginative thinking requires, therefore, a language which is rich in words and which has a highly complex and branchlike structure. This delicate structure will always be the crucial characteristic of a civilized language. Starting from this fact it may well be expedient at times to carry out some more or less drastic abstractions. But these abstractions are only possible when a rich and natural language is available initially. The telegraphic style is thus only one of many possible abstractions which emanates from the natural abundance of the various language-games. In other words: from its very origin no natural language is concerned with pure information. The tightly knotted grid of the various language-games shapes the particular mother tongue which, after a little careful pruning here and there, forms an entity. And the 'various mother tongues are the real data' as B. L. Whorf stated. This is a suitable base for every linguistic investigation which refers to speaking or to the practical 'communications instrument' language.

All these mother tongues, whether English or German, Chinese or Indonesian, Russian or Turkish, are full of natural redundancy. This fact not only facilitates the normal process of understanding between people of the same language but it also makes it possible for the foreigner to understand it; or be understood even though he may perhaps only understand every second or third word or cannot express himself very clearly. The verbosity of the mother tongue is fortunately not only limited to the word-tools. It is precisely the boldness in the lay-out of grammatical patterns (with reference to the language-game it is the surplus of linguistic rules) which is characteristic of every natural language. Communication will still be possible even if certain rules are violated at times. But the more rules are broken the more difficult communication becomes. Thus the structure, the framework of language which is marked out by these rules, plays a very important part (see page 41).

What kind of answer should one give to the question 'should one count words?' For the time being we can only reply: Whoever wishes to, or has to send a telegram will be well advised every time to count the words of his communication. In this case redundancy is very expensive. Superfluity is quite superfluous because one has to pay for it. Only in this instance is it sensible to make use of an abstracted telegraphic style. A telephone conversation, or a brief informative chat in telegraphese would be a frightful, highly fatiguing process. A scientific dissertation, a textbook, a newspaper article, the commentary to a film—they all prefer a

hungry man . . . restaurant . . . lunch . . .

evading payment . . . police . . . arrest . . .

The verbosity of the natural languages often permits one to relate stories with simple word chains. The grammatical pattern appears to be completely abolished. But every listener or reader fills in the vacant places himself, depending on his experiences in the language-game. He knows about the construction of a sentence, of typical texts and contexts. This story would have to be told with far more redundancy if it had been the policeman who did not pay his bill; this would have been a less likely situation.

73

language, which is concise and precise but which never will, and never can do without redundancy. Is telegraphese then only a technical recipe in order to save money? Or is there a deeper meaning to the method of counting words? The philosopher C. F. von Weizsäcker explains how the existence of the telegraphic style can point beyond this narrow field:

'The telegraphic style is derived from reflecting about the number of words, about something which is apparently entirely external to the language. But in human life there is nothing entirely external. This style expresses a characteristic trait of the language. Something about the nature of all that about which one can converse shows up much clearer today than it did in any former way of speaking, in a language which has been developed with regard to its information content; and the pure telegraphic style is so to speak the march past of this drill.'

Such a linguistic-philosophical reflection is still of no help to us in our search for the answer to the question about the measurability of the language, or better still the information contained in the language. Measurements, as they are normally carried out in the natural sciences, are quite different from the simple counting of words. But the counting of the words which are sufficient for formulating certain information, can be regarded as a useful preparation for a measurement. Every simple counting process could be regarded as the first step towards a mathematization of a particular field of research. Counting marks out a preliminary, albeit modest region which is characterized by the order of the natural numbers: one, two, three, four, etc. But as soon as one tries to measure the temperature—for instance by reading off the temperature of the air in a room— then the counting changes to a measurement. Mathematically speaking one changes from the natural numbers (one, two, three, four, etc.) to fractions ($\frac{1}{2}$, $6\frac{1}{4}$, 0.85, etc.). Why should it not be possible to state the redundancy of a text in terms of numbers, similar to the room temperature, or to measure it in a similar way? What would an instrument look like which would allow us to analyse and measure the body of the language? Can we then make statements about information and redundancy in a language in a similar way to 'The temperature in this room is $19.7°C$'? One ought to be able to say: 'The information value of this text is...' or 'the redundancy of this text is...'. One would then have to insert figures, the numerical values of the measurements, into the *blank spaces* indicated by the dots. Up to now we have not advanced sufficiently far in this direction. Galileo would not yet be satisfied with us; we speak of information and redundancy without having found the corresponding numerical values of measurement. Only unambiguous numerical values, quantitative statements, will turn these expressions into the specialized meanings of the exact sciences; they then become a precise tool in the hands of the scientist. Simply to say 'redundancy' instead of 'superfluousness' would be nothing else but charlatanism and would not get us anywhere. In a way we could say that our reflections about information and redundancy up to now were pre-galilean. But after all, all thoughts related to this subject right up to the first few decades of our century were more or less pre-galilean.

In order to track down the required numerical values we shall have to do some more preparatory work, particularly along mathematical lines, because information theory is a mathematical theory. It would simply be futile to pretend that this mathematical apparel did not exist. Mathematics does not create any difficulties to the understanding of basic ideas. On the contrary, every abstract theory contains regions which are relatively simple and which are accessible to most people. These regions and, at the same time, a hole in the fence of the exact sciences, have only to be found in order to penetrate into them. For the time being, however, we shall carry on without mathematics, in the same way as we have done so far: highly redundantly.

3.2 It 'can be said in three words'
Preliminary ideas about the elimination of redundancy

The verbosity of our natural languages is a well-known fact. Whether the mother tongue is English, Russian, Finnish or German we always speak with redundancy in every-day affairs. We have seen that this is a good thing: in this connection redundancy means certainty. On the other hand there are also situations where this superfluousness can be very effective. 'The less people understand a subject, the more they feel qualified to talk about it.' This is how Wilhelm Busch described the situation. Why is it that one refers to verbosity in the natural sciences by the word 'redundancy'? Is it possible that this originally Latin word sounds more scientific? Questions of this type are very popular with people who like to see things as they come about naturally and not in the distorting mirror of a science.

Charlatanism has no place in science. The fact that the physicist prefers to speak of *gravitation* instead of *heaviness*, or *elec-tricity* instead of the *force of amber*, that the chemist prefers *valency* to *binding* has various important reasons. First of all we know how easy it is to misunderstand one another if we use similar sounding building bricks from different language games. If Mrs Smith asks her cobbler to put her shoe on the *last* because it hurts she knows that she is not using the same language-game as if she were to confront her husband with the question: 'And where were you *last* night?', or with the threat: 'If you go on like this our marriage won't *last*.' In this example the three linguistic regions are very clearly recognizable and misunderstanding cannot occur. The differences become more subtle when politicians speak of *freedom* or *emergency*.

But let us choose an example from physics. When a physicist speaks of *mass* then generally he and his fellow physicists know quite well what is meant by it. The non-physicist, however, on hearing this word will automatically conjure up all sorts of ideas as to its meanings. To many people it will mean something heavy, weighty, full of energy. In each case it will represent something which takes up space, which possesses a rigid shape, or something deformable like a pastry mixture. The physicist will be very unhappy about these misinterpretations and will explain that he did not exactly mean it in the way other people have interpreted the word and that what he wanted to convey was something quite different. He will then embark on a more or less detailed explanation of the concept of mass and on the linguistic use of mass in physics. No doubt he will elucidate many ideas of Galileo and Newton and perhaps even some of Einstein. He will then clearly distinguish between *heavy* and *inertial* mass and point to the importance of the equality of heavy and inertial mass in modern physics.

The misunderstanding of his ideas would perhaps not have been quite so great had the physicist used, for instance, the latin word *massa* in his artificial and ingenious language-game. There are, of course, far more obstinate critics; they will protest that one speaks of masses of people, mass production and of mass meetings, not to mention that somebody has amassed a lot of money. If these people who are so keen on arguing have no feeling for what physics is about, if they come to the definite conclusion that the concept of mass in physics is too narrow or even wrong, they can drive many a physicist to despair.

These arguments are based on a misunderstanding of the character of the language which the physicist uses. The language-game of physics has largely developed into an articulate artificial language. These languages, as we shall see in the following chapters, differ from the natural languages which have been the subject of our discussion so far.

The physicist Georg Christoph Lichtenberg (1742–99), who became well-known for his penetrating aphorisms, coined a very fitting phrase: 'It is a great shame; most of our words are misused tools which often still smell of the mud in which previous owners desecrated them'. This invariably happens when linguistic building bricks which seem alike are used carelessly in different language-games. We only need to recall Wittgenstein's comparison between word and tool. Two different knobs, one of which forms part of the dashboard of a motor car and the other forms part of a vacuum cleaner can be as alike as two peas in a pod. Although these knobs are operated in the same way, by a slight pressure of the fingers, their effects can be very different. Whilst the first knob may perhaps switch on the head lamps of the car, the second starts a motor (see page 32).

Let us return to our question: Why does one speak of redundancy in linguistics if one can express oneself just as clearly with words like superfluousness, verbosity, or wordiness? This is just as ambiguous as the word mass discussed above. The linguist talks of redundancy because it expresses a clearly defined and specific term belonging to his scientific

The word 'mass' conjures up the most diverse pictures in the mind: a physicist thinks of an abstract property of material bodies, a student perhaps of the comparison of masses with the beam balance. But quite different visions can be created which have nothing whatsoever to do with the linguistic usage of 'mass' in physics.

mass?

$$\underline{f} = \boxed{m} . a$$

the 'mass' is a
scalar property
of bodies

mass?

comparison of masses with
the beam balance

mass?

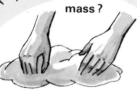

doughy   pliable

mass?

solid   massive   enormous

language; and he knows that his colleagues will use this word in the same way. Furthermore this word does not exist in colloquial language. There are consequently no problems concerning its linguistic use; the English scholar knows the meaning of this expression just as well as the Swede or the Italian. This word 'redundancy', which comes from the Latin expression redundantia is Redundanz in German and redondance in French. A translation from one language to another presents no difficulty. The structure of this word is clearly so 'artificial' that it can be interchanged at will. The individual mother tongue plays no part in this. Why should this be so?

According to our discussions this may appear somewhat surprising. Again and again we have referred to the importance of the natural languages which actually shape the 'words of the particular languages'. We have already spoken of artificial languages. The word redundancy belongs to such an artificial language and forms a 'clearly defined term' as the scientist would say. Such a word is part of the vocabulary of an artificial language (see page 49). Many a meaning assumes a different aspect in an artificial language, and fortunately in some cases with a considerable simplification, compared with a natural language. This will be discussed in the following chapters. For the time being it suffices to know that there exist artificial languages and that the exact sciences use them.

Let us try once more to probe certain regions of language by means of our natural language and investigate them with the tool 'redundancy' taken from the standard toolbox of the exact sciences.

In particular let us consider the regions of information such as messages, news, stories, poems etc. Every linguistic structure which was formulated for the purpose of transmitting information belongs to this category. We have met this idea when developing the telegraphic style where a natural verbose collection of words, our colloquial language, was depleted in redundancy or enriched in information by abstraction. As Weizsäcker said 'the language was geared to its information content'. The required information is formulated with the least expenditure of words.

Our task was always directed towards low redundancy because this is connected with a high degree of information. But low redundancy in speech is not necessarily contained in telegraphese only. We are all familiar with the News section of a newspaper or the News on radio or television where information is the essence. The language is short, clear and informative. Nobody would expect here to be told verbose and pleasing stories. What matters is the message, the news without comment, without evaluation or explanation. Ideally, we should have a dry sober statement of facts and occurrences; from the linguistic point of view a simple report. The language of this kind of news style is related to the language of observation of the physicist. It is by no means an artificial language (see page 49). It is very similar to our everyday language and uses abstractions carefully and rationally. It can no more guarantee complete objectivity of description than the observation language in physics. What does such a message look like? We have taken a short text from a

Munich daily which might be typical of any newspaper. In a slightly modified form it could appear in any language in the world and would be of interest to many people.

'Higher entrance charges to the stadium

The two Munich football clubs TSV 1860 and FC Bayern have raised the entrance charges to matches played in the stadium with effect from now. They have been forced to this decision in order to remain competitive as leading clubs in the league. A seat will now cost 20 marks (14 until now) and standing room 5 marks (4).'

This is of interest to thousands of football enthusiasts; essentially they represent the addressees. The information is directed at them. That the note is meant for football enthusiasts can easily be understood. If they want to watch a match in the stadium then they will have to pay more. The style of this news item is geared to information. The abstraction is perhaps not quite as severe as in the case of the telegram style and the text therefore reads far better. The language has very largely remained natural; and yet one can notice a certain linguistic drill. The news editor, the man who wrote this text is perhaps a great football enthusiast himself and is probably very angry about this increase in charges. Yet he formulates the message in a very detached and brief manner, as objectively as possible and does not embroider it with redundancy in order to let his feelings go. After all he might equally well have written:

'Wave of price increases hits football!

Munich's football enthusiasts note with indignation that they are being robbed of their hard-earned income at the stadium. The man in the street again has to foot the bill...' In this way a linguistic structure is being erected which has nothing whatsoever to do with decent journalistic reporting. The information is embroidered with redundancy. Feelings are being roused, readers might even be encouraged to some kind of 'action'. No news agency whether it supplies news to a paper, radio or television, should see this as its main purpose. News is always formulated in an impersonal redundancy-free way. 'Explosives,' if necessary, can only be placed 'between the lines.'

Do not let us forget that we wish to discuss redundancy in different texts. Quite a lot of modern poetry also largely avoids verbosity; the redundancy is very small. And yet there is quite a difference between these texts and the previously discussed telegrams or reports. But even here the shaping of the language is clearly recognizable. Economy of style is very important. Poetry which sets out to reflect our time realistically will be expressed mostly with urgency and economy of language. This is not to be confused with poverty of language. On the contrary the store of building bricks of the various natural language-games, of the artificial languages of the sciences, even of the jargons of the research establishments and discotheques, army barracks and film studios is after all immensely rich. And it is precisely the linking of words from different linguistic regions which can enhance the charm of a poem and reveal new nuances.

This is particularly apparent in the poems of Gottfried Benn who regarded poetry as a 'laboratory of words'. He considers that the poet 'models, creates words, dissects them, explodes them, demolishes them in order to recharge them with intensity'. In this way a poem contributes towards the recognition of reality. A poem also produces a 'world of the particular language' which, like the world of modern physics, differs considerably from that of daily life (see page 41). Benn, therefore, spoke of 'piercing the context', of the 'destruction of reality' in modern poetry. It is only this linguistic freedom which laid wide open the possibilities for the poetry of our time. Let us illustrate this with a few lines of one of Benn's poems.

'Lost ego, shattered by stratospheres,
Victim of the ion—: Gamma-ray lamb—
Particle and field: chimeras of infinities
upon your grey stone of Notre-Dame.'

Within the framework of our discussion it is not necessary for us to understand the meaning of what the poet is saying. What interests us is his choice of word-material. Gottfried Benn manipulates in his poem the vocabulary of the physicist, creates new linguistic relations and thus builds up unfamiliar realities. In this way exact science and modern poetry open up new landscapes of language and with it also of thought. Benn can be regarded as one of the most important teachers of the language engineers whom we have already discussed (see page 41). 'Making use of what could possibly be conceived' was M. Teste's challenge which applies equally to poets and scientists (see page 46). In the above mentioned poem *Lost Ego* by Gottfried Benn we find the following bitter truth:

'The world thought to pieces. And space and times
and what mankind weaved and weighed,
Function only of the infinities—
the myth lied.'

He who thinks the world to pieces will destroy it. But what is 'the world'? We learnt that it depends on language. The only worlds in existence are those created through language. Language is not 'the' world but it is a very familiar one. Space and time are always only 'recepts from culture and language' as B. L. Whorf remarked (see page 51). Modern poetry often sees the world in a far more radical light than does Einstein's theory of relativity. Is its way of thinking, therefore, meaningless? This should not be answered too rashly and superficially. No doubt the view of poetry is often most unusual and certainly unsuitable for science and every-day life. But what Whorf said about the relativistic way of looking at Nature and natural phenomena holds even more so for the view of modern poetry. We quote once more, but with a slight change:
'It (the view) hardly appeals to the common sense of the average man; not because Nature herself refutes it but because it must be talked about in what amounts to a new language.'

This is how we can see the field of language of modern poetry. It is based upon a rich vocabulary, a verbal domain which has not been reduced to bareness and which has not shrivelled up miserably like that of the telegram style. It transcends considerably the linguistic regions of colloquial language, even those of science. Yet, here too, words are used sparingly and economically.

The very intricate net of the lines of thought which the natural language and its grammar prescribe is not limited to a few safe paths as in the case of the telegram style. On the contrary; new grammatical arrangements open up numerous new ways of thinking. Signposts are being put up, signals, which stimulate independent thought. The restriction of the word-material in concise sentences, in austere strings of words, in unpretentious shapes of word-units—however one might name the products of language engineers —keeps redundancy down.

'On the wall was written in chalk
THEY WANT WAR
The man who wrote it
has already been killed in action.'

These four lines were written by Bertold Brecht. This concisely formulated poem helps us to explain the effect of the signpost. Is it not that words which are left unsaid here are put into the thinking reader's mouth? An arsenal of horror which is connected with the situation war has been confined into four concise and meaningful lines. Brecht's innermost thoughts have not been uttered; they have been circumnavigated. Yet Brecht's poem, because of its strong political allusions, remains much closer to the reality of every-day language than does the quoted poem of Benn.

Thus, low redundancy can be found in varied texts; they have all been formulated to speak to certain groups of addressees in order to convey information to them. These texts require a public. Nevertheless they display considerable differences. Is this entirely due to the different types of public? Let us try to enumerate the points where this diversity in the texts becomes apparent. Telegrams, newspapers, radio and television present their public, their addressees, with news items; information which contains a more or less pronounced element of surprise. The important thing of such a communication is that it is new. The English word 'news' is a clear indication of this. Also in the title of various publications we find formulations like *News of the World* or *Newsweek*. We are trying to obtain the latest news about what is going on in the world from newspapers, late night News on radio and television. The element of surprise is certainly something that the sender of news desires; news also wants to be sold. An American journalist wrote at the end of the last century: 'When a dog bites a man that is not news, but when a man bites a dog that is news.'

Do we expect to get news from a poem? Certainly not. New poems of a particular author only interest a small circle of addressees (literary critics, lovers of poetry, etc).

The feeling of expectancy of people who read poetry is quite different; poetry pleases us somehow, it speaks to us, it makes us perhaps enthusiastic. In this context Immanual Kant, the great philosopher from Königsberg (1724–1804) spoke of 'disinterested pleasure'. For all that, the contemporary Spanish philosopher Ortega y Gasset expressed the opinion that a poem could 'attack us like a buffalo'. This will naturally depend not only on the poem but also on the temperament of the addressee. 'But the right sort of public must have poetry in its heart before it becomes acquainted with it. The poet does not tell news; rather, the public to whom what he says is news, is not his public.'

Egon Friedell, a brilliant Austrian thinker who was hounded to death by the Nazis, gave this clear characterization: 'A poem which was formulated to present news was posted to the wrong address. This does not mean that a "poème engagé" is not topical. It can make use of the latest news and comment upon it. But the news about which it is written must have been made public, it must already exist'.

Let us recall the 'mould in the head' which Goethe spoke about (see page 57). This mould is the structure of the communication. Sound, rhythm of speech and grammar knit a characteristic network from strings of words. The building bricks of words mark out the knots in this network. Traditional grammatical links can be ruptured rigorously in order to lay bare new language and thought regions. Helmut Heissenbüttel, whom we have met previously, urged contemporary poetry to 'penetrate into and to take a foothold in a world which still appears to run away from language'.

Modern poetry seems to be concerned with linguistic virgin territory, with that which cannot be said as yet. The boundary regions of silence are therefore of utmost importance to modern poetry. This linguistic closeness to silence means in every case: lack of verbosity in language, thus extremely low redundancy. Exactly as in the telegraphic style one tries hard to exclude redundancy. How differently, though, is this accomplished;

how different is the result. In Paul Celan's poem *Voices* much that we have already said becomes clear about modern poetry. The last verse of the poem reads:

'*No*
voice—a
belated rustle, unaccustomed to time,
devoted to your thoughts, here,
at last come round; a
fruit leaf, eye-sized, deeply
scratched; it
bleeds, it won't
heal.'

Our expression *strings of words* represents the linguistic situation very well. In the case of Celan the signposts point to a region of reality which is different from that of Benn or Brecht. There is no doubt that many readers will find this redundancy-deficient expression of modern poetry not only highly unusual but also highly superfluous, nonsensical even. After all our discussions about the broad theme of *thought—language—reality* we must be careful not to equate unusual with nonsensical. Human thinking also takes place in such languages and worlds are formulated through them; they formulate realities beyond the reality described by our every-day language. No doubt the appeal of Celan's poetry is very limited. But even here Egon Friedell's sentiments apply:

'Every piece of poetry is nothing but a challenge to the public to compose poetry. It is here where its attractiveness and its value lies. The more room it leaves for manoeuvre, the more vacancies it leaves, the more meaningful it is. A new poet

The Soviet poet Yevgeny Yevtushenko recites poetry before a Moscow audience.

is born in every person who has an understanding for poetry. A thousand interpretations are possible and all of them are right.'

The theme of this discussion is low redundancy. It does not have to be brought about forcibly by a distortion of the word-material. Telegrams and modern poetry avoid the superfluousness in language. The breaking up of conventional linguistic structures, the reorganization of grammatical rules can avoid verbosity in poetry. The structure becomes clear and transparent. Words become precision-tools, simple in form. In this way it becomes possible, according to Ezra Pound, that words 'are charged with meaning to the utmost possible degree'.

Ferdinand Kürnberger, the Viennese writer who lived during the last century and who could be referred to as Karl Kraus' predecessor, provided the motto to Wittgenstein's *Tractatus Logico-Philosophicus*: '...and everything one knows, not merely the rumblings of one's mind can be said in three words.' Wittgenstein's book has provided modern poetry with an idea. This scholarly text lacks redundancy; it is almost free of superfluousness. One could almost speak of a barren, crystalline stone which is made of words. The lucidly arranged sentences are transparent and are written in a severe and

83

logical style. Wittgenstein's sentences map out an unadorned and cold sort of world structure. The foundation is well-cemented in the first few sentences:

'1. The world is everything, which is the case.

1.1 The world is the sum-total of facts, not of things.

1.11 The world is determined by the facts and also by these being *all* the facts.

1.12 For the sum-total of the facts determines what is the case and also what is not the case.

1.13 The facts in logical space form the world.

1.2 The world divides into facts.

1.21 Something can be the case or not be the case, and everything else remains the same.

2. What is the case, the fact, is the existence of basic relations.'

The last sentence, number seven, of the *Tractatus Logico-Philosophicus* reads: 'Words that cannot be spoken must be left unsaid.' We have reached the limits of what can be said. In the often quoted *Philosophical Investigations* Wittgenstein considerably extended the extreme puritanical thought pattern and broke through the rigidity of the *Tractatus*. Yet he found

The writing of concentrated specialist literature, with which the expert addresses his colleagues, forms an important part of scientific activity. The scientific publication is not and cannot be formulated in order to be generally comprehensible. Reproduced here are the title pages of two important publications in modern physics.

that 'because. of the contrast and the background' of his way of thinking the trains of thought of his *Philosophical Investigations* were put into the right perspective. Many contributions to the analytical philosophy of our time which are based on Wittgenstein's thoughts are formulated in a manner which is likewise lacking in redundancy. As an example one can quote Ryle's thoughts on thinking (see page 23f).

Finally one has to point to the publications in the exact sciences which in most cases were and still are being written without much redundancy. The rigorous method in scientific investigations contributes considerably towards avoiding verbosity. A purposefully built technical apparatus which questions Nature in an unambiguous way, a system of formulae, hardly tempts one to indulge in wordiness.

Let us quote one example. When the first Nobel prize winner in physics, Wilhelm Conrad Röntgen, made his sensational discovery of X-rays in 1895 he published it in a very dry and concise report. We give the first few sentences as an example of a language of observation (see page 49) which is full of information. One has to bear in mind of course that Röntgen's report was directed towards fellow-scientists; they and only they were his public and not the interested layman. Therefore a number of expressions were used (Hittorf vacuum tube, Rumkorff coil) which only the physicist would understand. *Concerning a new kind of rays* is the title of this very famous paper. It is not part of the aims of this book to interpret and explain the following extract. Like the passages taken from the poems of Gottfried Benn and Paul Celan

we only want to see them as a textual structure without commentary, as a structure built from definite words which are arranged according to certain rules.

'If one discharges a fairly large Rumkorff (coil) through a Hittorf vacuum tube or a sufficiently evacuated Lenard, Crooke or similar apparatus and if one covers the tube fairly closely with thin black cardboard then, in the completely darkened room, one can see the bright fluorescence of a paper screen placed close to the apparatus and painted with barium-platinum cyanide. It is quite immaterial whether the painted side or the reverse side faces the discharge apparatus. The fluorescence can still be observed at a distance of two metres from the apparatus. One can easily see that the cause of the fluorescence is the discharge tube and nothing else.'

We have considered different regions of information in the language where redundancy was kept low. At the same time naturalness of the language has more or less been lost. Mostly so in the telegram style and also to a considerable extent in modern poetry. Both adulterated forms of language represent certain dangers to human thinking. If systematically cultivated the telegraphic style could dry up our channels of thinking. Modern poetry on the other hand can think *the* world to destruction, and so destroy the world of our colloquial language. Such languages are very pointed special tools which cannot be used everywhere. Compared with them our colloquial language, due to its high redundancy, forms the universal tool for our communication.

4. BIT, THE ATOM OF INFORMATION

4.1 Means of transport for information
The Morse telegraph

Our discussions about language and information have so far been rough background sketches of the precise panoramic view that the exact sciences give us. We have already indicated that information theory is a rigorous mathematical theory; but as yet we have seen very little of it. No doubt most readers will not be exactly unhappy about this, because for the majority pure maths is not exactly pure fun. It would however be senseless to describe a mathematical theory as though it had nothing whatever to do with mathematics.

Why is it that most people are afraid of mathematics? Is mathematics really nothing but a dull assortment of formulae, an exercise in pretentious incomprehensible mental gymnastics? Unfortunately the creation of this peculiar impression is and has been due to the haughtiness of many mathematicians. Lichtenberg, whose barbed writings we have already come across, once remarked rather maliciously but regrettably somewhat aptly: 'Mathematics is indeed a splendid science but mathematicians are not even fit for the gallows'. This was written by a man of whom Egon Friedell said: 'his language "works" with the sensitivity and certainty of a precision tool'. But why did mathe-

maticians of the time spark off such bitter reactions in Lichtenberg? He found that among them were 'people whose heads are stuffed with rubbish, incapable of any other occupation that requires contemplation unless it can be done directly by that easy linking of symbols which is a matter of routine rather than thinking'.

And so Lichtenberg attacked the assumed haughtiness of some mathematicians, the haughtiness of those who confuse mental gymnastics with mathematics. Anyone incapable of using the complicated apparatus of modern mathematical formulae finds that the representatives of this craft have placed a *NO ENTRY* sign on the fence around their science. They endorse a remark made by their eminent precursor Copernicus, that one writes 'about mathematics only for mathematicians'. They would be most happy if only they could build up the mass of formulae to such an extent that an outsider would not be able to see anything that goes on within their exclusive game. Only after several years of study at a university is one allowed to penetrate this inner sanctum and can then be considered worthy of belonging to the initiated.

This kind of snobbery together with all the signs of a secret sect is simply ridiculous if one considers how strongly modern mathematics influences and shapes our lives and our surroundings. How can this snobbery exist in an age when experienced teachers manage to impart the basic ideas of the theory of sets to

Claude E. Shannon (born 1916), the American technologist who developed information theory.

primary school children? In many an advanced country twelve year olds don't look lost and helpless when one talks of 'associations', or 'functions' or 'equivalence relations'. Thank goodness they have no connection any more with the dull compound interest calculations with which their parents were plagued. Perhaps soon we may all think back with disapproval to the times when sixth-formers had to swot up the hardly intelligible integral calculus.

But let us stay in the not too rosy present where mathematics still possesses far too few friends. The blame for this lies largely with the very much neglected popular literature in mathematics which exists to a considerable extent only in English speaking countries. In these countries great mathematicians like Ber-

trand Russell, Alfred N. Whitehead and Lancelot Hogben manage to interpret contemporary mathematical problems in very simple terms. Other mathematicians in other countries did not take much pleasure in making contact with outsiders. They preferred to remain amongst themselves. What the public did get to know were nothing but amusing geometrical constructions, cheap tricks from the magical box of algebra and all sorts of knick-knacks from the fringe of what one might call 'pastime mathematics'.

Should one of the books reserved for the exclusive circle of scholars accidentally fall into 'wrong' hands then the 'sinner' must be confused and shocked. He must be made to feel his 'unworthiness'. A feeling of amazement and awe

In the development of the telegram style superfluous words which only carry information ballast are separated out. The quantity of words originally present is thereby divided into two partial sets. In the right hand diagram the set of superfluous words is shown in red, the set of the necessary words in green.

The combination of the set of necessary words (green) and the set of superfluous words (red) yields again the original set of words (right).

should get hold of him. This is how Thomas Mann described it in his delightful novel *Royal Highness*:

'What he saw confused his senses. A fantastic hocus pocus, a witches' sabbath of entwined symbols, covered the pages in an irregular, childlike writing. Greek letters were joined with roman letters and figures in different places, interspersed with crosses and lines, arranged like fractions above and below horizontal lines, capped like a tent by other lines, equated by short double lines and combined to form large masses of formulae by round brackets. Individual letters standing out like sentries were placed on the right above the brackets. Cabbalistic signs, incomprehensible to the layman, embraced letters and numbers with their arms whilst numerical fractions preceeded

them, and figures and letters floated round their heads and feet. Curious syllables, abbreviated secret words were interspersed everywhere, and between the necromantic columns were sentences and notes, written in everyday language, whose meaning was so to speak so high above all human things that when one read them one would not understand any more than one would a magic incantation.'

But this impression must not be allowed to be created if the interest of the non-mathematician is to be awakened for this fascinating all-embracing science. Mathematics must not become a magic incantation, a fantastic hocus-pocus to anybody. Most mathematicians nowadays see it this way. Naturally they are altogether no longer as arrogant as some of them have been in the past. But one of these overbearing mathematicians can well destroy more than ten sensible ones can put right. The figure of the arrogant mathematician unfortunately played a considerable role in the history of the exact sciences. Most mathematicians have not yet taken the trouble to clear the clouded relations between their science and the interested public. They admit that it does harm when one surrounds mathematics with the myth of a 'secret science' but do very little or nothing to correct it. At the threshold of the 'mathematical age' this has become a problem of society, a problem which affects us all.

Let us then try to define more precisely the rough outlines of thoughts; in other words let us try to put them partially into mathematical forms. We wanted to track down the information content of a text and to do this we have traced out the development of the telegraphic style. A very simple and instructive example—grandmother cables grandson—illustrated this process vividly. The first elementary connection with mathematics was the counting of words. Let us look at it in a different way: the superfluous words which only carried information ballast were put aside. In this way we could sort out the original quantity of words. The letter of our example represents the originally existing quantity of words which was analyzed. By this means we have created two partial lots; on the one hand the words required for the telegram and on the other hand the superfluous words. Together of course they again form the original number of words of the letter. Our figure (page 89) illustrates this idea very clearly.

This sorting out of words does represent a complete elimination of redundancy. We have already seen that in the telegram the three words 'I shall arrive' the two words 'I arrive' or the one word "arriving" produce practically the same information. In other words the message does not become richer or poorer in information whether we use one, two or three words. The *word* is not a definite unit of information. The smallest bit of information must be something else.

Even the single word can contain more or less information. Whether the telegram says 'arriving' or the slightly shorter 'arrive' the value of the information has practically not changed. And if Mr Smith says that he is going by motor-car we don't learn any more from him than if he had said he is going by car. The words motor-car and car contain the 'same' information. This is still a very vague information. As a precaution we have put the word 'same' in inverted commas. What the meaning of the 'same amount of information' is has not yet been clearly stated. To this purpose we require a little mathematics and this is what we shall do carefully, step by step. At the same time we shall make the use of the language more and more precise.

The difficulties of information theory regarding the word-unit in the language are increased by the tiresome complications of the philosophy of language which we discussed in detail in connection with Wittgenstein's *Philosophical Investigations*. The words of the natural language simulate tools with different fields of application (language-games) and have no well-defined, clearly established and delineated 'meaning'. It is exactly this which is important for the telegraphic transmission of information. That is to say the information contained in the text of the telegram does not need to be understood generally. The character of the language-game which we have discussed already is still preserved in the unnatural telegraphese. The best way to illustrate this is with a Jewish joke from the collection of Salcia Landmann:

'During the communist troubles in Hungary after the First World War a Hungarian Jew exchanged telegrams with his wife who was staying in Karlsbad at the time.
The wife: "He says operation operation."
Reply by the husband: "He says operation operation."
The authorities suspecting some kind of secret code between revolutionaries summon the husband. He explains: "This is quite simple. My wife is in Karlsbad taking the waters and had consulted a specialist there. She then sent the wire: '"The doctor said I ought to have an operation—shall I go through with the operation?"' and I replied: '"If the doctor said you ought to have an operation then you should naturally have the operation."''

The exchange of information requires clarity; as far as is possible the message should be generally understood. This was clearly not the case with the word 'operation' in our example. If one did not know that 'he' in the telegram is a doctor then one could quite well assume in certain situations that a revolutionary gives the signal to attack. Our natural language contains many such ambiguities which, as already mentioned, are due to the fact

that within the language one can cheerfully play with building bricks that sound alike and yet are part of different language-games. Normally this does not create any difficulties. In the normal way of speaking the redundancy of the natural language is sufficiently large that no serious misunderstandings need arise. Should such misunderstandings arise now and then they will be cleared up in the course of the conversation. The two parties in a conversation will pretty soon discover that they were using similar-sounding tools in different ways. This kind of control, however, does not apply to the text of a telegram. When the sender uses a certain words, e.g. operation, then he must be certain that the addressee understands his linguistic use of operation.

Incidentally, in the customary scientific use of the language one speaks of homonyms, words which sound alike but have different meanings. Having learnt the weaknesses of meaning as pointed out by Wittgenstein, we only refer in passing to this technical word. In the example by Landmann the tool character of words and sentences becomes particularly clear. The one sentence: 'He says operation operation' expresses two quite different messages. The information values transmitted by them are basically different. According to Weizsäcker such considerations make us regard our colloquial language as a 'non-transparent structure from the point of view of information theory'.

Nevertheless we shall have to begin with this 'non-transparent structure'. After all, the natural language existed long before information theory. We have emphasized often enough that it represents a very reliable tool within the compass of information theory. In any case in order to talk about information theory we have to use colloquial language. Let us then recapitulate: we are looking for a useful building brick of information, the smallest unit of information. The *word*, as we have seen, is not suitable; how then can we tackle this problem?

Perhaps we shall have more luck with the syllable as a building brick. By segmenting the language into syllables we interfere more sensitively with the natural flow of the sounds than we do by cutting out words. This refers of course to the spoken language and not to the written or printed one. As we know, our written language is a language made up of letters. And language is not spoken writing. When sending a telegram it is useful, as we have already established, to count the words. But the word is not a clear unit of information. Would it perhaps be better to count syllables? What do we find if we were to count syllables in arbitrarily chosen texts in arbitrarily selected languages (novels, poems, official notices, Stock Exchange reports etc)? In German, English and French texts we shall be surprised with the high incidence of monosyllabic words. This is particularly apparent in English no matter whether we look up Shakespeare or the *Scientific American*. Let us just select two lines from *Hamlet* to illustrate this point. The first line consists only of monosyllabic words:

'He's fat and scant of breath,
Here, Hamlet, take my napkin, rub thy brows.'

If one counts the syllables in various different texts then one finds that on average English texts contain more than seventy per cent of monosyllabic words whereas German contains approximately fifty-five per cent.

About seven out of ten English words are monosyllabic. The duosyllabic words in English, amounting to twenty per cent, also represent a fair proportion of the total. Only every tenth English word consists of more than two syllables. The following twenty monosyllabic words take up about one third (!) in a simple conversation. We have arranged them according to their frequency of occurrence: the-of-and-to-a-in-that-it-is-I-for-be-was-as-you-with-he-on-by-not.

Such simple tools contribute no doubt to the fact that English scientific or even philosophical texts still sound intelligible. This was only mentioned in passing. Let us return to the problem of the frequency of occurrence of syllables in different languages without any attempts at interpretation. In doing this we shall use the results obtained by a working party under the direction of the physicist Wilhelm Fucks at the Technical University of Aix-la-Chapelle.

For every language in which the words can be resolved into syllable building bricks one obtains characteristic frequency distributions. The simplest way of visually representing these distributions is by means of block diagrams, that is graphical representations; we restrict our discussion to one-, two-, three-, and four-syllable words. Words of more than four syllables hardly carry any weight.

What do these diagrams reveal? The keyword is 'frequency'. Frequencies can easily be counted and computed. Their values are obtained from observation.

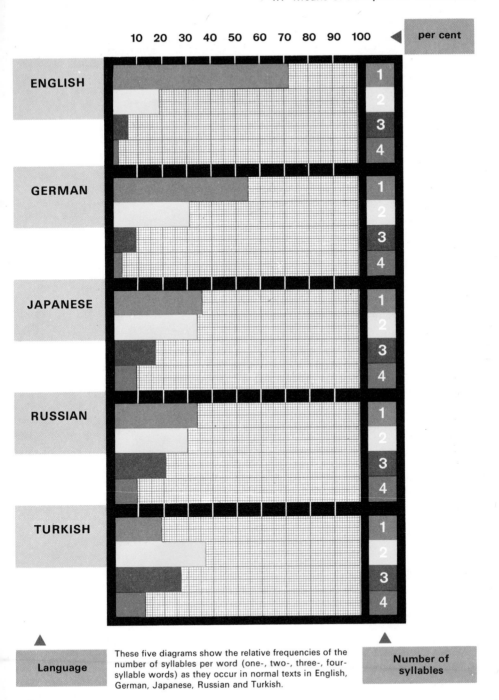

These five diagrams show the relative frequencies of the number of syllables per word (one-, two-, three-, four-syllable words) as they occur in normal texts in English, German, Japanese, Russian and Turkish.

93

4. Bit, the atom of information

The expert refers to them as 'empirical values' (see also page 161). They help to formulate statistical statements, statements which refer to 'relative' frequencies. Let us look more closely at some of these diagrams. It becomes evident that in the English language monosyllables play the major part in the building up of words. In Russian or Japanese texts there are approximately as many duosyllabic words as there are monosyllabic ones. One also finds three-syllable words quite often in Russian. A similar picture is obtained from the frequency distribution diagram for Turkish; here in fact two-, or three-syllable words occur more frequently than monosyllabic ones.

From these empirical values one can compute that only 140 syllables are required to build up an English text of one hundred words. A German text of the same number of words requires more than 160 syllables, a Russian around two hundred and a Turkish as many as about 250 syllables. This yields the following table for the average number of syllables per word:

English	1·41
French	1·57
German	1·63
Italian	2·04
Japanese	2·11
Russian	2·23
Latin	2·39
Turkish	2·46

These are characteristic mean values for normal texts in these languages. In addition to these numerical values there is one simple conclusion we can draw; it is this: in each of these languages each word is made up of at least one syllable. This seems trivial but very important for

a mathematical treatment. The occurrence of 'null-syllabic' words is excluded. This means that individual vowels like *e* (e.g. *and* in Italian) or consonants like *j* as in the combination *j'ai* (*I have* in French) are regarded as monosyllabic.

But are these two characteristics of a language (the average number of syllables and the exclusion of null-syllabic words) sufficient to describe languages mathematically? This is not really suggested by the various diagrammatic illustrations. As is the case so often, however, the first glance is deceptive. Wilhelm Fucks found a distribution law which enriched the landscape of mathematical statistics. Is our language governed by chance? This is how Wilhelm Fucks sees it:

'In all languages in which words are formed from syllables it is done in such a way that no word has less than one syllable. Apart from this a certain statistically irregular background and the choice of the individual author are superimposed on one another. If we were to take mean values from the works of very many authors then the peculiarities associated with the choice which individual authors make are cancelled out more effectively the more authors we consider.'

In the diagrams shown so far these mean values have already been taken into account. For the sake of comparison, however, we shall consider some individual distributions. One of the diagrams compares the distributions of syllables in Goethe's *Wilhelm Meister* and in Rilke's *Cornet*, the other those of Shakespeare's *Othello*, and Aldous Huxley's *Antic Hay*.

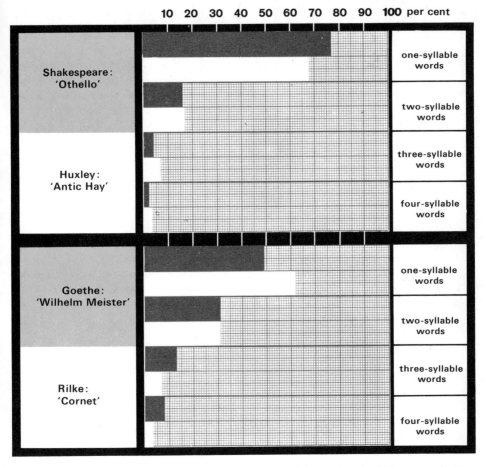

These diagrams show the distribution of the relative frequencies of the number of syllables per word of four texts of world literature. The similarity between the two English and between the German texts is clearly recognizable:

The relation between the two German and between the two English texts is clearly recognizable.

Fucks was able to confirm the statistical irregularity of the formation of words with a simple apparatus. This is how he explains his model experiment:

'In this model the syllables which are to be distributed are replaced by balls. The apparatus consists of the starting cells, the statistical distributor—rows of nails between which the balls have to move—and finishing cells. If, by means of this apparatus, one now wishes to reproduce the frequency of distribution of the syllables in words, for example in the Latin language, one begins by filling each finishing cell with one ball. This satisfies the condition that each word contains at least one syllable. The mean-value condition requires further that 139 balls

95

4. Bit, the atom of information

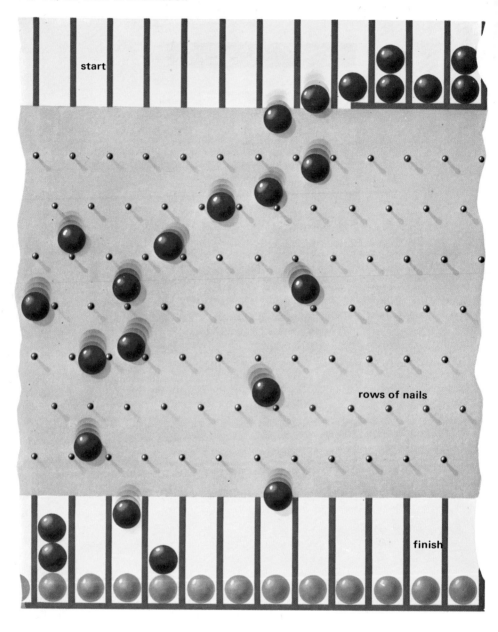

Wilhelm Fucks succeeded in confirming, by means of a very simple device, the statistical irregularity which occurs in languages whose word formations can be divided into syllables. The rows of nails which are traversed by the balls act as statistical distributors between the starting cells and the finishing cells.

(239 less 100) should be distributed as uniformly as possible amongst one hundred starting cells. The balls are now allowed to move through the statistical distributor where they are scattered irregularly by the nails. One finally obtains a definite distribution in the finishing cells containing one, two, three etc. balls. Experience shows that if the board is sufficiently long and the number of rows of nails large enough then the distribution of the balls in the finishing cells corresponds to a good approximation to the distribution of the number of syllables per word in the Latin language. A corresponding result is obtained for the other languages investigated. This proves that the distribution is determined by statistical randomness and our two conditions.'

Chance and speaking; there is no doubt that a connection exists between them. Does chance, therefore, control the information in the language? At least, in view of the close link between the fields of language and information we cannot simply answer with 'no'. Frequency, probability, entropy, etc; with these tools of the exact sciences a considerable amount of informative deductions about the formal structure of texts can be made. Before being able to use these tools on information we shall, however, have to delve into some mathematics. We shall encounter again all the specialized terms mentioned above (see especially page 158f). Our excursion into mathematics shall be done as gently as possible. For this purpose we shall first discuss a simpler way which will lead us to information.

Perhaps we can learn again from tele-graphy. Words which contain more than fifteen letters are, from the point of view of charges, counted as two words by the post office. Thus long words consisting of more than fifteen letters are charged double rate. Do the individual letters play the leading role in the transmission of information? Do they represent the atoms of information?

On average the alphabets of our natural languages contain twenty-five to thirty different letters. Thus the English alphabet a, b, c...x, y, z contains twenty-six letters, in other words twenty-six different symbols. The signal f looks quite different from the signal g or the signal z. The material symbol, the real 'body' of the language manifests itself in twenty-six different forms. This presents no problems as far as a printed message is concerned. Compared with the abundance of sounds of our colloquial language its representation by writing constitutes quite a useful abstraction in order to enlarge the areas of human communications (see page 64). The purpose of letters, newspapers and books is the exchange of information through the written word. 'For what one possesses in black and white one can happily take home'—this is how Goethe in his *Faust* commends the products of the printer's press. If we wished we could even 'take home in black and white' the text of the telegram. But this case is not quite so straightforward because the letters which make up the words in the telegram have gone through a lengthy process of transmission and have been through a few changes. Consider the situation with the help of the old Morse-telegraph. Any layman will easily understand how it works.

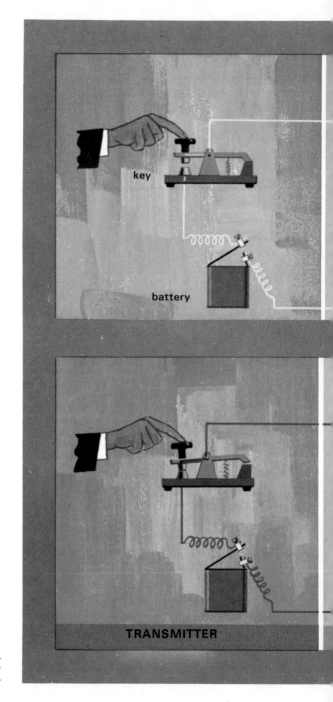

key

battery

TRANSMITTER

The American painter Samuel F. B. Morse developed an electro-magnetic telegraph in the last century.

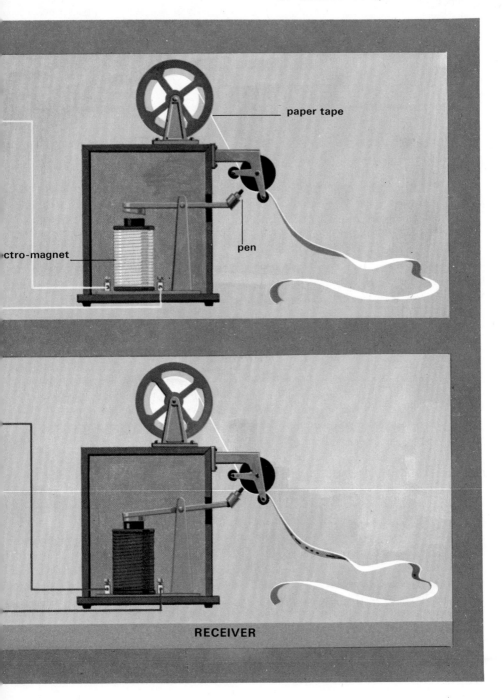

paper tape

pen

ctro-magnet

RECEIVER

99

4. Bit, the atom of information

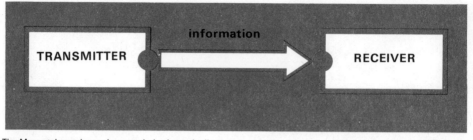

The Morse telegraph may be regarded schematically as a means of transport for information—from the transmitter to the receiver.

Our diagram shows the schematic arrangement of an electro-magnetic telegraph which was developed by the American painter Samuel F. B. Morse in the years 1835–8. The left-hand side of the diagram shows a key whose most important component part is a small, spring-loaded metal level with a press button. By simply pressing this button the key closes an electrical circuit. In the normal position of the lever the circuit is interrupted at the point of contact S, in other words no current flows. The current flows only when the circuit is closed. The closed circuit is drawn in red in the figure. The current in this circuit is direct current—it always flows in the same direction—and is supplied by a battery. This battery pumps electrons round the circuit whenever contact is established at S. The circuit incorporates an electro-magnet, a coil of many turns of copper wire which surrounds an iron core. Whenever a current flows through the coil the iron core becomes magnetic and attracts an iron lever situated above it. The other end of this lever carries a pen which presses against a uniformly moving paper tape. The pen draws a line on the tape.

If the circuit is provided with long copper leads then the key of this appara-

tus could be situated in place A and the electro-magnet and pen in place B. The apparatus in place A is called the transmitter and that in place B the receiver. We have thus become familiar with an apparatus which can transmit information from one place to another. In such a situation we can also speak of 'communication'.

Here again we become acquainted with an abstraction which is so important in the exact sciences. The actual technical problems of this apparatus (the compensation of the electrical line losses, efficiency, constructional problems of the electro-magnet etc) are of no interest in this context.

Incidentally the linguistic meaning of information and communication is not standardized in scientific literature. Both words are often used synonymously, i.e. no distinction is made between them. They are interchangeable at all times. This is what we have done so far although it may not always have been obvious. From now on when we meet situations in which the transport of information plays an important part, especially when a technical transmission mechanism is involved, we shall speak of 'communication'. This distinction is merely one of convenience. It does not tell us anything about the nature of this structure; and there is no need that it should do so. Only the progressive use of mathematics will eventually lead us to clues which will be able to shed some light upon the character of information (see also page 118).

The important discipline of communications technology has perfected not only telegraphy and telephony but also broadcasting and television without giving a clear definition of the linguistic meaning of communication. In other words in modern technology there exists no clearly defined concept of communication. This, no doubt must be a terrible thing to a classically inclined philosopher. By the way, did not Wittgenstein recognize that 'concept' is just as unclear as 'meaning' (see page 27)?

We direct our attention once more to communications, the information which was used by the Morse-telegraph in its role as a means of transport. According to our way of speaking the information contained in the telegram is a phenomenon of communication. This communication is not transmitted in its original form as a hand-written or printed

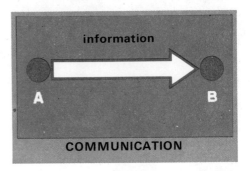

If information is transported from a point A (transmitter) to a point B (receiver) then one can speak of a communication which is being transmitted.

text. We have already spoken of the changes that are involved: pressure on the key—current impulse in the circuit—activation of the electro-magnet—line on the paper tape. But is a line a communication? What information does the line contain?

Let us attempt to clarify the connections between this technical apparatus, the telegraph, and a theory of information. After all we do want to find the measurable building bricks of information. Whenever the key is depressed in the transmitter A the receiver B inscribes a line on the paper tape. The mere exis-

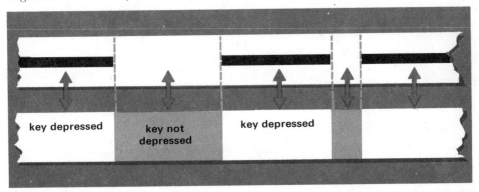

The key of the transmitter of the Morse-telegraph can either be pressed or not be pressed. At the receiver a pencil line is drawn on the paper tape when the key is depressed. If it is not depressed the tape remains clean.

tence of a line on paper does not, however, bring any information. It only tells the operator of the receiver that the apparatus works. He does not know whether his colleague at the transmitter presses the key constantly or whether the lever of the key is jammed thus making contact. But a key which is constructed in such a way that it can be depressed or released offers two possibilities to give signals:

(a) the case where the key is depressed at the transmitter corresponds to the line on the tape at the receiver.

(b) the case when the key is released (or not depressed) at the transmitter corresponds to a blank tape (or no line on the tape) at the receiver.

The availability of signals depends on a simple alternative: either the key is depressed or it is not depressed. These are the two possibilities of expression. What can be *said* in this manner? To begin with we shall have to interpret this signal: the operator of the transmitter could mean *yes* when pressing the key, or *no* when not pressing the key. If the receiver of this communication did not ask any questions to start with this interpretation does not make much sense. The sender could perhaps say 'I am here' when pressing the key and in the case of not pressing the key it means 'I am not here'. In such a situation the transmission of information would not be very promising.

More important is the following question: how can the alternative *key pressed or not pressed* be used in order to denote the twenty-five or thirty letters of the alphabets of our mother tongues? Only then will it be possible to telegraph in the

usual way. Since the words of the text of the telegram are made up of letters the following solution could be considered: we agree to a telegraphic alphabet where the letter a corresponds to pressing the key once, the letter b twice, c three times etc. This requires that in order to transmit a single letter we would have to press the key up to thirty times. Although this would be possible in principle it would certainly be awkward and strenuous for the operator. The receiver, too, would have great difficulties in deciphering this involved translation of letters into lines on paper tape. This is inexpedient and uneconomic (see page 66).

Samuel Morse approached this problem far more rationally. He chose two basic signals, short and long depression of the key. This was recorded as dot'·' and dash '-' respectively on the tape of the receiver. These two basic signals by themselves produce two signals: '·' means 'e' and vice versa; '-' means 't' and vice versa.

Before developing the Morse alphabet any further let us pause to consider why he associated the dot with e and the dash with t. It would have been only natural to call '·' a and '-' b; after all the alphabet does begin with a and b and not with e and t.

The natural way is however by no means the most economical way. As an American Morse's mother tongue was English. If one takes the trouble to take any newspaper and count the letters on the first page and if one arranges them according to their frequency of occurrence then one will find quite early that the letter e occurs most frequently followed by the letter t. The result would hardly be

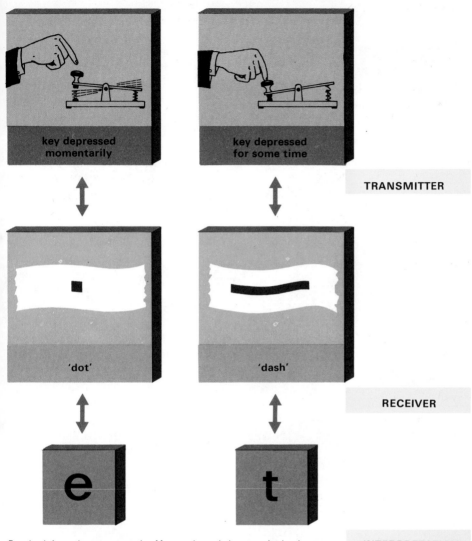

key depressed momentarily	**key depressed for some time**

TRANSMITTER

'dot'	'dash'

RECEIVER

e	t

INTERPRETATION

For the information transport the Morse telegraph has two basic signs: a short or a longer depression of the transmission key results in dot and dash at the receiver. These signals correspond to the two letters 'e' and 't' respectively.

different if one were to take the letters of any other English text; it could be a few pages from Lewis Carroll's *Alice in Wonderland*, the texts of the Beatles' songs or a sonnet by Shakespeare. Even texts from the exact sciences would not be different.

What applies to English applies in a similar way to German, French or Italian; 'e' is the most frequently printed or

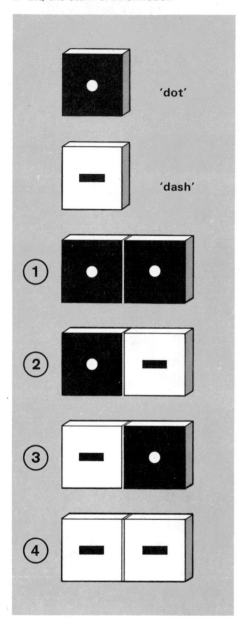

'dot'

'dash'

Signal pairs which are formed from the basic signs dot and dash result in four compound signs.

written letter. Had one of these languages been his mother tongue, Morse would still have associated '·' with 'e'. The association of '-' with 't' is characteristic of English. The second most frequent letter in German is 'n', in French 'a' and in Italian 'i'.

There are many more letters in the alphabets of our mother tongues. 'e' and 't' alone don't say overmuch in any language. Only the word 'tee', of significance to golf players, can be represented with this modest amount of symbols. The same sequence of signs on the tape of the telegraph, dash-blank-dot-blank-dot, means 'tea' in German.

Now Morse has developed telegraphy neither for tongue-tied golfers nor for reserved tea drinkers. With a store of symbols like '·' and '-' one can surely say more than just 'e' and 't' if one introduces signs made up of two or more of the basic symbols. This combination of the elements dot and dash shall also be made up rationally. The number of elements required for the various signs shall be increased step by step. To start with we have the two basic symbols themselves, giving the two possibilities

(1) dot

(2) dash

If we now use combinations of two elements of the two basic signals then the possibility of expressing ourselves is increased by four composite signs:

(3) dot-dot

(4) dot-dash

(5) dash-dot

(6) dash-dash

We can add a further eight composite signs by using all possibilities of groups of three of the two basic symbols:

(7) dot-dot-dot
(8) dot-dot-dash
(9) dot-dash-dot
(10) dot-dash-dash
(11) dash-dot-dot
(12) dash-dot-dash
(13) dash-dash-dot
(14) dash-dash-dash

If we now build up composite signs from two basic symbols 'dot' and 'dash', using four elements per sign, we can add a further sixteen to our list. These are shown in the figure.

Altogether we have now thirty different signs each one corresponding to a definite letter and vice versa.

This one-to-one correspondence represents such a clear and important relation between various elements that the mathematicians have introduced a special symbol, a double arrow ⇔ to describe such a situation concisely and without ambiguity. The expression 'e ⇔ ·' means 'the element e (from the alphabet of the natural language) stands in a one-to-one correspondence with the element · (from the Morse alphabet)'. In other words the letter e corresponds to the dot and conversely the dot corresponds to the letter e.

We have already seen that a clear relation between the spoken sounds and the written letters does not exist (see page 64). It is for this reason that we said that sounds are only indicated by letters. We shall come across this one-to-one correspondence again later; and we shall then define the mathematical language somewhat more precisely.

If the two basic signs dot and dash are grouped in fours one can form sixteen compound signs. The two single signs, the four sign pairs and eight groups of three increase the store of Morse signs to thirty.

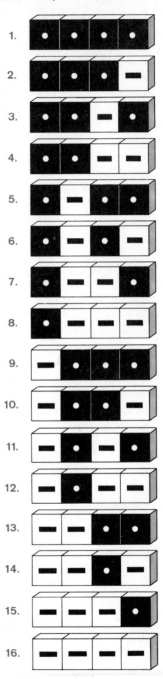

Turning our attention to the Morse alphabet, which is shown in the next figure and with which many readers are no doubt familiar, we see that it consists of groups of the basic symbols dot and dash. These groups are called Morse signs or Morse code; that is '-' or '· ·' or '· - ·' or '- · · ·' are Morse signs for t, i, r, and x respectively. We have Morse signs formed from one basic symbol, or from two, three or four. Each of these signs corresponds unambiguously to a letter of the alphabet. A translation from the natural writing to the artificial Morse code or vice versa becomes therefore very simple. By means of simple machines one can formulate texts in this code, transmit them over long distances and then store them.

Apart from the one-to-one correspondence between the elements of the two alphabets what is the determining characteristic of technical information transport? The telegraph accepts the telegram text, which has already been suitably trimmed with an eye to information, in the form of a sequence of short and long depressions of the key. This is what takes place at the transmitter. These depressions are transformed into short and long current impulses which travel to the receiver.

Here they activate the magnet and produce dots and dashes on the paper tape. Thus at the receiver a sequence of signals is produced which is very similar to the sequence of depressions of the key. At least they can easily be correlated, the dot corresponding to a short depression of the key and the dash to a long one, and vice versa. The information given to the transmitter is reproduced in a comparable way by the receiver.

What then does the telegraph transmit? To be sure it is not information by itself. The form, the concrete body, at the transmitter is not the same as that at the receiver. This rather vague way of expression is naturally due to the fact that we still don't know exactly how we can measure the information. But we can say this much: what is transmitted by the sender to the receiver is something like a building instruction. The commodity to be transported remains at the transmitter, whilst the receiver reproduces a closely resembling structure. The instruction comes over the wire in the shape of current pulses. Communications can therefore be regarded as some kind of building instruction. As we shall see this points very clearly to the most exact of all the exact sciences, to mathematics.

Every Morse sign corresponds reversibly and uniquely to a particular letter of the alphabet. The double arrow (red) is the symbol for this correspondence. Examples 'q ↔ - - · -' and 'u ↔ · · -'.

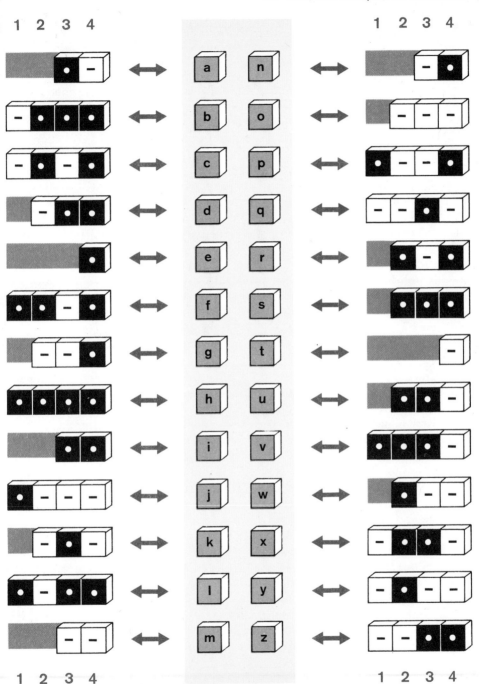

4.2 A morsel of information—bit by bit
The 'binary digit'

We are still searching for the atom of information, the smallest measurable quantity of information. The information which was transported along an artificial transmission line, and which we recognized as some kind of building instruction, was called communication. 'Information is information; it is neither matter nor energy.' The words were coined by Norbert Wiener. The decisive thing here is the subordinate clause: information is not matter, not energy. It is therefore not possible to describe it with the two principal characteristics of physics. The word building instruction points towards mathematics. In an essay published in 1902 Henri Poincaré says: 'Mathematics advances by construction, it constructs more and more complicated combinations'. Our discussion on information will therefore have to penetrate deeper and deeper into mathematical regions. These regions, however, are parts of the exact sciences which are still relatively unknown. And we shall enter these regions at the points where it is easiest to do so.

What might the smallest quantity of information look like? It can not be material nor can it be energy. We know that information lies hidden in the language, in this 'opaque structure from the point of view of information theory' as Weizsäcker said. We also know that the words, the building blocks of the natural languages, are not suited to play the part of the atom of information, the smallest bit of information. We have seen this when eliminating redundancy in formulating the text of the telegram.

Things are equally vague when considering the building brick of ordinary writing, the letter symbol. We know that letters only indicate the sounds of the natural language, that there are many fewer letters than there are speech sounds in use. This is a useful abstraction in the particular writing which we have already referred to. To return to letters or sounds would not make much sense in this connection. An abstraction which was usefully carried out should not be reversed. But what was the point of explaining the Morse code? With this code modern technology has given language a new artificial body whose material signs, groups of dots and dashes, stand in a one-to-one correspondence with the material symbols of ordinary writing. And because we recognized ordinary writing as a highly useful abstracted tool the Morse script must also have advantages due to the close relation existing between them. Technically it is a very effective and useful body of the natural language. This natural language when used for telegraphy has been trimmed for economic reasons to become the telegram style. It is concerned only with information.

As we learnt from the construction of a telegram text we can also learn from its economic transmission by the telegraph installation. The key at the transmitter is depressed for a short or slightly longer period and the receiver records a dot or dash. This is an artificial, arbitrarily arranged alternative: either the one or the other is being transmitted or received. And it is exactly this situation, as banal as it may appear at first sight, which is a considerable step forward in the search for the building block of information.

It is always a good thing if the deciding characteristic of a situation can be highlighted by examples from similar situations. In this particular instance we find Goethe helpful with a brief episode from *Faust*. In the first part of the tragedy, in the garden scene, the following takes place:

'Margarete: Let it be! (She picks up a daisy and plucks the petals, one by one)
Faust: What is it to be? A bouquet?
Margarete: No, it is only a game.
Faust: What?
Margarete: Go away! You are making fun of me. (She plucks and mutters to herself)
Faust: What are you muttering about?
Margarete (in an undertone): He loves me—he loves me not.
Faust: Your gracious heavenly countenance!
Margarete (continues): Loves me—not—loves me—not— (plucking the last petal jubilantly) he loves me!
Faust: Yes my child! Let this flower image be a sign of the gods to you. He loves you!'

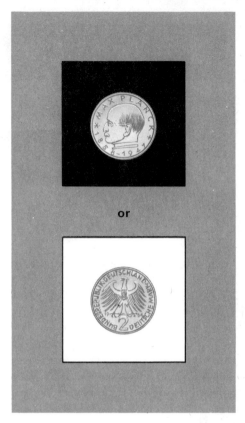

or

The toss of a coin is a yes-no decision. A tossed coin lands either on one side or on the other; the decision is 'heads' or 'tails'.

What does this poetic love scene have to do with information theory? What is the similarity with the sender situation of the telegraph? Without destroying the lyrical quality of this scene we might well say: the flower image of Faust is based upon a clear-cut alternative: either 'loves me' or 'not' in Goethe's words. To put it more precisely: 'love' or 'no love'. A pop song is more banal in this respect but clearer as far as information is concerned:

'Im counting on my buttons,
Yes—no—yes—no—yes,
whether I stand a chance with you,
yes—no—yes—no—yes.'

4. Bit, the atom of information

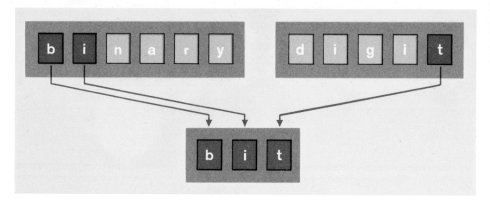

The expression 'bit' is not synonymous with the English word bit (small quantity); it is an artificial contraction of 'binary digit'. The Americans Shannon and Tukey are responsible for this meaningful word.

All these situations—the sending of Morse signs, the plucking of petals, the counting on the buttons—they are all leading to yes-no decisions. The alternative is always clear: say yes or no to something. Or receive a yes or no answer to something you have said. We can choose between two states, no more no less. The very popular tossing of the coin also belongs here. A coin thrown into the air falls on one or the other side. When the coin comes to rest the decision becomes a clear and simple fundamental situation in the exchange of information. Something happens or something does not happen. Whoever says or is told something, communicates or learns something respectively. To say or be told yes or no, in whatever connection, is information; it may be a very limited but is, no doubt, a very effective information. It is so or it is not so. Yes or no. A third possibility does not exist. Could this be the situation in which morsels of information can be given out or taken in bit by bit? Is the yes-no decision the smallest amount of information?

In fact it is expedient to define the yes-no decision as the smallest bit of information. As it happens many processes described in the exact sciences and modern technology can be represented as a sequence of yes-no decisions or at least can be traced back to such 'two-steps'. We shall be able to confirm this on various occasions. Each yes-no decision where one has to take sides for or against can be taken as a discrete unit of information. Contrary to the day-to-day use of the language, 'discrete' in this context means separate. Information is given out or taken in bit by bit. In the English-speaking world these units of information are called *bits*. Thus each yes-no decision defines one *bit* of information.

Incidentally, the word *bit*, the unit of information, which was introduced by Claude E. Shannon, is made up from the first two and the last letter of '*bi*nary digi*t*'.

This is the English name for the yes-no decision. Associated with the introduction of this name in 1948 was Shannon's colleague John W. Tukey. The same year saw the publication of *Mathematical Theory of Communication* by C. E. Shannon and W. Weaver which turned information theory into an exact science. Much preliminary mathematical work had already been done by the American Norbert Wiener and the Russian Andrei N. Kolmogorov. We shall hear of both these mathematicians later on.

It would certainly be completely wrong if we were to plunge impetuously into the mathematical foundations of information theory. The body of formulae is so intricate to a non-mathematician that it is far better to continue with our method of carefully and gradually increasing the precision. Consider once more the name for the yes-no decisions: binary digit.

The word 'digit' in colloquial language denotes a figure used in arithmetic to represent a number, or it can denote a finger. 'Binary' characterizes the property of a system which can only assume two different states; this is nothing else but the well-known yes-no decision.

What would such a yes-no decision look like in figures, with a key or even with a finger? Why could this yes-no decision not be expressed simply by the two figures **1** (yes) and **0** (no)? Here again we have a one-to-one correspondence.

$$\mathbf{1} \Leftrightarrow \text{yes}$$
$$\mathbf{0} \Leftrightarrow \text{no.}$$

'**1**' means 'yes' and '**0**' means 'no' and vice versa. We can realize such a yes-no decision by means of a key. Key depressed means yes, key open means no and vice versa. Also a finger can be used to signal yes and no; thumb up means yes, thumb down means no. This is quite an arbitrary definition but it can be useful. In order to play the yes-no decision we can make use of all sorts of signs. **1** and **0** are

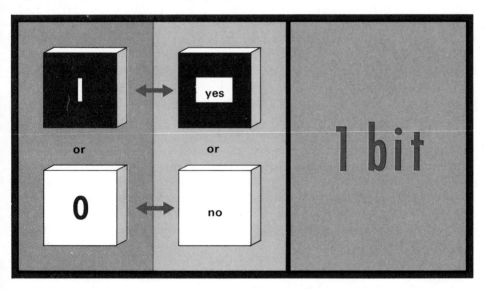

A yes-no decision can be expressed by the two figures 1 and 0; 1 stands for 'yes' and 0 for 'no' and vice versa. The two double arrows again express the uniquely reversible correspondence 1 or 0, yes or no. This corresponds to one bit of information.

numerical signs, a depressed key or a raised thumb are signs of a different kind. But they all are signs which we can interpret.

A binary digit, a yes-no decision, occurs exactly then when signs or signals of a special kind are being used. They must be signs which come from a sign-store which only contains two signs like yes—no, 1—0, key down—key up, black—white, right—left, dot—dash, current—no current etc. These pairs of signs, which have not yet been interpreted and are therefore meaningless, are known as binary symbols. They can be interpreted whenever necessary. For instance for the pedestrian the two colours green and red of the traffic lights mean

green $\Leftrightarrow$ go
red $\Leftrightarrow$ wait

Often we find that this completely arbitrary interpretation, which is so useful to the unimpeded flow of traffic, is amplified by pictures of a walking or standing figure. But in principle this is quite unnecessary; the two binary symbols in this case are green and red; they yield the required information.

Incidentally, these pictures of the figures which amplify what the two coloured lights already say form a further contribution to the theme redundancy. It is quite sufficient to associate green with go and red with wait. This system is now being enriched: green and walking figure and bottom light mean go; and red, standing figure and top light means wait. Thus additional and relevant information is being given.

It can be seen quite clearly that redundancy is being used to avoid misunderstandings. Not necessarily every-body knows the rule that when the red light is on one should not cross the road. For such people the picture of the figure is very helpful. Moreover there are many people who are colourblind; they cannot distinguish between red and green but they can see whether the top or bottom light is on. We can again say: redundancy means safety.

Now that we have found the atom of information, the bit, we can count the corresponding yes-no decisions (binary digits) of the situation in which information is being exchanged. We record 1 *bit* for every either-or for which the decision has been made. In this way the quantity of information can be given in terms of numerical values: 1 *bit*, 2 *bit*, 3 *bit*, 4 *bit* etc. Again the numerical values are natural numbers 1, 2, 3, 4 etc. We shall see later that expressions like $2 \cdot 75$ *bit* or $6\frac{1}{2}$ *bit* can and do make sense; but this only after further mathematical reflections. For the moment we shall disregard this; after all $2 \cdot 75$ yes-no decisions can hardly be visualized and neither can $6\frac{1}{2}$. The yes-no decision forms the starting point of our line of thought.

Again we choose a simple example. Mr Smith arrives at the station of a small town where he is a stranger. He intends to spend the night at the 'White Swan'. Although he was told that it is only a ten minute walk from the station he does not know in which direction to go. So he asks the porter for information. Porters on the whole like to express themselves with high redundancy and this has its reasons; not everybody who is given information has such a power of comprehension as Mr Smith. From the wordy description he extracts the following information:

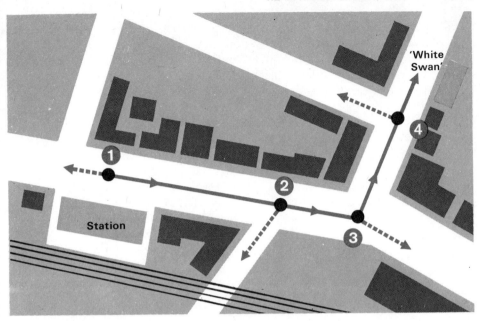

The direction given for the route from the station to the inn represents a quantity of information from which the necessary bits of information can be extracted as a sequence of two-steps. In this case four binary digits are required for the right route.

(1) Turn right and not left!
 (this corresponds to 1 *bit* of information)

(2) Go straight on and not right!
 (1 *bit*)

(3) Go left not right!
 (1 *bit*)

(4) Go straight on, not left!
 (1 *bit*)

The diagram illustrates the way Mr Smith is going to take. The fundamental situation to fix the way is the fourfold repetition of the binary digit. It is important that in each case only two choices exist.

(1) right or left (selected: right)
(2) straight on or right (selected: straight on)
(3) right or left (selected: left)
(4) straight on or left (selected: straight on)

Each decision for the one or the other possibility costs 1 *bit* of information. Hence Mr Smith must be given at least 4 *bit* of information in order to find his way from the station to the White Swan.

In the way we have described this example Mr Smith receives more information than he actually needs. But this ensures that the 4 *bit* of information which he actually needs are received by him with certainty.

Consider these facts by playing a game with black and white bricks as shown in the illustration. The board is divided into yellow and blue squares. In the first row (the lowest) there are only two large squares; the left square contains a black and the right square a white brick. Black or white brick in the yellow (left) or blue (right) field is 1 *bit*. The bricks take the place of binary signals; they form our binary digits.

Let us choose the black brick to start the game. There are two possibilities of moving it into the next row; either into the left (yellow) square or into the right (blue) square. In the former case we

follow the red trace and in the latter the green one. Similar moves can be carried out with the white brick in the right half half of the board.

We now fill the four squares in the second row with one brick each so that in the left half of the board we have a black brick per square and in the right half a white one. Then we add bricks to make groups of two. We merely have to add a black one or a white one in each case. The four pairs of bricks are: black-black, black-white, white-black, white-white. Thus we have a choice of

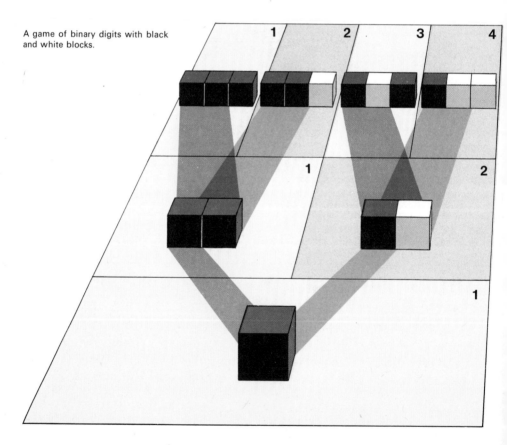

A game of binary digits with black and white blocks.

four possibilities corresponding to 2 *bit* of information.

If we repeat this game in the third row then we obtain eight groups of threes from the binary signals; we have already met this in the Morse code except that our binary symbols are no longer dot and dash but black and white bricks. The choice of eight possibilities corresponds to 3 *bit* of information.

Naturally the game does not end here. In a further row we would have 16 squares and the same number of groups of fours of black and white bricks. This would

correspond to 4 *bit* of information.

These reflections show that with, say, 20 *bit* there would be quite a considerable quantity of information available. How many possible choices would we have? One hundred? Five hundred? One thousand? Perhaps even ten thousand? Wrong. There are exactly 1,048,576 possibilities to go left or right twenty times, to group twenty black and white bricks or to arrange twenty dots and dashes. How this amazingly large number can be calculated we shall discuss in the following chapter.

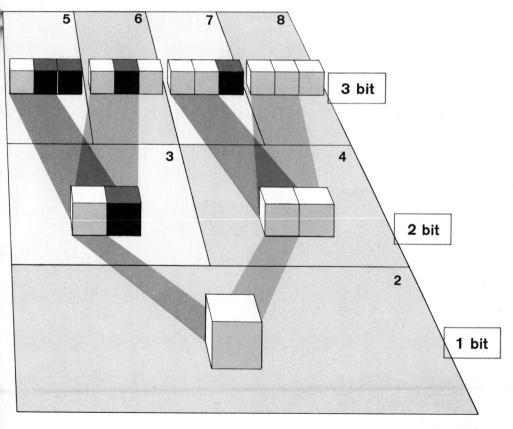

5. 'INFORMATION JOURNEY' WITH FORMULAE

5.1 Mathematizations through games
A more precise form of information

'Render measurable what is not yet measurable'. In our foregoing discussions about the information in the language we tried to remember this aphorism which Galileo once recommended to all exact sciences. This was much more difficult at first than one would have suspected. The yes-no decision was of considerable help in brightening the contours of the somewhat blurred image of a measurable quantity of information. We have managed to extract a distinct amount of information from the opaque structure of everyday language; this information is composed of discrete morsels, the bits. Each two-step (binary digit) makes up 1 *bit*.

The yes-no decision, although seeming somewhat artificial, has provided a very simple and well-tested germ cell for a measurable quantity of information. It is an offspring of technology although it seems the most natural thing in the world to be able to say yes or no. In order to do this one has to ask questions; and not every question can be answered by the two informative words.

But, first of all, let us recall the starting point of our discussions. We set out from a situation typical of our technological environment, the sending of a telegram, a telegraphic communication, a little bit of communication technology.

Nowadays important concepts of modern mathematics can be 'discovered' in a playful sort of way. Our way into the mathematical information theory begins therefore with the block-doubling game.

Was it merely a fanciful idea that a technological situation was chosen as the starting point of our deliberations? Certainly not. Information theory was invented by technologists and its problems show up most clearly in fields which were created by technology. The reason for this is fairly obvious. Technology has been created by man; it is his technology. It is the outcome of human activity which produces more and more complex and efficient tools. Everything connected with this technology is considerably easier to comprehend than Nature which is so enormously complicated and into which we humans were placed; we, who ourselves, are built in such a very intricate way. This is certainly no accident. This complexity, together with the almost incomprehensible complex structures of the building blocks of the living world, is necessary for a living creature to survive in hostile surroundings. To put it pictorially, the livelier things happen in Nature, the more difficult, many-sided and stratified become the natural relations and connections, which means the more difficult become the mathematical descriptions of natural facts.

By the way, as far as this aspect is concerned, it is well worthwhile to compare two companion volumes to this work, *Modern Physics* and *Modern Biology*. In physics one explains what are really very simple facts by highly sophisticated and complex images or models accompanied by precise mathematical descriptions. In biology, on the other hand, one must try to produce some order among the enormously complicated phenomena of life by means of less efficient models. If we may exaggerate a little we can say that its range of research contains far too many facts. Biologists, therefore, rely in their investigations on certain methods and tools which open up certain regions of life whilst they know almost nothing or very little about others. In most cases this concerns those problems which, to many of us, are of particular interest. Thus biology will never be able to answer questions like 'what is life?' If the biologist does give answers to such questions then they turn out to be useful definitions, conventions, which can neither be true nor false in an absolute sense. This has to be said although many people thirsting for knowledge will not like to hear of it; certain quarters may even reproach one for being definitely resigned to this. One just has to put up with it.

To come back to information theory. We have indicated frequently that this theory has close links with mathematics which fills the well furnished tool box of the exact sciences and modern technology. This cannot be altered. Whoever tries to convey to the layman ideas of modern physics or even of information theory or cybernetics without any mathematical help is doomed from the start. Whoever tries to present physics without formulae, information theory without mathematical ballast, either tells untruths or bypasses reality. Once again we wish to state quite clearly: information theory is a mathematical theory which was developed within the field of modern technology. Our discussions will therefore have to deal with both fields of research.

Just as we previously placed our exposition behind the caption 'language and information' we can now take our theme as 'information and mathematics'. We already met Wiener's description that information is neither matter nor energy. What is it then? 'Information is information' said Wiener. And if this is not to be a highly banal statement then information must be something fundamental. Our first reflections on the linguistic use of the word 'information' did not, however, point in this direction (compare with page 59). But information theory is a very young science whose fundamental ideas will only gradually become part of what is generally accepted. We have already learnt that the yes-no decision is the atom of information. Perhaps it can help us further.

Before going on let us once more put up a warning sign. In the early fifties the psychologist George Miller compiled a list of what information, within the framework of a mathematical information theory (or mathematical theory of communication), is not. Measurable information has nothing to do with meanings in other words nothing to do with semantics in the wider sense. This was stressed emphatically by Claude E. Shannon and Colin Cherry taking the viewpoint of technologists. Yet technologists themselves have often acted as 'semantic trappers' as for example Shannon's co-author Warren Weaver; the ambiguous word information just tempts one to do it (compare also with page 59). The philosopher Y. Bar-Hillel also has thoroughly examined the technical word 'information'. (*An Examination of Information Theory*, 1955.)

We have to keep this in mind: the roots of measurable information lie outside the language; communication begins with extra-linguistic events. It was for this reason that our search for the atom of information is like looking for a well-hidden Easter-egg; it could not be found in the field of language.

The yes-no decision is the smallest quantity of information, a bit of information. It is no doubt clear by now that this yes-no decision as such has nothing to do with energy or matter. It merely suggests a decision. Do either one thing or the other. Say yes or say no to something. Choose this or that. One deals with doing, saying, choosing; these are activities which can or should be carried out.

This keyword 'activity' helps us to progress a little further. The Dutch mathematician Luitzen Brouwer once said very appropriately: 'Mathematics is more like an activity than a tenet.' This is an obvious but often ignored thought. The mathematician does something; he works with *operators* and *symbols*, he constructs patterns of symbols, he interlinks various kinds of figures, etc. Our century has produced a group of mathematicians, the constructivists (compare *Modern Mathematics*), who again and again refer to this fundamental situation in mathematics. To base mathematics on these definite operations has given important new ideas to the exact sciences.

We shall also keep this in mind in our discussion. To do mathematics means to carry out mathematical activities. To speak about mathematics means to speak about mathematical activities. According

'Mathematics is more like an activity than a tenet.' This view held by the Dutch mathematician and logician Luitzen Brouwer is shared by many of his colleagues. At the beginning of the mathematical activity stand simple, schematic operations with mathematical symbols. Essentially these activities do not differ from the activity of a bricklayer who lays bricks according to a scheme.

to this view the mathematician makes his own objects, he constructs them as he needs them. He does not make any remarkable journeys of discovery into an ethereal platonic land of ideas. He does mathematics and does not discover metaphysics (see page 22).

In the simplest case the representatives of this exact fraternity carry out modest schematic operations. The mathematician Paul Lorenzen wrote:

'Everybody is familiar with schematic operations with figures. When building a wall for example the bricks are laid one on top of the other according to a certain scheme. Everywhere in mathematics, also in the higher stages of its development, we always find schematic operations. In order, for instance, to solve equations like $3 \cdot x + 7 = 10$ one always learns certain transformations. From

119

$a + b = c$

we get

$a = c - b$

from

$a.b = c$

we get

$a = c/b.$

In the language too we find many schematic operations which are known as logical deductions. From the statement "Not all Cretans are liars" we deduce that "Some Cretans are not liars"...

For the purpose of the schematic operation it is quite immaterial whether the figures with which one operates are bricks, mathematical symbols or words.'

So much about Lorenzen's thoughts on schematic operations which were taken from his book *Introduction to Operative Logic and Mathematics*. These schematic operations have the advantage that one only has to observe how to do things. The activity is the thing that matters (compare page 30). The operator does not need to speak in order to tell his partner what he is doing. He does not need to use everyday language, 'this opaque structure from the point of view of information theory'. Some onlooker could quite easily find out what he operates with and how he does it.

In this manner somebody plays a game for someone else's, the onlooker's, benefit. The onlooker having watched every detail and knowing the scheme of the game, the pattern of behaviour in this game, will be able to copy the game step by step. One might usefully name the first or fore-player, the 'transmitter' and the second or after-player, the 'receiver'.

So far the linguistic use of these two words has been somewhat different; so we will take stock. When we discussed the apparatus of the Morse-telegraph we called one part of this extensive installation the transmitter and the other part the receiver. Between them there is the long telegraph line, an artificial channel for transmission, as the expert calls it. The transmitter transmits signals over this channel and the receiver takes them up. Thus Information is being transported (see page 100). It is something that is neither matter nor energy.

We shall now apply this image to the two players. (It should be noted that we are speaking of an image which we intend to use, or to compare it with another. We do not define the concept; we don't inquire whether this fact comes under the heading of a concept or can be encompassed by a concept. Wittgenstein quite rightly said: 'Concept is something like an image which is used to compare objects.')

This is how it goes. Somebody demonstrates a game to somebody else; he operates schematically, with any kind of bricks. For the sake of argument we assume that the fore-player begins with two black discs and then places a white disc next to it. Now he adds three black discs to this configuration, then again three black ones, a white one, three black ones, a white one, another white one, three black ones, a white one etc. The after-player will soon have learnt that the game begins always with two black discs. They are the basic figures or basic symbols. It is obvious that we are dealing with binary symbols (page 114). There are two rules of the game which the behaviour of the fore-player reveals.

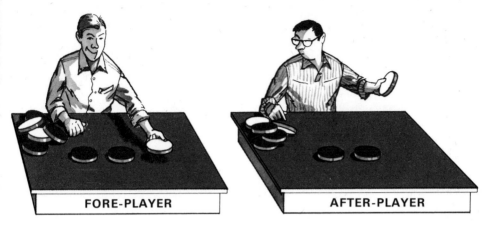

Somebody demonstrates a simple schematic game. The 'fore-player' makes figures from black and white discs. After a while the 'after-player' has 'got the message' of the scheme of the game. He learns the rules of the game for the allowed figures of black and white signs.

(1) One white disc may be added to each configuration produced in the game. Thus from the figure ●●○○ one can make ●●○○○ . Using rule 1, in the simplest case, one can change ●● into ●●○ .
(2) One can add three black discs to every figure produced in the game. If one uses this rule then one can change ●●○ into ●●○●●● .

A verbal communication between fore-player and after-player is superfluous. After a very short time the latter will understand how he can or cannot play. Simply by watching he learns to operate schematically in the same way as the fore-player. Naturally, to do this the after-player, like the fore-player, requires black and white discs. In other words both players possess a common sign store.

Summarizing we can say that for the after-player to copy the game of the fore-player correctly he must learn the rules. For the simple schematic operation he can do this by watching. The two players do not have to talk to each other. In other

words the after-player simply copies the activity of the fore-player. But to do this he must be familiar with the pattern of behaviour. The thing he copies is a pattern, a scheme, a structure, how to follow the rules. We could also say that he learnt the rules of how to construct the patterns which are allowed.

Whichever way we put it, nowhere is there any mention of things that could be linked with matter or energy. Only information-structures, of the kind mentioned above, are at the disposal of the after-player; they are his information. To make the communication click and so to reproduce the game requires the transport of a certain type of information, from the transmitting fore-player to the receiving after-player. For this reason it is quite useful to refer to the fore-player as transmitter and to the after-player as receiver. In addition there is also the common sign store which in this case consists of black and white discs. This situation is illustrated in the figure.

121

5. 'Information Journey' with formulae

Can we from now on always use the words scheme, pattern, pattern of behaviour, construction rules, instead of the words information or communication? We can do this but it depends on what we wish to emphasize. Consider once more the transport of information when sending a telegram. The two words transmitter and receiver have been applied to the fore- and after-player of a simple game in which schematic operations are being carried out. As we know

this is a simple mathematical activity. In this sense each of the two players is a mathematician. And when he plays a game then we can follow Wittgenstein who said: '"To play" must mean in this case: to act in accordance with certain rules.' Such rules can be very simple but can also be fairly complicated. The important thing is, however, that they define certain operations which can be carried out with arbitrary blocks, building stones and similar things. These are

When operating schematically with black and white discs, fore-player and after-player can be regarded as transmitter and receiver. The games discs belong to their common sign store. The information can be regarded as the building instruction which is transported from the transmitter to the receiver.

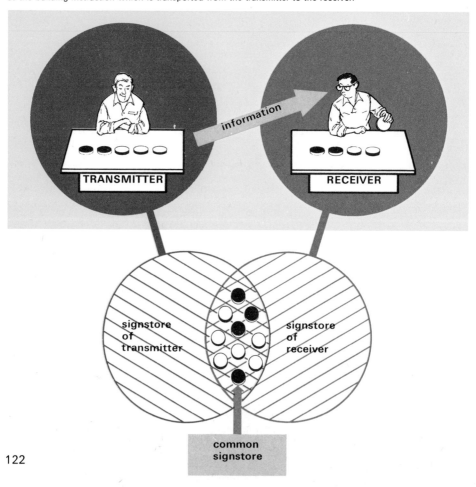

material structures, symbols. And just as the game described above was played with black and white discs, with binary symbols, it could equally well be played with the binary signals 'dot' and 'dash', the basic signs of the Morse alphabet. Dots and dashes as games blocks? Why not? Surely one does play a meaningful game with binary symbols at the transmitting station of the telegraph: a communication is translated into a sequence of dots and dashes; it is formulated in 'Morse code'.

By the way 'code' is an important word. Messages can only be encoded when they are already formulated; they must normally exist as a familiar textual structure formed with the letters a, b, c etc. Only then does the translation into the Morse code become possible because of the one-to-one correspondences between the symbols of the various alphabets (see page 105). The code depends normally on the peculiarities of the transmitting channel and when we discussed the telegraph we mentioned why Samuel Morse chose dots and dashes as basic signals.

The signals as such are not being transmitted. Dots and dashes become short and long current impulses and eventually again dots and dashes on the paper tape. In the game which we discussed above we have referred to the fore-player and after-player as transmitter and receiver and we have managed to understand the transport of information from one to the other. Let us now look at the technical situation of the telegraph from the point of view of a game. The bricks are Morse signs. The transmitter plays first. The receiver copies. The telegraph wire, the channel, trans-mits the sequence of dots and dashes to the receiver. As a consequence of this information transport these concrete Morse signals, the bricks, can be assembled at the receiver as a copy of the sequence at the transmitter. This is done purely mechanically with the pen attached to the magnet pressing in the corresponding rhythm against the paper tape.

The information required by the receiver can be regarded as the rules of construction. According to the transmitted scheme the receiver constructs his own material Morse signs. It does it in such a way that they are very similar to the sign sequences at the transmitter. This helps us to characterize reasonably well this apparently non-tangible structure 'information'. It is the construction rules which have to be transmitted in order to make the communication-games work. Figures and patterns of arbitrary material signs have to be brought into shape or form not only at the transmitter but also at the receiver; it is in this sense that we can understand the verbal meaning of information. This however required a few preliminary thoughts. Only when the particular construction rule is known as information is it possible to form the material signs.

The decisive thing here is solely the form, the construction. For this reason thoughts on information theory must necessarily be mathematical. But in this context mathematical, is not to be equated with difficult. This has been shown before in our discussion on schematic operations. As Poincaré remarked 'Mathematics advances by construction' (see page 108). The preceding discussions help us to advance within the mathematical terrain of information theory.

We have seen that the quantity of information 20 *bit* represents a very large number of possible choices, in fact 1,048,576 (see page 115). In other words: an information of twenty binary signals (e.g. dots and dashes, black and white signs, etc.) conveys precisely 20 *bit* of effective information and so expresses a decision; the decision to select one possibility out of 1,048,576 possibilities. We shall consider this avalanche-like increase in the possibilities of choice in more detail.

In the previous chapter we have sketched a simple game with binary signs where black and white bricks could be moved on yellow and blue squares (see page 114). We have been able to relate the multiplicity of the possible moves in

The block doubling game may be regarded as an introduction to the mathematization of information theory. Each block contains twice as many pieces as the one before it. In each case the pieces added on are shown with a red border.

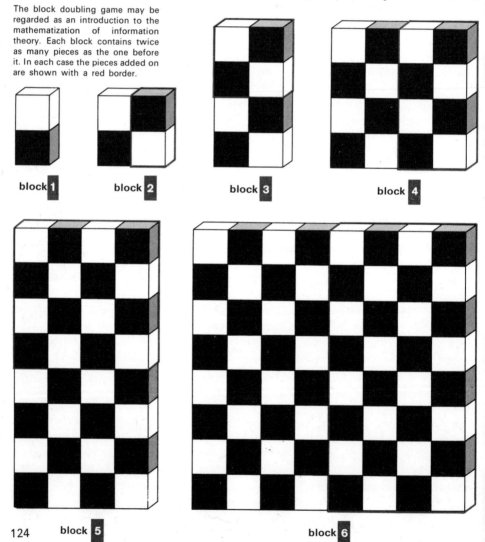

block **1**   block **2**   block **3**   block **4**

124   block **5**   block **6**

the game and the possibilities of grouping the bricks with the amount of information. But on that playing field one gets so easily lost that we only illustrated three steps diagrammatically. We will now clear the field and play another similar game with black and white pieces. For reasons which are easily apparent we shall call it 'block-doubling'.

The game is quite simple. We take a black and a white piece and place one on top of the other. We shall call this figure 'block 1'. From the point of view of information theory block 1 tells us: black or white, a two-step, 1 *bit*; in other words, in the game block 1 expresses the smallest amount of information.

As a next step we add to block 1 another similar block which is also made up of black and white. This is block 2 composed of four pieces, two black and two white. In the game block 2 formulates the amount of information 2 *bit* (four choices).

If now this second figure is doubled we get block 3 which is composed of eight pieces; the amount of information 3 *bit* offers eight choices and is represented by block 3. We can easily see from the illustration how the game progresses. If we represent the doubling of the blocks in tabular form we get:

block 1   2 pieces
block 2   4 pieces
block 3   8 pieces
block 4   16 pieces
block 5   32 pieces
block 6   64 pieces
block 7   128 pieces etc.

So far the increasing number of pieces can still be deduced from the illustration.

block **7**

One can easily see how to continue. Each successive block contains double the number of pieces of the preceding one. Each step doubles the number of pieces. Since block 7 contains 128 pieces (black and white), block 8 contains 256, block 9 512, block 10 1,024, block 11 2,048 and block 12 4,096 etc.

This process then yields for block 20 1,048,576 pieces. And because the twentieth block of our game expresses the situation 20 *bit* it means there are 1,048,576 choices.

This simple game has taught us a type of mathematical structure known as a sequence of numbers. The terms of this sequence 2, 4, 8, 16, 32, 64, etc are all natural numbers; they are all even numbers because they can be divided by 2. That each number of this sequence is divisible by 2 can easily be seen. Each number in the sequence is formed from its predecessor by doubling. And if something can be doubled then the original can be obtained from the double simply by halving the latter. To halve means to divide by two. In the sequence of our blocks of black and white pieces this simply means that we have to go in the opposite direction to the one we took for block-doubling. Our game then becomes block-halving.

Some reader might now ask: What about this constant game-like to-and-fro within a row of blocks? Surely it is a simple matter, schematically, to build up or take down these blocks. Certainly. We have again described a schematic operation, admittedly a very simple one but one from which we could learn a good deal. To quote again Poincaré's words: 'Mathematics progressesses by construction; it constructs more and more complicated combinations.' Our game with black and white blocks forms a good illustration of this statement. The black and white blocks can be combined in fairly complicated ways.

The importance lies in the way Poincaré continued his thoughts:

'For the construction to be useful and not to represent an unnecessary strain on thinking, to serve as a jumping board for those who want to go higher, it must possess a characteristic which allows us to recognize in it more than just an accumulation of elements. To put it more precisely: one has to recognize the advantage in preferring to consider the construction rather than the individual elements.'

It is thus a matter of clearly pinpointing the particular construction principle. In our case this refers to the keyword 'doubling'. We have to form a sequence of blocks where each successive block is twice as large as its preceding one.

In order to comprehend such constructions clearly the mathematicians invented their very unpopular formula-language. Prejudices in this case are superfluous. Formulae represent a very solid and handy tool which no mathematician will ever do without. For most mathematicians these formulae are the be-all and end-all of their science. Even the constructivists, whom we have already mentioned, constantly use these tools although they see the formulae merely as a 'means to help the memory by fixing and communication'. This at least is how Hermann Weyl, one of the foremost constructivistically thinking mathematicians, saw it. Whether they are regarded as indispensable formulations or merely as shorthand notes these formulae are always used and valued as precise tools.

How can we represent our elementary block-doubling game by a simple formula? In order to do this we rewrite our table in a somewhat different form:

Block	Number of pieces
1	2
2	2.2
3	2.2.2
4	2.2.2.2
5	2.2.2.2.2
6	2.2.2.2.2.2
7	2.2.2.2.2.2.2

etc.

The construction rule for the doubling of blocks shows up quite clearly; each term of the sequence is double the preceding term. The block number corresponds to the number of times one has to multiply 2 by itself, i.e. the block number 4 corresponds to 2.2.2.2 or the number-symbol 4 uniquely corresponds to 2.2.2.2. in terms of symbols we write

$$4 \rightarrow 2.2.2.2$$

The single arrow '$\rightarrow$' indicates a unique correspondence (this is not to be confused with the double arrow $\Leftrightarrow$ which represents the one-to-one, or reversibly unique, correspondence). This artificial signal '$\rightarrow$', which we have agreed to give a meaning to, is the expression of an artificial language. There shall be no doubt about it; whenever the symbol '$\rightarrow$' appears in a formula it means: 'uniquely corresponds'. We have already spoken of artificial languages (compare particularly page 49). Every language of

formulae which is used in the exact sciences is such an artificial language. The two signals '$\rightarrow$' and '$\Leftrightarrow$' and the numerical symbols '1', '2', '3' etc are typical building bricks of an artificial language.

The natural numbers 1, 2, 3, etc form very simple structures with which we have been familiar since our childhood. As the mathematician Kronecker said in the last century in a much quoted sentence they 'were made by God Almighty'. This means that the significance of these numbers lies in the straightforward counting, in the very familiar activity of counting.

As far as the signs of the two arrows '$\rightarrow$' and '$\Leftrightarrow$' are concerned we can indeed speak of meanings and use an artificial expression which we have carefully avoided when discussing colloquial language.

Artificial languages differ considerably from this natural language. We have described the complicated tool-character of the words of our every-day language. The image of the 'meaning' in this case is not generally applicable. Meanings should be clearly defined, unambiguous and unequivocal. This can easily be put into practice with the artificial structures of the artificial languages. The meaning of each sign has been agreed upon. One says: 'By this I understand this and that and nothing else.' Remember what Wittgenstein said about meanings?: 'That philosophical concept of meaning has its place in a primitive idea of the way language functions. But one can also say that it is the idea of a language more primitive than ours.'

An artificial language in which the

meanings are clearly laid down and can be interpreted uniquely is in fact a far more primitive language than our colloquial language which has taken thousands of years to be shaped in natural surroundings. The colloquial language is a natural language which, as we know, consists of a widely dispersed network of different language-games. In an artificial language the use of the language and the terminology have been worked out to the last detail. In the case of artificial languages, depending on particular requirements, there are always language engineers, linguistic toolmakers busily constructing a language machinery. It functions precisely whenever it has been properly serviced. It just is artificial. The French mathematician André Revuz noted appropriately: 'The expressions of the mathematical language are related to the expressions of the colloquial language like a safety key to an ordinary key.'

Let us return again to practial mathematics. We look once more at our small table in which the following unique co-ordinations are carried out:

$$1 \rightarrow 2$$
$$2 \rightarrow 2.2$$
$$3 \rightarrow 2.2.2$$
$$4 \rightarrow 2.2.2.2 \text{ etc.}$$

This way of writing has the great disadvantage that composite expressions soon become involved and long. We can easily see why this is so; we only need to think of the very intricate structure

$$20 \rightarrow 2.2.2.2.2.2.2.2.2.2.2.2.2.$$
$$2.2.2.2.2.2$$

which is part of this sequence of composite terms. Furthermore it is very trying and disadvantageuous to write 2 twenty times. A useful abbreviation is '2^{20}' (read: two to the power twenty). Here 20 is called the exponent. 2^{20} can be regarded as an instruction: multiply twenty 2's together. In this way, for example, 2^3 (two to the power three) can be written '2.2.2' or '8'; '2^7' is '2.2.2.2.2.2.2' or '128'. These expressions can be mutually interchanged, i.e.

$$`2^3 = 2.2.2\text{' or '}2.2.2 = 2^3\text{'}$$

The equality sign is also an important symbol of a language of formulae. In this way of writing it simply means that we can replace the expression 2^3 by 2.2.2 and vice versa. Furthermore if '2' can also be written as '2^1' then our sequence of correspondences becomes:

$$1 \rightarrow 2^1$$
$$2 \rightarrow 2^2$$
$$3 \rightarrow 2^3$$
$$4 \rightarrow 2^4$$
$$5 \rightarrow 2^5 \text{ etc.}$$

This is a sequence of composite expressions which we can regard as a sequence of sentences written symbolically. The first sentence can be read as: 'One and two to the power one correspond to one another uniquely.' If we were to regard this sentence as a rule of construction then we could read: 'Establish a unique correspondence between one and two to the power one!' One version emphasizes an existing relation, the other one focuses on the operating instruction. It is not difficult to see that both interpretations do not contradict one another. The other expressions have to be read in a similar way, e.g. 'Four and two to the power four correspond uniquely to one another' etc.

Notice that the exponent in the composite expression on the right of the arrow always corresponds to the natural number at the left of the arrow. It is tempting therefore to describe this situation in a general way. The mathematician describes this case by the following formula: $a \to 2^a$

An expression like this actually looks relatively simple. The building bricks are: the numerical sign '2', the correspondence arrow '$\to$' and a letter 'a' which occurs twice. In the two versions discussed above this structure could mean: 'a and two to the power a correspond uniquely to one another' or 'Establish a unique correspondence between a and two to the power a!'

One can not really imagine anything by this expression. The reason for this is solely the symbol 'a'; what does it mean? It alone is responsible for turning our sentences like '$3 \to 2^3$' or '$17 \to 2^{17}$', into a sentence scheme or briefly into a formula. 'a' is not the name for something in the usual sense. It is neither a nameplate for numbers like '1', '2', '3', etc nor does it represent a relation or an operating instruction like '$\to$' or '$\Leftrightarrow$'. 'a' signifies here a 'hole' a blank space in the expression. Yet it is the most important building element of the formula.

Our illustration helps to make this situation clear: blank spaces exist to mark out certain positions in an expression which the mathematician calls a formula. In the simplest case, as in ours, these blank spaces can be filled with natural numbers. Thus 'a' does not denote a fixed numerical value but signifies a variable value; it is called a 'variable'. Such variables are simply place reservations for numbers. The sign 'a' denotes a space which is going to be filled. This is similar to a passenger in a train putting his coat on a seat to indicate that it has been taken. This, of course, only makes sense when the passenger later on actually does sit down on his seat.

Similarly, a mathematical formula makes sense and fulfills its purpose only when the blank spaces are being filled, in our case with the natural numbers 1, 2, 3, 4, etc. In other words numbers are being substituted for the vacant places indicated by variables. This, too, points to a mathematical activity.

The natural numbers represent the region of the particular variables. Thus, in our example, the natural numbers 13 and 20 belong to this region, the store room of the variable a. For each blank space in the formula marked by 'a' one has to substitute the same number. If we were to take say the values 13 and 20 then we obtain the two expressions $13 \to 2^{13}$ and $20 \to 2^{20}$. They are expressions of the sequence which is described in general by the formula $a \to 2^a$.

Nobody will doubt that it is very useful to employ relations like $a \to 2^a$. They tell us a great deal in a very concise and unique way if only we understood how to use them. Had we restricted ourselves to the tools of the colloquial language we would have to depend on a long and often awkward description which in the end would not be as clear and general as a mathematical formula.

If we glance once more at our game we find two definite lots of numbers whose elements correspond uniquely to one another. As far as one lot is concerned we spoke of block numbers and as far as the other lot is concerned of the number of pieces. Both lots are made up from the infinite store of natural numbers. We

5. 'Information Journey' with formulae

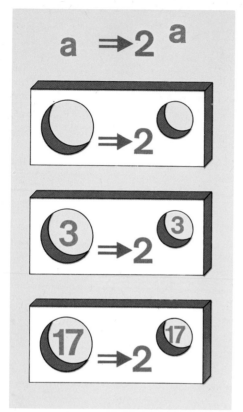

Letters often occur as building elements in mathematical formulae. As variables, they indicate vacant places which can be filled with numbers.

have to say infinite because the sequence 1, 2, 3, 4, etc does not come to an end; there is no 'largest' natural number.

The scheme $a \rightarrow 2^a$ expresses an important relation between block number and number of pieces. In addition the equals sign '=' permits the formulation of the following expressions:

$$2 = 2^1$$
$$4 = 2^2$$
$$8 = 2^3$$
$$16 = 2^4$$
$$32 = 2^5 \text{ etc.}$$

The numbers on the left of the equals sign are the numbers of pieces whilst the numbers of the blocks appear on the right as exponents. As regards our game the expression $8 = 2^3$ can also be read as follows: 'The exponent producing eight in the sequence of blocks is three.' And for the example $32 = 2^5$ we can say: 'The exponent producing thirty-two in the sequence of blocks is five.' But our game is called doubling of blocks; therefore the number 2 plays an important part. It forms the 'base' of the exponents: 2^1, 2^2, 2^3, 2^4, etc. As regards our two examples we can also say:

'The exponent producing eight to the base two is three.'

'The exponent producing thirty-two to the base two is five.'

Let us well remember these two sentences. They will help us to introduce in a simple manner a somewhat dreaded word in mathematics, the word 'logarithm'. We shall do this in the same way as in the advertisement for a washing powder. We shall replace the word exponent in the two sentences by the word logarithm. Thus our slogan becomes: 'Force exponent out, force logarithm in.' Our sentences then read:

'The logarithm of eight to the base two is three.'

'The logarithm of thirty-two to the base two is five.' This way of writing is far too cumbersome to a mathematician. Hence he writes simply:

$$\log_2 8 = 3$$
$$\log_2 32 = 5$$

Again replacing 8 by 2^3 and 32 by 2^5 our two expressions become $\log_2 2^3 = 3$ and $\log_2 2^5 = 5$. We can already recognize the general form of these expressions in terms of the variable a: $\log_2 2^a = a$

which reads: 'The logarithm to the base two of two to the power a is a.'

This makes it clear, once again, that the logarithm of the one version corresponds to the exponent of the other version. It so happens that few readers will topple over the sentence 'The exponent to the base two of two to the power a is a' because they will consider it as an explanation. The logarithmic way of writing, which one can easily get used to, will help us now to give a clear mathematical form to the mathematical structure 'information'.

As we know the amount of information is measured in *bit*. In our game the black and white blocks represent, as binary symbols, the sequence of simple units of information: 1 *bit*, 2 *bit*, 3 *bit*, etc. Why did we stack up the pieces into blocks? It can be seen from the large block diagram on page 124 that whilst the sequence of simple stacks of pieces, where we simply place one piece upon another, grows very rapidly, the morsels of information welded together into blocks increase quite uniformly. This arrangement into blocks corresponds precisely to the logarithmic description. In this manner the picture becomes much clearer if one has to operate with large numbers. Once more, usefulness is the principal guiding line.

If we take the individual blocks 1, 2, 3, etc which we now call amounts of information I_1, I_2, I_3, etc then the first few terms of the sequence become

$$I_1 = \log_2 2 \ (bit) \text{ or } I_1 = 1 \ bit$$
$$I_2 = \log_2 4 \ (bit) \text{ or } I_2 = 2 \ bit$$
$$I_3 = \log_2 8 \ (bit) \text{ or } I_3 = 3 \ bit \text{ etc.}$$

Again recalling the expressions $\log_2 2^1$, $\log_2 2^2$, $\log_2 2^3$, etc., we can see the general scheme for writing the corresponding formula. For this purpose we shall again make use of the variable a:

$$I_a = \log_2 2^a \ (bit) \text{ or } I_a = a \ bit$$

Thus, when using binary signals, the particular quantity of information I_a (a = 1, a = 2, a = 3, etc) in *bit*, corresponds exactly to the logarithm to the base two of that natural number which gives the number of all possible choices. And from the many examples quoted we know that we can say quite generally: a *bit* gives us 2^a possibilities of choice.

5.2 'Force "logarithm" in!'
General formulae for quantities of information

If two people have a chat then they exchange information in a more or less redundant manner. In order to define the quantity of information we had to learn the fundamental concepts of an exact science—the theory of measurable communication or information theory, whatever you like to call it. We can say, that even in the case of such simple and familiar chats communication is being conveyed. By communication we understand the type of scheme in which information is transmitted from one point to another. This also applies when one speaks 'man to man'. The particular channel along which information is being sent in this case is however neither technical nor artificial. It is the natural environment which is used in the transmission. Both parties in that chat make use of a natural language. They speak, produce intelligible sounds which represent their common sign store.

Although this situation seems to us highly natural we can nevertheless construct an artificial transmission mechanism which will contribute decisively to the understanding of the situation. The persons who are having a chat also act alternately as transmitter and receiver. From the point of view of information theory the question of material and energy changes are hardly interesting; this is something that falls into the province of the physicist or engineer. (Incidentally, it is only a very modest amount of acoustical work which the speaking sender produces. More than nine-tenths of the total sound energy is used up simply to warm the surrounding air by an imperceptible amount. In order to increase the amount of energy the sender would have to strain his vocal chords and to shout. This would hardly be expedient unless there happens to be a large amount of noise present. In fact, just the opposite would apply. Understanding would become more difficult, the sounds distorted, the ears of the receiver would begin to ache, etc.) We know that information is neither matter nor energy. It is a casting mould, a scheme, a construction rule, a structure, an instruction for use depending on which aspect of the situation we want to look at. What is decisive is not the amount of energy but the amount of information. And we do know now what this amount looks like in the simplest cases.

In order to gain the first definite contact with measurable information we considered the simplest of all communication systems. Moreover we confined our attention to situations where one operated with binary digits. In an ordinary chat, in a written text of 'normal' literature there always occur more than two basic signs. After all, the natural alphabet has a sign store of twenty-six different signals. In principle they can be translated into the binary system. The translation of the alphabet of our written symbols into the Morse alphabet which consists of binary symbols is, as we know, a one-to-one correspondence, it is a codification. But our books, newspapers and other printed matter are not formulated in the binary code. Besides not everybody is familiar with the Morse code or can read it without difficulty.

Yet this system of codification will be of assistance to us in our discussion. There is a one-to-one correspondence of signs from two sign stores. This is a clear and simple mathematical relation. We know that the Morse alphabet contains composite signs of different lengths; thus 'e' is represented by the single digit '·' whilst 'y' corresponds to the four digits '- · - -'. One might now be tempted to draw the following conclusion: the dot, the symbol for 'e' in the Morse code corresponds to 1 *bit*; the symbol for 'y', the sequence dash-dot-dash-dash, to 4 *bit*. There is no doubt something in this idea. Because of the relative rarity of 'y' compared with 'e' it might be more informative to receive 'y' instead of 'e'. The only trouble is that the numerical description of amounts of information by 1 *bit* and 4 *bit* does not apply.

So let us proceed step by step again.

The length of the encoded messages, in our case dot and dash-dot-dash-dash, is not the only thing which is important for the amount of information. Equally important is also the abundance of the alphabet in which the message was formulated before translation into the Morse code. Here we have twenty-six familiar symbols a, b, c,...x, y, z. This alphabet forms an ordered set of twenty-six letters. The telegraphic transmission of one of these twenty-six symbols means that exactly this one symbol and not one of the other twenty-five was cabled. If, say, 'f' is received (dot-dot-dash-dot) then only 'f' is registered and not 'a' or 'b' etc. For the dot, the Morse 'e', this would mean the following: if the dot were only to represent 1 *bit* then the alternative could only be dot or dash, Morse 'e' or Morse 't' nothing else. The remaining twenty-four letters, which are absolutely necessary for composing the normal verbal messages, cannot however, be left out. It is for this reason that we can speak of 'amount of information'. A definite amount of symbols, a definite number of possible messages, is at our disposal. If we now select one of these symbols as the message then the other elements from the remaining set of messages have not been chosen although the possibility existed to select any one of them.

Even an information amount of 4 *bit* for each of the symbols in our example is still too little. They only admit sixteen possibilities of choice, exactly ten too few, for the twenty-six elements of our natural alphabet. On the other hand 5 *bit* offers thirty-two choices, six more than is necessary. Can we say, then, that a letter of our natural alphabet carries between

4 *bit* and 5 *bit* of information? This sounds quite reasonable but what does it mean? We can understand four binary digits, four two-steps, and we can understand five binary digits. But what happens in between? Our imagination fails us.

Here the expression $I_a = \log_2 2^a$ can help us further. We have, so far, only considered the sequence of 'natural' information quantities $I_1 = 1$ *bit*, $I_2 = 2$ *bit*, $I_3 = 3$ *bit*, etc. We have established this formula for the case of binary symbols. These were the black and white pieces in the block-doubling game. This scheme can be generalized further to apply not only to binary signals but also to three, four, or more diverse types of signs.

To begin with let us consider the case of three basic symbols. As arbitrary elements of this three-set we shall choose one black, one grey and one white disc. If we formulate a message by a single, isolated symbol then there are only three possibilities of expression: black or grey or white. If we form composite signs (figures) from two out of the three basic symbols say by combining a white and a grey disc or two black discs the power of expression increases considerably:

> black-black
> black-grey
> black-white
> grey-black
> grey-grey
> grey-white
> white-black
> white-grey
> white-white

This combination—the formulation of pairs from three basic signals—yields nine expressions compared with the pair combination from two basic symbols (binary signs) which leads only to four figures

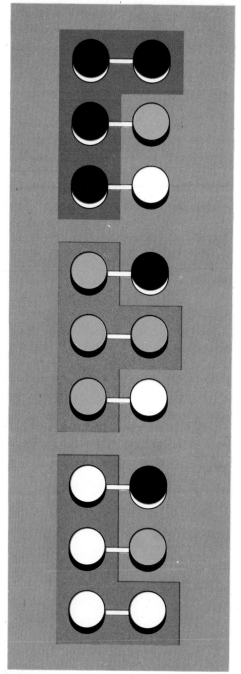

(compare with page 104). In order to take the comparison further we shall develop the set of figures whose elements are composed of three of the three basic signals. We know that in the case of a treble grouping of binary signs we can form eight composite signs (see page 105). Thus we obtain the following possible treble combinations of black, grey and white discs:

black-black-black
black-black-grey
black-black-white
black-grey-black
black-grey-grey
black-grey-white
black-white-black
black-white-grey
black-white-white
grey-black-black
grey-black-grey
grey-black-white
grey-grey-black
grey-grey-grey
grey-grey-white
grey-white-black
grey-white-grey
grey-white-white
white-black-black
white-black-grey
white-black-white
white-grey-black
white-grey-grey
white-grey-white
white-white-black
white-white-grey
white-white-white

In this way we have produced 27 figures. Why exactly 27? This can be clearly seen from the diagram. A threefold trebling has been carried out which is indicated by the red section. A threefold trebling corresponds to the arithmetical

From three basic signs (black, grey and white discs) one can form nine figures each of which consists of two of these basic signs.

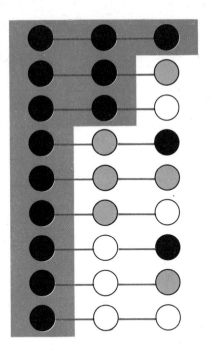

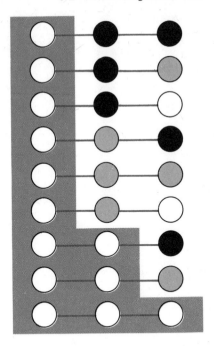

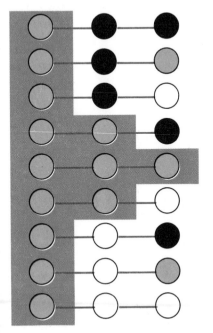

From three basic signs (black, grey and white discs) one can form twenty-seven groups of three.

expression '3.3.3' which can be read as 3^3 (three to the power three) equal to 27. Thus the corresponding equations are:

$$3 \cdot 3 \cdot 3 = 27 \text{ or } 3^3 = 27.$$

It now becomes clear why the threefold doubling in the case of binary signals leads to only eight configurations:

$$2 \cdot 2 \cdot 2 = 8 \text{ or } 2^3 = 8.$$

From three basic symbols we managed to form nine pairs:

$$3 \cdot 3 = 9 \text{ or } 3^2 = 9.$$

In the case of binary symbols this pair formation produces four figures:

$$2 \cdot 2 = 4 \text{ or } 2^2 = 4.$$

These examples are sufficient for the time being to clarify the general scheme:

If a is the number of building bricks in a figure made up of b basic symbols then we can always produce b^a (b to the power a) figures.

We can also say: with a signs from a store of b basic symbols we can always formulate b^a messages. Again a and b represent variables; they indicate vacant places, places into which natural numbers can be substituted. Further examples will make this unusual structure 'b^a' more familiar to us. Mathematicians call this, as well as the expression 2^a, a 'term'.

Mrs Miller had been shopping. On her kitchen table is a small basket of cherries and next to it a box containing cocktail sticks. Her small son Peter takes a handful of cherries and the cocktail sticks. And because he can count to five he wants to make figures with five building bricks from the cherries and cocktail sticks. Such a figure could consist of say five cherries in a row, or the configuration cherry-cocktail stick-cherry-cocktail stick-cherry, or the sequence cherry-cherry-cherry-cocktail stick-cocktail stick, etc. How many such figures can be made? At first glance such groupings seem quite pointless. Mrs Miller will probably be very angry at seeing her son play with these particular building bricks. From the mathematical point of view the situation looks different: Peter has a store of two basic symbols. Cherry and cocktail stick are his two binary signals. He constructs figures which represent combinations of five of these two basic symbols. The two vacant places a and b in the term 'b^a' can be replaced by natural numbers with b = 2 (binary basic symbols) and a = 5 (number of building bricks per figure). Thus the number of all possible figures is $2^5 = 32$.

Take another example. It is intended to arrange the vowels A, E, I, O, U of the natural alphabet in pairs, e.g. AE, IA, OE, UI etc. How many such pairs can be produced? We know the term for the general case, b^a. Here b = 5 (five letters as basic symbols) and a = 2 (figures as symbol-pairs). Thus the required number is $5^2 = 25$.

We have already discussed the meaning of 2^a at great length. Now we can say: the term '2^a' is a special case of the general term 'b^a'. The vacant place denoted by b has been replaced by the numerical value 2. But this term 2^a occurred in our general scheme for the amount of information, $I_a = \log_2 2^a$, where we operated with binary symbols. We remember that the word logarithm was substituted for the word exponent. We can also read this expression as: the amount of information, I_a, equals the exponent in two to the power a.

This scheme is clearly formulated for binary symbols; the base for the exponent a is two. If we were not to specify this base but to indicate it by the variable b then we could say more generally: the amount of information, I, equals the exponent of b to the power a. b represents the natural numbers. Again using our slogan, force 'exponent' out, force 'logarithm' in! we can then say: the amount of information, I, equals the logarithm of b to the power a. Or, $I = \log b^a$.

The theoretician will now consider the following: if, for a message of length a consisting of b basic signs, the amount of information is $I = \log b^a$ then one obtains for the smallest amount of information, for a single sign, $i_b = \log b$. In the case of the binary signs (b = 2), the simplest case of information encoding, we obtain the expression $i_2 = \log 2$. And now we see why it is that the logarithm to the base two plays such an important part in information theory. There are good reasons for choosing the information $i_2 = \log 2$ as a unit. In this case then we must have $\log 2 = 1$ and this is so if one chooses the logarithm to the base two. For we have $\log_2 2 = 1$. The exponent of 2 equals 1 when 2 is taken as the base: $2^1 = 2$.

And so we have again arrived at the atom of information. Whereas before we pictured it as a binary digit, a two-step, we have now come back to it in a purely formal manner. From now on we shall denote this unit quantity of information by $i_2 = 1$ *bit*. (The suffix 2 indicates that the sign store consists of two types of signs.) The quantity of information i_1 points to a sign store of only one type of signal. But we know that this is not sufficient to convey an information. The signal (a pictorial symbol, a constant tone) would have to be there or not be there and this implies that we have already stepped into the domain of the binary sign. Thus we must have $i_1 = 0$ *bit*. By definition we have $2^0 = 1$ ('two to the power zero equals one'). This is an equation which cannot be proved. For the single sign from a store of b basic signs the following general relation holds:

$$i_b = \log_2 b$$

If we now apply this relation to our natural alphabet with its twenty-six basic signs then each letter carries the amount of information

$$i_{26} = \log_2 26$$

So far we have established that each of these letters possesses an amount of information between 4 and 5 *bit*. Now we know it more accurately; the information has the value of $\log_2 26$ *bit*. This is a somewhat unusual numerical value which does not occur in this form in day-to-day problems. Can it not be written differently? We have come across the transformations $16 = 2^4$ or $32 = 2^5$. 'Twenty-six equals two to the power...?' In such a case one indicates the vacant place by dots. We might also ask 'twenty-six equals two to the power what?' This is a very popular type of problem in school mathematics in which the proverbial 'x' the 'unknown' makes its first appearance. One would then write $26 = 2^x$ which reads 'twenty-six equals two to the power x'. What is the value of x? x is a variable just like a and b, though here the unknown indicates so to speak a special place. It can only be filled by a definite number if the equation is to be satisfied, i.e. when the value of the term on the left of the equality sign (26) becomes equal to the term on the right of it. This is the case when $x = \log_2 26$. Thus we can write

$$26 = 2^{\log_2 26}$$

(which reads: 'twenty-six equals two to the power logarithm to the base two of 26.') But as we said before, to most people $\log_2 26$ is a most unusual number. We shall try to transform it to give it a more familiar look. The natural numbers 4 and 5 are not all we have; between them there are fractions as for example, in the familiar decimal notation, $4{\cdot}5$, or $4{\cdot}25$ or $4{\cdot}863$ etc. Values like $\log_2 26$, $\log_2 29$, $\log_2 30$ can indeed be approximated by such decimal fractions. For our purpose it is sufficient to say that tables of values of logarithms to the base two have been worked out in which these approximate

values are listed. For every natural number b we have the relation
$$b = 2^{\log_2 b}$$
Therefore for every natural number b we can represent the exponent of 2 as a decimal fraction, at least approximately. There exist three-, four-, and five-figure tables of logarithms. We reproduce the first 32 values of a three-figure table (see page 139). A glance at this table shows us that the logarithm to the base two of 26 has the value of 4·7. In other words the exponent of two is 4·7, i.e. $26 = 2^{4·7}$. So we can say: the amount of information associated with each individual letter of the natural alphabet is 4·7 *bit*. This value (formulated as a decimal fraction) lies between 4 *bit* and 5 *bit*, and indeed nearer to 5 *bit* than to 4 *bit*. After all 26 lies nearer to 32 (2^5) than to 16 (2^4). We shall consider a few examples in order to become familiar with the table of logarithms: how much information is carried by a single one of the ten numerals 1, 2, 3, 4, 5, 6, 7, 8, 9, 0? These are 10 basic signs (b = 10). A glance at the table shows us that each of these signals carries an amount of information of 3·322 *bit*.

When tossing a coin (heads or tails) we have two basic signals, binary signs (compare with page 109); hence b = 2. The amount of information per toss is thus exactly 1 *bit*. A throw with a dice (b = 6, because it has six faces) gives 2·585 *bit* of information. The spotting of any single card out of a pack of 32 carries 5 *bit* of information. For the game with black, grey and white discs which we described above (b = 3) each disc carries the amount of information 1·585 *bit*.

Since each individual sign from a store of b different types of symbols carries

the information $\log_2 b$ *bit* the amount of information increases in proportion with the number a of signs participating in the message. We can therefore write for the total amount of information I:
$$I = a \log_2 b \ (bit)$$
This schematic expression can also be obtained by simply transforming the formula
$$I = \log_2 b^a.$$
For the transmission of information we have to use material signs (letters, Morse-signs) or various forms of energy (current, no current, sounds etc) which are capable of being encoded. The code is thus a typically technical product which exhibits the property of a reversible, one-to-one correspondence between different sets of signs. The twenty-six letters form one such set of signs. The alphabet a, b, c,...x, y, z represents an ordered set; the elements form a definite sequence. Other sets of signs can also be arranged alphabetically An alphabet is thus an ordered set consisting of b basic signals. The quantity of information however is determined by the number of 'a'-signals which are required to formulate the particular message. If, from ordinary numerals, one forms the six-digit number 735639 (a = 6, b = 10) then it carries the information $I = 6\log_2 10 = 6 \times 3·322 = 19·932$ *bit*. If one were to translate this into letters and words 'seven-hundred-and-thirty-five -thousand-six-hundred-and-thirty-nine' the amount of information increases to $I = 56\log_2 26 = 56 \times 4·7 = 263·2$ *bit*. There is thus no doubt that a rational and appropriate formulation of information depends very much on the code. We shall pursue this idea further; at the same time

b	$^2\log b$	b	$^2\log b$
1	0	17	4,09
2	1	18	4,17
3	1,585	19	4,248
4	2	20	4,322
5	2,322	21	4,39
6	2,585	22	4,46
7	2,807	23	4,524
8	3	24	4,585
9	3,17	25	4,644
10	3,322	26	4,7
11	3,459	27	4,755
12	3,585	28	4,807
13	3,7	29	4,86
14	3,81	30	4,91
15	3,91	31	4,95
16	4	32	5

Logarithm to the base two of the natural numbers 1 to 32.

we shall meet again the concept of redundancy in a more precise shape.

Of the preceding discussion there is one thing we wish to keep in mind: the mathematical trick with the logarithm has enabled us to fill the gaps which lie between the 'natural' integral quantities of information 1 *bit*, 2 *bit*, 3 *bit*, etc.

6. IMPROBABILITIES

6.1 'Of the silent king who liked to eat roast pork'
Preliminary thoughts on codes

We have done some thinking about thinking, and we soon found out that our power of thinking is inseparably linked with our speech in every possible way. Our thinking is organized in terms of language. The recognition of this close relation between speaking and thinking is due to the cooperation between modern linguistics, behaviourism and unconventional philosophy as practised for instance by Ludwig Wittgenstein. He who wants to think must have his facts ready in language form. Yet, although we recognize this close relation there still exist hundreds of ways of traversing this rich landscape of thinking and speaking. We could only choose one of these, the one which seemed useful to us. Our guide was Wittgenstein who was one of the most original and unconventional thinkers of our century and who questioned so many things which appeared obvious to many. This is why his deliberations often began with hyper-critical questions as for example in the following extract from his *Philosophical Investigations*:

'Arbitrariness of the linguistic expression: Could one say: Although the speaking of a particular language has to be learnt by a child, not so the thinking, i.e. he would think of his own accord, even without having learnt any language? But I mean,

if he thinks, he makes his own images and these are, to a certain extent, arbitrary inasmuch as other images would have rendered the same service. And on the other hand the language has also developed naturally, i.e. there must have existed a first person who for the first time expressed a certain thought verbally. In any case the whole thing is immaterial because every child who learns the language, only learns in such a way that it begins to think in it. And I mean begins suddenly. There is no preliminary stage during which the child uses the language, for communication as it were, but does not yet think in it. There is no doubt that the ordinary man thinks in terms of a mixture of symbols of which the truly linguistic ones form only a small part.'

In our discussion on the theory of information we have placed the emphasis on communication. We don't want to ignore the fact, however, that by doing this we only look at one aspect of language. In order to speak about languages, natural or artificial ones, we always need the colloquial language.

Wittgenstein wrote:

'All our efforts to make a language intelligible already presuppose the existence of a language. This means that in a certain sense the use of language cannot be taught; i.e. it cannot be taught through language as, say, one could

This unusual snapshot was taken by a photographer during the fitting-out stage of a jet-plane (top J. Fowler, bottom I. S. Smith).

141

teach piano playing by using language. This means nothing more than: language does not help me to escape from language.'

This is an essential statement for all discussions about the information theory of natural languages. Incidentally Carl Friedrich von Weizsäcker wrote something very similar:

'Language which has been completely transformed into information is the hardened tip of a not hardened mass. Nobody who talks about language should forget that one of the functions of language is information. Furthermore, nobody who talks about information should forget that language as information is only possible in the context of a language which has not been changed into clear-cut information.'

Finally let us note what the mathematician Friedrich L. Bauer said in this connection:

'Any statement made in a language about that same language means nothing to a person who does not yet know this language.'

We have therefore tried in our discussions so far to convey a certain reverence for the ordinary every-day language, the colloquial language, as it is and as it has developed during the past millenia. Rightly Wittgenstein was of the opinion that: 'It would be strange if human society had been speaking all along without managing to produce a single correct sentence.'

Unfortunately many mathematicians, scientists and technologists speak at times so disdainfully about natural language that one might lose respect for this, our most solid tool of communication. This is ultimately in no small measure due to the oversimplified image which many

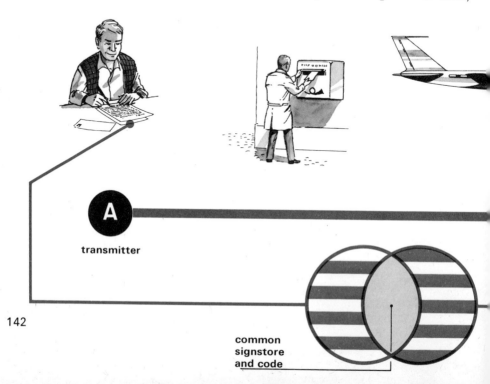

transmitter

common
signstore
and code

philosophers had of our language (see page 27). The natural language, as it has evolved, is by no means simple. It 'must have the many-sidedness of a signal-box which triggers off the actions corresponding to its sentences.' At first sight it seems that Wittgenstein's image of the language and the signal-box is too artificial, too technical. But in fact a signal-box, with its many levers and push-buttons, offers a similar, and therefore dangerous, uniform appearance to our language with its words. A pressure on a push-button can release the most diverse activities or mechanisms. Wittgenstein explains this in the *Philosophical Investigations*:

'As one uses the handles inside a signal-box to carry out many different tasks, so one does with the words of a language which correspond to handles. One handle may belong to a crank which can be adjusted continuously; another may belong to a switch which can be either on or off; a third may belong to a switch which can be set to one of three or more positions; a fourth is the handle of a pump which can only be moved up and down, etc., but they are all handles, they are gripped by the hand.'

In mathematics we have also encountered the clear indication of a handle, of activity (see page 119). The emphasis on human activity often prevents most effectively a digression into the fields of metaphysics. This applies also to the situations obtaining in communication if one considers and describes them from the point of view of information theory, i.e. mathematically. We have regarded information as a recipe, a building instruction. This is a useful view. According to Wittgenstein 'Every instruction can be understood as a description, every des-

channel

The most varied situations associated with communications can be imagined with the technical words transmitter, receiver, channel, common sign store and common code. The models of communication can be built up from these basic objects just as with a building set. Here a simple example of a one-way transmitter is shown.

receiver

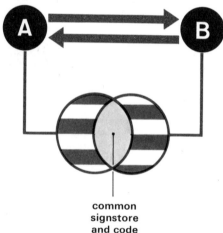

common
signstore
and code

Two persons are having a chat, man-to-man and by telephone. These are two examples of a two-way transmission. What applies here is that which is stated unintentionally humorously in an official memorandum: 'It is expedient, though not binding that always only one partner speaks'.

cription as an instruction.'

We have often spoken of 'communication'; it is a fashionable word of our time. One speaks of 'the world of communication', of 'communication patterns', of 'means of mass communication'. The word communication conjures up many vague ideas; there exist many explanations and definitions. We have learnt a few basic principles of information theory which forms the mathematical part of research into communication. The title of Shannon's paper *Mathematical Theory of Communication* points to this. It was therefore necessary for us to sketch out some mathematical ideas in order to obtain a clearer view of the problems in this region of research. We have met communication in many situations; messages were being formulated and transmitted. Depending on the situation we speak of message, information, news, communication, report. We cannot and should not always speak in precise and well-defined terms. This is not only very tedious but also limits our range of thinking. For the sake of clarity it is often advisable, indeed essential, to be more precise, to mathematize, to construct. But let us never forget the rich landscape of our natural language-games, which ought to be practised constantly. Don't let us forget Wittgenstein's warning: 'Language does not help me to escape from language.'

Artificial languages should be compared with highly specialized precision tools, with highly developed machine tools. Nobody would ever think of throwing away a hammer, a pair of pliers or a file just because there are such things as automatic tools. The latter are of little use if one wants to hammer a nail into the wall. Something similar applies to the well-stocked tool-box of the colloquial language.

Different ways of speaking produce different models of things or draw different pictures of situations. Thus, language is capable of emphasizing useful points. In connection with our discussion of information theory we can say the following:

Communication takes place from transmitter to receiver, from sender to addressee. (As we have seen this image can be applied to very familiar situations.) The appropriate transmission channel which we can also call communications channel, or information channel, or briefly channel, lies between transmitter and receiver. This channel is a physical structure (compare page 131). It can be a natural one, like the atmosphere surrounding us, or an artificial one, like a metallic conductor of electricity.

There are numerous models of communication of which an accurate picture can be formed by means of the building bricks; transmitter, receiver, channel, common sign store and common code. There is, to begin with, the simple chat between two people. In this case information is being conveyed reciprocally. Both partners act not only as senders but also as receivers; both can speak. The sounds of the natural language represent their common sign store. They are both fully conversant with their common mother tongue: English or Russian, Chinese or French, etc. The common mastery of such a language provides them with the ability to encode and to decode. The (natural) channel is the air which transports the sounds in the form of sound waves.

The situation changes only little—from the point of view of information theory—if both have a telephone con-

A speaker, acting as transmitter A, sends out messages to his listeners, the receivers B,C,D. This is a one-way transport of information as long as the audience does not interrupt.

145

versation. The channel becomes an artificial one. An additional codification takes place at the sender where the sound waves are changed into electrical impulses which travel as information recipe to the loudspeaker of the receiver where these impulses are decoded into sound waves. Of the sound picture of the speaker only the rules of construction are transmitted and a very similar sound picture is reproduced at the receiver. Here too the technical installation permits information to be conveyed reciprocally. The transmission becomes one-sided if somebody sends a message in a letter or telegram to somebody else.

Let us recall the first picture of an information transmission (see page 101). Information is being transported from a point A to a point B. This represents the simple one-sided mechanism of transmission. If information can be conveyed not only from A to B but also from B to A then this transmission is reciprocal; we speak of two-way transmission. Considering these two basic situations of information transport one can draw various

pictures depicting communication. Our figures show a few examples.

We have often spoken of codes as well. Here too the linguistic meaning is not quite uniform. The French mathematician Louis Couffignal said: 'A code is a law for the translation of one language into another language.' In a technical dictionary we read: A 'not necessarily reversible and unique correspondence between sets of cyphers (letters, figures, symbols)'. This describes the facts in a very concise and precise manner far better than we did further back. In most of the cases which we considered information and communication are formulated to begin with in our 'natural' written language and are then translated, encoded. If the explanation refers to a 'not necessarily reversible and unique correspondence' then the accent is on 'reversible'; the correspondence must be unique in every case. In our examples the double arrow ⇔ always clearly indicates the reversibily unique correspondence. The two sets of signs to which these correspondence relations apply are usually

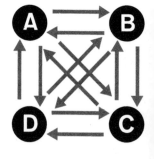

A round-table discussion has to be regarded as a more complex scheme of information transmission.

ordered sets, i.e. alphabets (see page 62).

The establishing of a unified terminology for information theory is mainly due to the efforts of Colin Cherry and D. M. MacKay. On the basis of their work we can draw the following distinction between code and encoding: a code is an agreed correspondence by means of which messages may be converted from one form of representation to another.

Encoding is a transformation of a message from one form of representation to another, carried out by using a code.

At times one might refer to all artificial languages as codes as for instance the logistic calculus which we shall discuss later (see page 188): but it is preferable if the words code and encoding, as explained above, are applied to typical situations only. We can speak justifiably of a Morse code, whilst the Deaf and Dumb Alphabet and the semaphore and flag signals may equally be considered as codes.

Our attention will now be directed towards the useful 'optimum' encodings. The two-steps and the formulae for quantities of information are of considerable help when comparing and ordering quantities of information. We can now say that an amount of information is greater or smaller than, or equal to, another amount. We can give its value in *bit* and even have a mental picture of this quantity if the *bit*-value corresponds to a natural number.

We have come to suspect that there are good and less good ways of encoding certain messages. Why is the decimal code so useful when formulating large numerical values? We have seen that six figures are sufficient to formulate the

The English communication scientist Colin Cherry (born 1914) wrote a book on information theory *On Human Communication* (1957) which is of interest not only to people working in this field. Incidentally the book is dedicated to 'his dog Pym'.

number 735639. This same information becomes a very cumbersome and uneconomic expression when written out in words, i.e. in the natural code of our written letters with its 26 basic signs. If compared in *bit* the numerical way of writing requires 19·932 *bit* whilst the worded version requires 263·2 *bit* (see page 138).

Naturally it would be completely nonsensical to try to interpret these two *bit* values in such a way that one associates the latter with a higher information value. When comparing figures one always has to keep the properties of the codes in mind. We therefore ask: what shall the code accomplish? In many cases a code shall be simple, unique and useful. How can these characteristics be tested? When

147

roast!

pudding!

gherkins!

cake!

is a code useful? We can say: the lower the *bit*-value for comparable typical performances the more economic will be the encoding. This thought requires more precision.

Again it is advisable to start with a very simple situation. We invent a short fairy tale and call it: 'Of the silent king who liked to eat roast pork'. This does not seem to have any connections at all with information theory but we shall see that this is not so.

Once upon a time in a far-away land there lived a little king who was fat, lazy and grumpy. All he wanted to do was to eat all day long. His favourite dish was a gigantic helping of roast pork. He would often eat great platefuls of chocolate pudding as well. And sometimes he licked his lips at the thought of pickled gherkins or a big strawberry cake. Apart from these four dishes nothing took his fancy at all. Day after day he would eat only

1) Roast pork
2) Chocolate pudding
3) Gherkins
4) Strawberry cake.

Sometimes the king could put away three lots of roast pork one after the other and still manage strawberry cake after that. But if he felt like it, then he would have chocolate pudding with gherkins afterwards. Or he might pick at a couple of platefuls of chocolate pudding between meals...

And so the little king became as gluttonous as he was empty-headed. As if this were not enough, he was also rather tongue-tied: he found ordinary speech a bit much to bother with. The silent king's favourite sound was a contented grunt after meals. But after all, he some-how had to let people know before meal times what he wanted to eat. As time went on, he even found calling out 'Roast Pork' a bit much for him. As for saying it politely, well this was quite beyond him.

So he decided one day to develop a code which would help him to signal his orders in the simplest way without having to open his mouth at all. The king thought that it should really be quite enough for him just to lift his left or right hand a bit for people to know what he wanted. We know that in this way he chose 'binary signs' to put over his orders. But those did not interest him in the least; all he cared about was his own comfort. So he decreed:

Right hand up a bit means: 'Bring me some pork!'

Let hand up a bit means: 'Bring me some chocolate pudding!' And that was as far as basic signs could go. If the king wanted to limit himself to binary signals he would have to use 'compound signs'. So he decreed further:

Right hand up a bit then left hand up a bit means:

'Bring me gherkins!'

Right hand up a bit then right hand up a bit means:

'Bring me strawberry cake!'

For the sake of simplicity we shall abbreviate the two binary signals 'right hand up a bit' and 'left hand up a bit' to **R** and **L**. The word 'roast!' shall replace the order 'Bring me some roast pork!' and in the same way we shall use the words 'pudding!', 'gherkins!' and 'cake!'. According to royal decree we have the following correspondence:

Roast! $\Leftrightarrow$ **R**

Pudding! $\Leftrightarrow$ **L**

Gherkins! $\Leftrightarrow$ **R L**

Cake! $\Leftrightarrow$ **R R**

No sooner done than the first difficulties occurred with the encoding. Assume that the king raised his right hand three times. In our abbreviated way of writing this is represented by '**RRR**'. What should this mean? Did he order roast pork three times or did he want roast pork followed by strawberry cake? Or perhaps he wanted strawberry cake first and roast pork after?

Obviously, the first royal code was ambiguous. But, after all, the king had a court mathematician. He summoned him to solve this problem. This was by no means simple because in order to explain the situation the king had to use ordinary speech; and he had to talk a good deal. It was very tiring and made him cross.

'Hmmmm' pondered the court mathe-matician stroking his beard. 'Your maj-esty has obviously used the binary code in your most illustrious wishes. Excellent, excellent.' 'I know that; I am the king!' interrupted his majesty indignantly in a typically regal way. (Of course he had not the slightest idea what encodings with binary signs were.) 'But it does not work' he said angrily. 'If I want straw-berry cake I get roast pork, if I want gherkins I get roast pork with chocolate pudding!' He puffed and snorted wildly and did not behave at all like a king.

'If your majesty will permit me to remark, this code is unfortunately not clear.' The mathematician was just about to begin his explanation when the king stopped him angrily: 'I know all that! After all I am the king! But you are my court mathematician! And what do I pay

The first codification attempt of the little fairy-tale king turned out to be ambiguous. Raising his right hand three times in succession could be interpreted as 'three times roast', or 'roast' followed by 'cake', or 'cake' followed by 'roast'.

you for? Just think of something and quickly too! I am already getting very hungry!'

With studious brow the mathematician withdrew. And almost in tears the king called out for his favourite dish: 'Double portion of roast pork!' He was afraid that were he to raise his right hand he would be served strawberry cake. There was a danger that this might indeed happen.

Let us now peep into the study of the court mathematician. Deep in thought he paced up and down his room. Royal comfort meant to him: produce a useful and appropriate code. The king had done some very good spade work by raising his right and left hand; he had chosen binary signals. But the difficulties set in when using compound signs: 'RR' could mean cake as well as two portions of roast pork. 'RL' could mean gherkins or roast and pudding. 'If he were to pause over a clearly recognizable time between the two signals then the problem is solved' pondered the mathematician; but he rejected this idea straight away: 'The king is definitely too lazy to be bothered with long pauses. What's more this pause would represent a third sign and this would mean to do away with the binary code. The pause would have to be counted as a vacant place. This would not do.' He did what mathematicians always do—he went to the blackboard and picked up a piece of chalk.

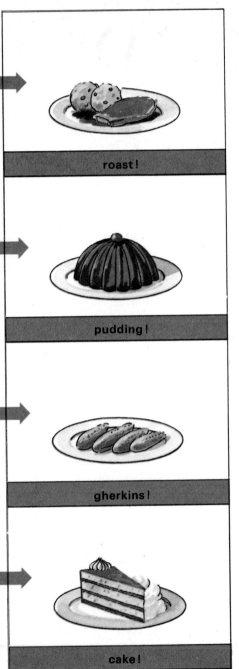

roast !

pudding !

gherkins !

cake !

He had to describe unambiguously four commands in the binary system in such a way that a sequence of binary signals could be deciphered without confusion. After a few trials he arrived at the following code:

Roast! ⇔ **RR**
Pudding! ⇔ **R L**
Gherkins! ⇔ **LR**
Cake! ⇔ **L L**

The code was clear and did not lead to confusion. The sequence

RRRRLRLLRL

could only mean: 'Bring me two portions of roast pork, then gherkins, then strawberry cake and finally chocolate pudding!' A confusion was no longer possible. What for example does the following sequence of signs mean?

'**LRRLLLRRRRLL**'

The code tells us: 'Bring me gherkins, pudding and cake, then two portions of roast pork and then again cake.' Obviously no normal human being would want to eat this but with the moody little king one could never tell.

Our little fairy tale took place a long, long time ago. This is all very well for fairy tales but as far as we are concerned it has the disadvantage that the royal court mathematician could not possible have heard of a binary digit and so could not imagine the humorous word contraction '*bit*' (compare page 110). Nevertheless we shall let him count his information in '*bit*' (No doubt he could understand English. And because he would say: 'Either the right or the left royal arm was

The court mathematician succeeded in developing a unique, unequivocal code for the royal culinary wishes. Even with long sequences of signals, erroneous orders are impossible.

raised a bit' we can imagine that he took the last word in this sentence to name the unit of information '*bit*'.)

If the silent king wanted roast pork which he expressed by the signals **RR** (twice lifting the right hand up a bit) the mathematician counted 2 *bit* of information. This same amount of information 2 *bit* was involved whenever the king longed for any one of the other three dishes (**RL, LR** or **LL**). Considering what we have said so far we can state: each one of the royal wishes is a signal which carries 2 *bit*; and altogether there are four such (compound) signals. If for example the royal menu consists of three roast porks, one chocolate pudding and two strawberry cakes the amount of information in this order is 12 *bit*.

RRRRRRLLLLL

This code was certainly unambiguous but was it also useful? It was well-known in the royal palace that his majesty's favourite dish was roast pork. He would eat it more often than anything else. On the other hand he chose gherkins least of all. In other words the signal **LR** was not expected to occur as often as **RR**. One was less probable than the other. In order to have an appropriate and useful code this point has to be considered. We remember that Samuel Morse chose, with good reasons, the shortest code signal, the dot, for the most frequently occurring letter e. For an optimum encoding it must be taken into account that the royal table contained a lot of roast pork and only a few gherkins. The code thought up by the court mathematician worked quite well because it was unambiguous but it possessed a certain amount of redundancy. The frequent orders for roast pork as well

as the rare orders for gherkins requires the same amount of information, 2 *bit*. This was by no means a favourable situation because of the very different occurrence of the dishes and the corresponding signals. We have now arrived at a stage where it is important to clarify this thought. An appropriate code must take account of the signal frequency. It is important to know whether a certain signal (or sequence of signals) occurs more often than another. We shall look at this situation again by returning to our fairy tale. The 'repertoire' of the four culinary wishes which occur with different frequencies has to be encoded economically.

'What does one do?' pondered the mathematician when he became aware of the problem of signal frequency. Like every learned man in high office he had an assistant. And he was given the job to observe closely the royal menu over many weeks. Day after day the court-mathematician's assistant sat in a corner and noted on paper the number of the particular dishes which were served at the royal table. Eventually he could report to his Lord and Master the following result of his investigations: on average the hungry king would eat eighteen individual dishes per day. Although the sequence changed continuously it was possible despite this to establish an unambiguous frequency distribution of the dishes consumed by the king per day:

9 lots of roast pork
6 lots of chocolate pudding
1 lot of gherkins
2 lots of strawberry cake.

The optimum encoding of the royal culinary wishes took into account that the king ate a lot of pork and only a few gherkins.

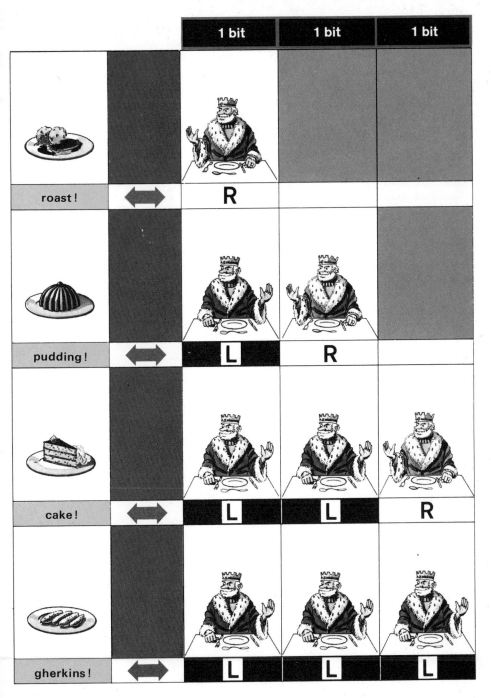

For optimal, unambiguous and useful, encoding one has to try to fix the shortest possible signal for the roast pork order. In contrast to this the order for gherkins could be expressed more lavishly, i.e. with a longer sequence of signals. In the course of a single day the king consumed eighteen dishes. In the existing code this required thirty-six *bit* of information since each order corresponds to 2 *bit* (**RR** or **RL** or **LR** or **LL**). The exact knowledge of the frequency distribution of the dishes helped the mathematician to devise a new, more economical 'key':

The favourite dish, roast pork, was given the shortest code name; this could be **R** or **L**. As the king was right handed and preferred to lift the right rather than the left arm the mathematician decided in favour of the **R**. Thus:

Roast! ⇔ **R**

In order to maintain the clarity of the code the following composite signal must be **LR**. The reason for this is that in a sequence of signals the combination **RL** would have meant that roast pork and something else, which has not yet been deciphered, was wanted. **LR** was unambiguous, **RL** on the other hand, was not. Thus:

Pudding! ⇔ **LR**

'...**RLR**...' in a sequence of signals meant '...Roast! Pudding!...' and '...**LRR**...' meant '...Pudding! Roast!...'. And this exhausted the store for signal pairs. For the encoding of the next popular dish the court mathematician appropriately again placed an **L** in front of the previous signal.

Thus the following correspondence applies:

Cake! ⇔ **LLR**

And for the last of the four dishes one could choose **LLL**. The code list therefore shows the following encoding:

Roast! ⇔ **R**
Pudding! ⇔ **LR**
Cake! ⇔ **LLR**
Gherkins! ⇔ **LLL**

The order of nine portions of roast pork per day required only nine *bit* (eighteen *bit* in the old code). In addition there are twelve *bit* daily for six chocolate pudding, six *bit* for two cakes and three *bit* for the one portion of gherkins. Altogether this came to thirty *bit* of information compared with thirty-six *bit* in the previous coding. No doubt this produced a far more advantageous code of the royal menu. Compared with the old days the lazy king saved himself six lifts of the hands per day. No wonder he was satisfied with this solution.

Thus the new coding was useful and unambiguous—it was economical. We shall practise it briefly on two examples. What did the king order when he sent the following sequence of signals?

LRRRLLR

In order to decode this message we proceed step by step: '**L**' by itself does not signify anything but '**LR**' means 'Bring me chocolate pudding!' Then comes '**R**': this was the royal signal for roast pork. '**R**' again: second portion of roast. Next comes '**L**' which again means nothing; even '**LL**' has no meaning but '**LLR**' means finally: 'Bring me strawberry cake!' In a similar way we can easily decipher **LLLRLLRLR**: 'Gherkins! Roast pork! Cake! Pudding!' demanded the king. Another interpretation was out of the question. The royal court mathematician found an optimal code for the culinary wishes of his majesty.

So much for our little story which like all nice fairy tales ended happily. The silent king was greatly pleased with his mathematician and promoted him to 'Chief court mathematician'. Over and above this the scientist was decorated with a very high order which was usually reserved only for the field-marshal. From now on the little king hardly spoke a word. And if he is not now dead then he still lifts his right or left arm from time to time, with great economy of effort, and follows this by eating roast pork, chocolate pudding, strawberry cake and gherkins with great satisfaction.

6.2 Signs with 'rarity value'
Probability and information

We shall now return from the fantasy world of the fairy tale about the little king and his coding problems to the somewhat more real world of pure information theory. We have already been able to learn that everything here does not need to be tedious and dry; mathematical expressions and formal dryness need not, by any means, go hand in hand. If we now shed the fairy tale cloak of our little story we are doing this only to recognize better the structure of information theory. Since our most useful instrument of communication, the natural language, is an opaque structure from the viewpoint of information theory, we had to take a rather unusual path in order to arrive at the kernel of measurable information. Only the seemingly artificial information-atom, the two-step, helped to create a useful basis for counting, ordering and comparing quantities of information. In order to create an appropriate measuring scale the theoreticians introduced logarithms; in fact, as we have seen, for purely practical reasons they use the logarithm to the base two. This finally helped to place the very densely packed amount of information. Our fairy tale gave rise to the idea of frequency of signals, whose effect on information it is our intention to determine in a more precise mathematical form.

First of all we saw that the information content of an arbitrarily selected sign depends on which sign store it came from, i.e. out of how many possibilities of selection it represents a decision. The larger the availability of signs the larger the amount of information carried by each sign. We came to the conclusion that a letter from the collection of twenty-six signs of our alphabet carries the information of 4·7 *bit* because, apart from the occurrence of the particular letter at a certain place in a text, there exist a further twenty-five possibilities to fill this place with another letter. It has been tacitly assumed here that all letters a, b, c,...x, y, z, occur with the same frequency. A quick glance at a newspaper or this book tells us right away: in English texts there are not as many y's as there are e's. (Again we shall ignore the use of capital letters and small letters.) We have already briefly discussed this fact when developing the Morse code (see page 102). Now the problem is to put this into mathematical language.

We have done good spade-work with our fairy tale. In order to encode a certain repertoire of messages or orders as economically as is possible a knowledge of the frequency distribution of these messages is required. If the encoding has been done properly then one finds: frequently occurring signals carry less information than rarely occurring ones; a sign will always represent more information the less often it appears. Thus in the 'good' code in the fairy tale the frequent call of the king for roast pork carried only one *bit* of information (**R**) whilst the less frequently occurring order for gherkins carried three *bit* (**LLL**).

Let us try to look at this more intuitively. It occasionally happens in printing that there are some words with letters missing. These missing letters can always be guessed more or less quickly. Of the two disfigured words 'box.r' and 'bo.er', the first word can be far more easily corrected to 'boxer' than the second word. The fact that it can be done at all is again connected with the much quoted redundancy. To begin with we are going to ignore all the other words of the text, the context of which could facilitate guessing the sense. The letter x does not occur in texts as often as the letter e. Thus x carries more information. It is far more noticeable if in a fragment of a text the x is missing than had it been an e. Do.s it b.com. mor. str.nuous to r.ad this s.nt.nc.? It is probably not very difficult although the letter e is missing from nine places. On the other hand it is not quite so simple to understand the following 'misprinted' sentence: Ale. the bo.er drives a lu.ury car. We know of course that the x is missing and it does not seem too difficult to read this sentence. But normally parts of sentences in which the e is missing are easier to guess than those where the x is missing. The letter x has 'rarity value' and carries therefore a considerable amount of information. In English x carries 9·5 *bit* whereas the more frequently occurring e only 3·2 *bit*.

One arrives at these values by a 'statistical' evaluation of English texts of different contents (compare with page 94). In addition to the size of the sign store, which exists as an ordered set in the particular alphabet, the amount of information is also determined by the frequency of occurrence of the signs. This naturally applies to all languages. And just as in English texts the letters *e, t, o* and *a* occur with highest frequency and so carry the least information, the same applies to *e, n, r* and *i* in German, to *e, a, s* and *n* in French, to *e, i, a* and *o* in Italian, etc. On the other hand the letters *x, j, k* and *q* occur infrequently in all these languages and carry therefore a relatively large amount of information. This is illustrated by an example each of an English and of a French text where the frequently and infrequently occurring letters are marked.

Incidentally texts printed in most Indo-European languages with all vowels missing can still be deciphered. The English sentence: 'Mr Sm.th .s . g.ntl.-m.n' as well as the German one: 'H.ns .st h.ngr.g .nd d.rst.g' can easily be guessed. Many shorthand systems in fact make use of this redundancy of the vowels. It is much more difficult to guess sentences where consonants have been omitted. This applies even to simple examples like 'i. i. ..e .o...a.' in English or '.e. .u.. ..ie.. i. .a..e.' in German. The reader will try, no doubt in vain, to fill these gaps and to complete, the sentence. The solution to all examples can be found on page 345.

The word 'frequent' has often been used in this discussion; this is important for the mathematical treatment. It has taken us into the field of 'probability theory'. If in certain texts a certain sign occurs frequently then it will also occur frequently in similar texts. It is a 'probable' sign, a sign to be expected. If, however, the sign occurs infrequently then it will also occur infrequently in comparable texts. The sign is 'improbable', it is hardly to be expected. Our task now is to build a bridge between the word 'frequency' which is well entrenched in linguistic usage and the theoretical 'probability'.

Probability and information—how are these two interlinked? Can we find a way to this problem starting from an everyday situation? Two simple examples may be of some help to us:

We have already met the saying of the journalist: 'When a dog bites a man that is not news but when a man bites a dog that is news.' (see page 81). News must have a surprise effect. We only need to look at the headlines of newspapers in order to understand what is meant. Just imagine the surprised face of Mr Brown when he reads the headline in his evening paper: 'Prime Minister bites dog'. Mr Brown definitely considers this as an unexpected event. It is, one might say,

Frequently occurring letters carry less information than less frequently occurring ones. In this example of an English text (Ian Fleming's *Dr No*) the letters carrying little information are shown in red, those carrying a lot of information in black. Half (!) the number of letters of this text consist of e-, t- and o- signals.

James Bond picked up his glass and sipped at it thoughtfully. It seemed pointless to go on bluffing. His story of representing the Audubon Society was any way a thin one which could be punctured by any one who knew about birds. It was obvious that . . .

e e e e e	t t t t t	o o o o o
e e e e e	t t t t t	o o o o o
e e e e e	t t t t t	o o o o o
e e	t t	o o

Most frequently occurring letters in English texts

La mathématique »moderne« serait, trop abstraite pour être enseignée aux niveaux élémentaires? A cette objection, les partisans d'une reforme opposent leur expérience. Dès le jardin d'enfants, certaines maîtresses font usage des notions mode . . .

e e e e e	a a a a a	s s s s s	n n n n n	t t t t t
e e e e e	a a a a a	s s s s s	n n n n n	t t t t t
e e e e e	a a a a a	s s s s s	n n n n n	t t t t t
e e e e e	a a	s s	n n	t t t
e e e e e				
e e e e e				
e e e e e				
e e e e e				

Most frequently occurring letters in French texts

The letter e has a clear lead, in the trequency distribution of letters in French texts. The example is a report on modern mathematics in the weekly *Figaro Littéraire*.

improbable. Or to put it into a more neutral way: it is an accidental occurrence, a chance happening. In colloquial speech one would say 'But this is most improbable!' or 'what a coincidence!' But this is precisely the point. The surprise effect of messages, news, informations will be greater the less probable they are, the less we expect them, the more they come about by chance.

Another example: 'Next winter is definitely coming!'. This is an obvious statement which one uses successfully in advertising. The news content, the information is practically nil in this case. Why? The sentences refers to an event which is generally considered to be a 'certainty'. One learns nothing new. What is said here is neither unexpected, nor improbable, nor accidental.

From the point of view of colloquial language there exists then a surprisingly good verbal relation with information. The information is greater the less probable it is. In this sense information is 'improbability'. To say it more precisely: the information of a signal is the measure for the improbability with which this signal occurs in a certain communication. We shall now put this idea into mathematical terms.

Before doing this, however, we have to sketch a few of the fundamental ideas of the theory of probability which the Russian mathematician Andrei N. Kolmogorov (born 1903) has placed on a most profound basis. These thoughts of A. N. Kolmogorov are described in *Modern Mathematics*, chapter 8.1.

We have often referred to 'sets' and also to 'subsets' (compare page 90). In a naive way this represented a 'collec-

tion', a lot of completely arbitrary things which are called the 'elements' of the set. The number of these elements is always taken to be finite. We must always be able to compile a list of finite length in which these elements appear. Then and only then shall we speak of a 'set' if we can form a clear and representative image of the particular structure. This image may be comparable with a basket of apples, a heap of coal or the natural numbers lying between 10 and 123. It will not interest us either that Kolmogorov's theory is constructed along strictly formal and axiomatic lines. After all we are doing 'applied' mathematics.

A certain number of elements can be collected to form a set. For example we can form a set M from the two letters a and e and the number 17:

$$M = (a, e, 17)$$

This set M possesses a certain number of subsets. Each element of a subset is also an element of M. Subsets of M are for instance $\{a, e\}$, $\{e, 17\}$ but also $\{a\}$ or $\{17\}$. Even M itself, i.e. $\{a, e, 17\}$, is by definition a subset of M. Furthermore the 'null-set' is a subset of M. What is this 'null-set'? We can imagine the set M being emptied step by step. To begin with we have three elements. If we remove one of them there remain two. If we remove another one we are left with one. If we finally remove this one as well then the set is empty. This empty set is called null-set and is denoted by 'o'.

We know now the meaning of sets and subsets in a finite region. But what use is all this to our discussion? Kolmogorov's theory allows us to determine the probabilities of random events. What is a random event? This is a type of question which we don't need to ask in a mathematical theory particularly if it is constructed like Kolmogorov's theory. It is better to ask: 'How do random events enter into the theory?' 'How do they occur?' Random events appear in this theory as subsets A_1, A_2, A_3, etc. It is therefore advantageous to know what a subset is. The totality associated with it is called the 'set E'. It possesses a finite number of elements, the 'elementary events'. Now to each of the subsets A or E there corresponds uniquely a (non-negative) number P(A) which is called its 'probability'. Thus these correspondences are:

$A_1 \rightarrow P(A_1)$
$A_2 \rightarrow P(A_2)$
$A_3 \rightarrow P(A_3)$ etc.

$P(A_1)$ should be read: 'P of A—one' and we say: '$P(A_1)$ is the probability of the random event A_1'. What sort of numerical values can $P(A_i)$ assume? (Here i is again a variable which represents a natural number.) We know that by definition the set E is also a subset of itself. Hence Kolmogorov defined: $P(E) = 1$. This reads: P of E is equal to one. Thus E expresses the event which is both elementary as well as random. In other words E is the 'certain event'. If the certain event is described by the one extreme value then the other extreme value must correspond to the completely uncertain, the 'impossible event'. It is represented by the other singular subset the null-set o. We have $P(o) = o$. All other values of $P(A_i)$ lie between the numerical values o and 1. If in the toss of a coin, the landing of heads or tails are equally probable events (A_1 and A_2 respectively) then $P(A_1) = \frac{1}{2}$ and $P(A_2) = \frac{1}{2}$. The chances for heads

or tails are fifty-fifty (see also page 109).
The correspondences with the probabilities are:

$A_1 \rightarrow \frac{1}{2}$
$A_2 \rightarrow \frac{1}{2}$

We can represent this in a simpler way by the following bracketed expression

$$\begin{pmatrix} A_1 & A_2 \\ \frac{1}{2} & \frac{1}{2} \end{pmatrix}$$

and the general expression is

$$\begin{pmatrix} A_1 & A_2 & \dots & A_i \\ P(A_1) & P(A_2) & \dots & P(A_i) \end{pmatrix}$$

But does it mean that the probability of the random event A_1, for example to land heads when tossing a coin, is $\frac{1}{2}$? If the coin is tossed ten times then it can quite well happen to land heads four times and tails six time. The frequency of occurrence $h(A_1)$ (read: 'h of A—one') would then be $4/10$ which reduces to $2/5$. How can the frequency of occurrence $h(A_1) = 2/5$ and the probability $P(A_1) = \frac{1}{2}$ be reconciled in this instance?

Frequencies are values obtained by experience, by observation. They are also referred to as empirical values. These empirical frequency values have to be clearly related to the theoretical probability values. If one were to toss the coin not just ten times but a hundred —or five hundred—times then the numerical comparison looks quite different. What is important is a relatively high number of throws or, to say it more generally a repeated realization of the experimental conditions. We can then apply the practical rule of probability calculus:

If a n-fold realization of the required conditions leads to a random event A_i in m cases then the frequency $h(A_i) = m/n$, differs only little from the probability

6. Improbabilities

$P(A_i)$. Written as a formula this means $P(A_i) \approx h(A_i)$ which is to be read: 'P of A_i is approximately equal to h of A_i'.

These theoretical findings can now be put to use in our little fairy tale. Four random events are of importance at the royal table:

A_1: The king orders roast
A_2: The king orders pudding
A_3: The king orders cake
A_4: The king orders gherkins

Also known are the frequencies $h(A_1)$ to $h(A_4)$. We assume that they are based on a large number of tries, i.e. that the royal court mathematician has observed his majesty's culinary habits over a long period of time. The frequency values are then almost identical with the probability values. We can thus write down the following expression:

$$\begin{pmatrix} A_1 & A_2 & A_3 & A_4 \\ 9/18 & 6/18 & 2/18 & 1/18 \end{pmatrix}$$

The sum of the probabilities $P(A_1) + P(A_2) + P(A_3) + P(A_4)$ always comes to the value 1, which can easily be checked in our example. Most of the probability values can be reduced giving

$$\begin{pmatrix} A_1 & A_2 & A_3 & A_4 \\ \frac{1}{2} & 1/3 & 1/9 & 1/18 \end{pmatrix}$$

Let us look at this situation from the angle of information theory. The king with his culinary wishes represents a source of information. He is the 'sender' giving out wishes (or orders). Hence his messages are A_1, A_2, A_3 and A_4. In other words the bracketed expression above which contains the royal information repertoire and the associated probabilities represents the 'image' of an information source. This image is indeed very abstract but it is simple and useful. We shall see its usefulness later.

The expression within the brackets tells us that the message A_1 occurs with a relatively high probability $P(A_1) = \frac{1}{2}$; on the other hand the message A_4 with a low probability $P(A_4) = 1/18$. To put it into other words: A_1 is more likely to be expected at any point of a sequence of messages than is A_4. Admittedly this sequence cannot be pre-selected; it is accidental. But in the end, one will obtain a clear-cut frequency distribution. This 'certainty' is the reason why it is possible to calculate an 'expectation value' for every message which occurs as a term of a sequence. In this case the expectation value means that this value shall represent a measure for the uncertainty as to which message is to be the next one in the sequence.

If now the king begins to 'transmit' or if he is in the middle of a transmission then the receiver (the servant or chef) will expect to receive every time the order 'roast pork' (message A_1) rather than the order 'gherkins' (message A_4). A_4 is far less probable than A_1 but carries more information than A_1. What is the amount of information, measured in *bit*, that is carried by a particular message? We know already that the smaller the probability $P(A_i)$ of a message A_i the larger is its information $I(A_i)$. Logarithmically we can express this as

$$I(A_i) = \log_2 \frac{1}{P(A_i)} \quad (bit)$$

$P(A_i)$ occurs in the denominator because the amount of information increases with decreasing probability. The logarithmic scale serves here only for better clarity. In order to obtain the numerical values of the informations $I(A_1)$ to $I(A_4)$ we apply the above to the four messages A_1 to A_4:

$$I(A_1) = \log_2 \frac{1}{\frac{1}{2}} = \log_2 2 = 1 \; bit$$

$$I(A_2) = \log_2 \frac{1}{1/3} = \log_2 3 = 1\cdot585 \; bit$$

$$I(A_3) = \log_2 \frac{1}{1/9} = \log_2 9 = 3\cdot17 \; bit$$

$$I(A_4) = \log_2 \frac{1}{1/18} = \log_2 18 = 4\cdot17 \; bit$$

These are the precise numerical values for the amount of information contained in the messages. But how can they be used to reveal the expectation value? The measure of the uncertainty as to which message will occur next in a sequence is the 'average information' usually denoted by H. The expression 'average information' indicates the way along which we have to proceed: it is necessary to calculate the average value of the amounts of information involved in this particular problem. The general expression for this is

$$H(A_1,...A_i) = P_(A_1) . \log_2 \frac{1}{P(A_1)}$$

$$+ P(A_2) \log_2 \frac{1}{P(A_2)} + ...$$

$$... + P(A_i) \log_2 \frac{1}{P(A_i)} \; (bit)$$

This average information $H(A_1,...A_i)$, which reads H of A_1 to A_i, is often called 'entropy'. The expression deduced here does in fact formally resemble an expression for entropy in statistical physics. In the latter case entropy is used to describe energy losses. Now information has nothing to do with energy (see page 106); therefore if we were to use entropy in our discussion we would run into dimensional difficulties. We shall consequently limit

our verbal expression to 'average information' and 'uncertainty'. To speak of entropy in this context is a rather enforced analogy which only creates more confusion (compare page 33). What then is the average information $H(A_1, A_2, A_3, A_4)$ in our example of the royal information source? We only need to substitute:

$$H(A_1,...A_4) = \tfrac{1}{2} \log_2 2 + \frac{1}{3} \log_2 3 + \frac{1}{9}$$

$$\log_2 9 + \frac{1}{18} \log_2 18 = 1\cdot614 \; bit$$

This value $1\cdot614$ bit does not tell us much as yet. What we need are comparative values and for this we have to do some calculating. We can say that the value which we have just calculated applies to a repertoire of four signs A_1, A_2, A_3, A_4. Naturally we could equally well have chosen four other signals: A, B, C, D or i, ii, iii, iv or the four kings in a pack of cards etc. We can arrange the signs for the 18 royal orders according to their frequency:

$$A_1A_1A_1A_1A_1A_1A_1A_1A_1A_2A_2A_2A_2A_2$$
$$A_2A_3A_3A_4$$

The first unique encoding with binary signals

$(A_1 \Leftrightarrow$ RR, $A_2 \Leftrightarrow$ RL. $A_3 \Leftrightarrow$ LL, $A_4 \Leftrightarrow$ LR)

produces the following frequency distribution

RRRRRRRRRRRRRRRRRRRLRLRLRLRLRL
LLLLLR

But the royal source of information has become much simpler. Since the king only sends binary signals the expression within the brackets becomes:

$$\begin{pmatrix} R & L \\ \frac{25}{36} & \frac{11}{36} \end{pmatrix}$$

163

The two probabilities $P(R)$ and $P(L)$ can be given in terms of the frequencies $h(R)$ and $h(L)$. The ordered sequence of signals is made up of thirty-six terms of which twenty-five are R's and eleven are L's. We can now calculate the average information $H_1(R,L)$ if we remember the following rule which applies to all logarithms $\log \dfrac{a}{b} = \log a - \log b$, thus:

$$H_1(R,L) = \frac{25}{36} \log_2 \frac{36}{25}$$
$$+ \frac{11}{36} \log_2 \frac{36}{11} = 0.883 \; bit$$

Now we have the two values $1.614 \; bit$ and $0.883 \; bit$ for the average information content of two sign stores, of which the former represents a repertoire of four and the latter one of two signs. But nothing can be said as yet as to which of the two codes is the more useful. So we have to continue our calculation. But before that we wish to determine a third value of the uncertainty or average information and that is the one corresponding to the code repertoire R, LR, LLR, LLL considered as optimal by the royal court-mathematician. Again we operate with binary signals. The ordered sequence gives the following frequency distribution

RRRRRRRRRLRLRLRLRLRLLRLLRLLL

This corresponds to the following image of the source of information:

$$\begin{pmatrix} R & L \\ \dfrac{17}{30} & \dfrac{13}{30} \end{pmatrix}$$

The corresponding uncertainty $H_2(R,L)$ is:

$$H_2(R,L) = \frac{17}{30} \log_2 \frac{30}{17} + \frac{13}{30} \log_2 \frac{30}{13} =$$
$$0.988 \; bit$$

Why was it that in our fairy tale we considered the second binary code as being more useful than the first? In the second case the king saved himself raising his hand six times in order to be served his daily routine of eighteen dishes. Comparing the average information we see that $H_2(R,L) = 0.988 \; bit$ is larger than $H_1(R,L) = 0.883 \; bit$. Thus each signal from the second code carries more information compared with each signal from the first code. We can say that a concentration of messages has taken place; the signals of the second code express more.

We have already explained this reasonably well by means of redundancy without, however, being able to make precise numerical comparisons. But now we can do it.

Binary signs carry $1 \; bit$ of information, i.e. R or L correspond to $1 \; bit$. This is as far as we had gone. But now we can be more precise: for binary signs, $1 \; bit$ of information forms the largest possible average information or the maximum uncertainty H_{max}. The uncertainty is always largest when all signals appear with the same probability. This is exactly what we have always tacitly assumed. Our thoughts about the amount of information have been made systematically more sensitive. We can also calculate the maximum uncertainty without difficulty. The bracketed expression for this case is

$$\begin{pmatrix} R & L \\ \dfrac{1}{2} & \dfrac{1}{2} \end{pmatrix}$$

and the maximum uncertainty is

$$H_{max}(R,L) = \tfrac{1}{2} \log_2 2 + \tfrac{1}{2} \log_2 2 = 1 \; bit$$

In the relevant literature one often finds the expression 'maximum entropy' for

The Soviet mathematician A. N. Kolmogorov (born 1903) has made a considerable contribution to making information theory into a precise tool.

H_{max} but for reasons already mentioned we shall not make use of it (see page 163). For the repertoire of the signs A_1, A_2, A_3, A_4 the maximum uncertainty assumes the value $H_{max} = 2 \; bit$; this is a result which can more easily be arrived at by reflection rather than calculation. The connection between the uncertainty H with the maximum uncertainty H_{max} leads to the expression for the redundancy r.

Groups of two or three (digrams and trigrams) occur frequently in every language. In English texts it is far more likely that a 't' is followed by an 'h' and an 'e' (the) than by any other letter grouping. Thus the letters following a 't' carry a smaller amount of information than in a mere chance pattern where the letters follow at random.

ENGLISH	FRENCH	GERMAN
t h e	e n t	e i n
a n d	l e s	s c h
i n g	q u e	d e r
i o n	e d e	i c h

165

It is given by

$$r = \frac{H_{max} - H}{H_{max}}$$

For the repertoire A_1, A_2, A_3, A_4 we thus obtain a redundancy of

$$r = \frac{2 - 1.614}{2} = 0.193$$

The redundancy in this case amounts to 19·3 per cent. What is the redundancy of the first binary code with the pairs of signals **RR**, **RL**, **LR**, **LL**? One can easily calculate that the value is 0·117 or 11·7 per cent. Thus there is less 'unnecessary chat' compared with the use of four signs. Finally the 'optimum' attempt of the court mathematician to condense the royal information (0·988 *bit*) yields a redundancy of 0·012 or 1·2 per cent. This is quite a noteworthy result.

Of course for the ideal case of optimal encoding the redundancy becomes equal to zero. This requires a completely uniform sign distribution, i.e. all signs must occur with the same probability. Every non-uniformity in the probability distribution benefits redundancy.

The highly non-uniform probability distribution of the letters in arbitrarily chosen texts of different languages, a topic we have already discussed, is to a large extent responsible for the redundancy in Indo-European languages, which lies between 50 and 75%. This is, however, of great advantage for natural as well as artificial communication situations. It actually guarantees the trustworthiness of the communication. We can follow telephone conversations even if the line is noisy, can read strongly fragmented texts tolerably well, can communicate quite well with one another despite loud noises etc.

Probability and information: the mathematical theory which Kolmogorov created in the early thirties is exactly what information theory needs. His theory was formulated far more generally than we have sketched it here. We have only used it to the extent that we looked for a simple introduction into the mathematical field of communications research; a simpler introduction than one would often get using the approach in technical literature.

There are other reasons, apart from the ones discussed here, why redundancy is relatively high in the texts of the various languages. There is no language in which the letters appear altogether arbitrarily. This may perhaps be so in a third of the cases. It is not by accident that a verb follows a noun; that within a word in English the letter a follows the letter e etc. Apart from sign store and sign frequency, another decisive factor in the amount of information is the intersymbol influence. Signals often occur in quite definite regular groupings. For instance in arbitrary texts letter groups appear in pairs as 'digrams' (or in threes as 'trigrams'). It can easily be checked that in German the letter pair *ei* occurs frequently, similarly *of* in English and *en* in French. But the best example of this intersymbol influence is q and u. Like Siamese Twins q and u always occur followed by u. Hence u after q carries zero information. The situation is similar as for the sentence: 'Next winter is together or more precisely q is always definitely coming'. Just as winter follows autumn so u follows q. A probability, an expectation value does not exist in this case.

Similarly, the sequence of other letters

is not completely random. It is limited by rules, by certain standard patterns. For example in German the letter combinations *schl, schm, schn* and *scht* can only be followed by a vowel. The maximum amount of information associated with the place following this group of four letters is $\log_2 5$ or $2 \cdot 322$ *bit*. Three-letter groups which frequently occur in English, French and German are shown in the diagram. Along with them goes a devaluation of information. Of course such phenomena can also occur in non-linguistic cases of communication: motorists have to pay attention to traffic lights with green, yellow and red signal lights. For the moment we shall ignore the fact that red and yellow can light up at the same time; we shall simply note this as yellow. On the basis of the signal store alone each signal would correspond to an information of $1 \cdot 59$ *bit* ($\log_2 3$). But this is too high. Because, within the sequence, red can never directly follow green or vice versa it follows that the choice is limited. There is no random sequence of the three signals. The quantity of information per sign is also decreased here due to the intersymbol influence between green and yellow and also between yellow and red. Yellow always follows green; yellow (actually red and yellow) always follows red. It would be futile in such situations to expect anything else but yellow. Since after yellow we always get red or green we can attribute 1 *bit* of information to this point in the sequence of signals. But it is important to design signalling devices of this kind with considerable redundancy. After all we are always concerned here with Safety with a capital s and not with the lack of it. In this particular case, in addition to the yellow light, this is achieved by the unique arrangement of signals: red is always on top, yellow in the middle, green at the bottom.

Although, strictly speaking, order seems to diminish information, to act as an opponent to information, the fact is that every kind of order or regularity limits the choices which enable one to make a decision. The feeling of expectation has been relaxed, the surprise effect has gone.

This may sound very confused at first but it is by no means a 'song in praise of chaos'. If we think of a typical situation in communication, e.g. reading a newspaper, a telegram, a telephone conversation, what would we have to say if all we were being told as receivers was the sequence of traffic signals: Green-Yellow-Red-Yellow-Green-Yellow-Red-Yellow...? Would we not prefer to leave to chance what we are going to read in the papers the next morning or what we are going to find out during our next telephone conversation?

7. 'BUILDING SITES' OF LANGUAGES AND THINKING

7.1 Good old redundancy
Balance sheet on the subject of 'Language and Information'

At the starting point of our unusual approach to measurable information stood the sign post binary digit: Yes or no, left or right, black or white, **1** or **0** etc. Its verbal contraction 'bit' provided us with a label for the unit in terms of which information could be counted and measured. This defined a tightly packed scale of information. So far all seemed to be in 'good' order.

But then we saw these titbits of information in a new perspective. The rich tool-box of modern mathematics suggested that we regard information as something accidental, as a logarithmic measure for improbability. Indeed 'order' turned out to be the opponent of information. But news which we expect in any case is not news—the information is then very 'thin'. The accident, the random event, however, is least popular with most people, certainly far less so than order. This may perhaps be one of the reasons why people who are professionally associated with accidental events, with improbabilities, do not command 'high public esteem'. According to opinion polls journalists, reporters, radio and television people do not have many friends. All 'newsmen' must always smell out, or chase after, the improbabilities of life. News offices are the exchange places for information from where news is sent out to the interested public. Reporters, correspondents, news agencies bombard their offices with local or international 'improbabilities'.

Every rigid order, every 'purely automatic' regularity is deadly poison for journalism if there are no gaps left for chance events. If we know precisely what the newspaper is going to say tomorrow then we just will not buy it. A journalist who always churns out the same thing has missed his vocation. When we glance at the paper, turn on the radio or television we always expect something new, whether it is news or background information from politics, economics, culture or science, a new thriller or a new pop song, a new show or a new society scandal. The presentation need not change at all or perhaps just a little. Newspapers have their typical lay-out. Shows and plays on television often have the same cast. Such fixed forms, 'signs of quality' and 'motifs' act as a useful counterweight for improbability. Nevertheless, here too one runs the risk of creating stereotypes.

Summarizing we can say: in all interesting situations of communication the 'state of suspense of the receiver' is always borne in mind. If news, messages and informations are to be what their names suggest they have to be accidental, improbable. In terms of information theory we say: the average information of the source should have large *bit* values, that is it should have a large uncertainty. But let us not forget what this means

---

'To think with thinking tools': This motto determines the following discussion. Just as today man uses his technical tools in quite a natural way, he will use his thinking tools without much ado tomorrow.

from the point of probability theory: from a randomly selected repertoire certain messages should not be sent too often or too rarely. Both cases act to the detriment of uncertainty; the average information decreases. The much disputed 'freedom of the press' can also be considered from this point.

Problems associated with communication can be dealt with quite well mathematically by means of the theory of probability. The 'network' for random events which we indicated on the basis of Kolmogorov's theory, contains a useful pattern for communications research. Does this, however, say anything about the nature of information? Does it help us to give a satisfactory answer to the question: 'What is information?' The honest theoretician has to shrug his shoulders regretfully and explain that he cannot answer such questions because he did not ask them in the first place. It was not the nature of information that interested him but the question of whether information can be rendered measurable. Many serious thinkers may well regret such questions. Is it to be wondered at that they do not like the answers given by information theory? Ever since an exact science existed, that is since the days of Galileo, such thinkers were always dissatisfied with the way that physicists, and later chemists and biologists and now also theorizing technologists formulate their questions. Counting and measuring: to many people these form even today reprehensible and inferior activities incapable of 'saying' anything.

As it turned out it did not make much sense in natural science that physicists should ask: 'Why does a stone fall towards the earth when I let go of it?, that the biologist should ask: 'What is life?, that the communications expert should ask: 'What is information?'. Much more useful were questions like: 'What do the patterns of communication look like?' or 'How does a particular process function in a living cell?' or 'How does a stone fall towards the earth when I let it go?' These are cases where mathematical tools can be of help. The German physicist and technologist Wilhelm Fucks, referring to the simplest of our examples, said:

'What process is there in the universe which could be less rational than a stone falling down once I have released it? For thousands of years men have tried to tackle questions of this type purely with the intellect. They have pondered about how Nature actually does it that a stone which to start with is high up will, a little while after I let it go, be farther down. Up to the present time this problem has not been solved. We don't know at all how it comes about that the stone when released does not remain where it is but changes its location. Neither the old theories of gravitation nor the modern field theories have changed anything in this situation. You all know that Galileo came and said the stone falls five metres during the first second, fifteen metres during the second and twenty-five metres during the third etc. What would a philosopher at the time have thought of this attempt to describe rigorously and quantitatively the process of the falling stone? He would have thought that Galileo did not even understand the first elements of the problem of free fall. Surely it is quite immaterial whether the stone falls a little bit slower at the beginning and a little faster later on. This may well be an interesting detail but such a quantitative description has nothing whatever to do with the actual understanding of the process. Surely one had to explain why the stone is on top at first and at the bottom later on. This is what Galileo did not explain. He deliberately bypassed the question of the nature of things and phenomena, the question which has inspired philosophers since the days of Aristotle. He selected one characteristic which, as far as the understanding of the essence was concerned, was highly insignificant.'

Nobody would deny nowadays that this new way of questioning was extremely useful. Modern physics and modern technology furnish thousands of proofs in the defence of Galileo. A very similar situation applies today when we consider information from the theoretical and mathematical point of view. We are certainly not in a position to weigh up the consequences. Without having come close to the 'nature' of information let us try to draw up a modest balance sheet about the mathematically established information.

It was not until our century that people became aware of the importance of information. The real thinking about the 'structure' of information started in the field of modern technology. It was triggered off by problems encountered in connection with artificial transmission channels. 'Faithfulness of sound' in the case of reproduction of music, 'intelligibility' in a telephone conversation, etc, these were the first qualitative terms with which the technologists set off to track down information. Telegraphy, telephony, radio and television had already been invented by the time the exact science of information—or communication theory began to take shape. It was mainly due to American theoreticians led by Harry Nyquist, R. V. L. Hartley and especially Claude E. Shannon, that a unified terminology was created. Mathematical communications research thus became the first important contribution of modern technology to the 'theoretical world-building' as the mathematician Hermann Weyl expressed it. Until then such contributions were reserved entirely for theoretical science, especially theoretical physics. It was the latter which created the precise terminology of 'space' and 'time', of 'matter' and 'energy' in order to describe the universe and its events theoretically. Information theory did the same for the initially vague catch word 'information'.

'Information is information; it is neither matter nor energy'; this, as we have already stated, is how Norbert Wiener described it. We have also seen that pieces of information can be regarded as activities, as simple mathematical operations. One is then always concerned with definite patterns, schemes, structures: shapes made by human hand or machine, constructions, operations which are all 'technically realizable'. Something always has to be made, a repertoire of signs or signals. C. E. Shannon gives a very good parallel to this activity: The transport of information resembles an endless belt which carries timber. The shapes of the pieces of timber are determined by the load limit and carrying capacity of the

C. E. Shannon compared the transport of information with an endless belt laden with timber. Turning the timber into planks, blocks, logs and shavings corresponds to information.

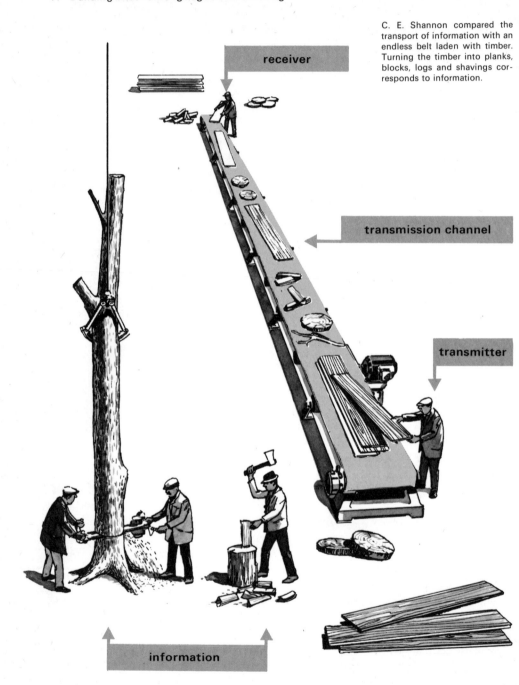

receiver

transmission channel

transmitter

information

belt. For correct loading the timber has to be cut up into planks, blocks, logs and sometimes even chips. This division corresponds to information. It always conforms to the dictates of the transmission channel (here the endless belt).

In his papers C. E. Shannon has also sketched the idea of characterizing the measurable structure 'communication' or 'information' as a sequence of signals which can be produced as a 'stochastic' process. Such a sequence is made up of elements which are selected in terms of a probability which depends on the directly preceding signals of the sequence. If adjacent signals (digrams) are characterized by transition probabilities then one speaks of a 'Markov-chain'. Such a sequence of signals has been named after the Russian mathematican A. A. Markov who produced a statistical analysis of digrams for Alexander Pushkin's *Eugene Onegin*. In the middle of this century when students gained access to computers a whole avalanche set in of such statistical evaluations of texts written in all civilized languages.

The sequences of signals of traffic lights (see page 112) represent incidentally a typical Markov chain. In this case one can see straight away that transition probabilities exist between 'adjacent' signals. Markov chains play a part in all situations of communication. This includes 'speaking' as a human behavioural characteristic. Is the Markov method also of interest to the linguist and to theoretical linguistics? There is no doubt that in this connection this method has been, and still is, overestimated. Y. Bar-Hillel dissociated himself from this method in a very clear manner: 'In the study of language there is no room for probability and statistics.' In fact we have pointed out several times that the roots of measurable information do not lie in the landscape of languages; information theory without probability and statistics does not exist.

So that communication can function, at least two people, but usually many more, must have access to the sign store. Only then is it possible to transmit information or exchange messages. Karl Steinbuch the German physicist and communications expert illustrated this situation by an event which was decisive in the history of communication:

'It was Johannes Gutenberg's invention to use movable cast types in the printing of books. This compares so to speak with the transmission of information: first of all one has to create a repertoire of type which both sender and receiver associate with the same meaning; without a store of signs common to both, transmission of the information is impossible. In the case of the written transmission of the communication the writer has to use a sign script which the reader will understand; in the case of the verbal transmission the speaker has to use sounds which are known to the listener.'

In this context we must remind ourselves of Wittgenstein's critical thoughts about the much used 'meanings'. We would prefer to speak of 'unique use' of signs or type (compare page 27). The emphasis is again laid on the human activity. Similar signs are used in similar ways. One can only establish a more or less strongly marked similarity; but this similarity suffices for communication.

173

This is an example where the recipient has to choose the message:— light fish and light birds, or dark fish and dark birds? (M. C. Escher).

But there are other activities which are important in communication processes. There is first the selection process of the sender. Out of a certain number of possibilities the sender decides to select a particular message and no other; this then appears at a particular point of the transmission sequence. If this communication is formulated simply and unambiguously then the undistorted reception will be clear-cut and definite (compare also page 153).

Such a selection process is at times also required of the receiver. If the transmitted message is not always unambiguous then the receiver has to be selective. This is shown very clearly by two fascinating illustrated examples by the Dutch artist Maurits C. Escher (born 1898). In the larger of the two illustrations depending on our choice of background, whether dark or bright, the information will be different: light fish or dark birds. Although the artist (sender) has formulated both messages with the same expenditure of signals yet the observer (receiver) initially chooses only one of the two possibilities. In most cases one

chooses spontaneously the message 'fish' and only rarely the message 'birds'. Only after looking for a while can one select arbitrarily one message or the other. The simultaneous comprehension of both messages is possible but, as is known from experience, gives rise to some difficulties. Our inborn cognition mechanism of the visual sense is not conditioned by nature to cope with such artificial situations. It is very much easier, in the smaller illustration, to distinguish between the two messages 'bright fish and bright birds' and 'dark fish and dark birds'.

The finite size of the sign store to which a transmitted sign belongs is the first important parameter of measurable information. Naturally the amount of information becomes larger if composite signs or signals are permitted. The information content increases with the 'length' of the compound signs. But there is one point which we always have to bear in mind. Out of how many possible messages which can be chosen does the selected message represent the only decision? If we assume that all signs used have the same probability then the corresponding amount of information can be computed from a simple formula (see page 138). The evaluation of the information is still not too difficult if the probability distribution of the signals varies (see page 162). The 'average information' of the particular information source is an important parameter in the latter case. It helps us to determine exactly and without difficulty the redundancy of the sender (see page 166).

As we have seen our colloquial language contains a good deal of redundancy. Here the information is normally strongly diluted, well packed and sufficiently safe-guarded. In most cases of information transport via natural or artificial channels verbosity is a 'good' rule; it helps to compensate for disturbances of all kinds. Is it not very useful if, at times, we can follow fragments of a conversation which we just pick up, or if we just half-listen to something? Thanks to redundancy we can understand strongly distorted telephone conversations, decipher badly printed or mutilated texts, ignore mis-prints etc. Of course this does not always apply with absolute certainty but mostly the communication is safeguarded. A distorted telegram text could read: 'arrive sigurday' or 'arrive saturdy' but the receiver will know without doubt that the sender will arrive on saturday. Even if all vowels are missing: '.rr.v. s.t.rd.y' the fragmented text still carries enough information regarding the sender's in-tentions. This is made possible only through redundancy. Yet, at times, there may be difficulties. If the sender intends to arrive on saturday night and the distorted telegram text says: 'arrive satur-day .ight' then even redundancy may not help to avoid misunderstandings.

Redundancy is concerned with safety in communication. In order to arrive at the root of information we had to remove redundancy. But what has been removed can, when necessary, be re-instated. This is a very simple but effective principle: What was systematically dismantled can again be systematically assembled. We have seen in our fairy tale how an 'opti-mal' code was created, how it was analyzed mathematically and why this code deserved this adjective. Its redun-dancy is almost zero; in the ideal case it is exactly zero.

For the use of top-secret information-transmission communication technolo-gists nowadays devise codes with high redundancy built in according to require-ments. Such codes are then checkable and correctable. Why?

Naturally one can illustrate all this mathematically. In the discussion of the optimum code we have used so much

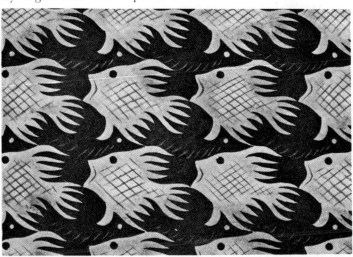

The recipient of a com-munication has to choose at times. In this drawing by M. C. Escher this selection process is par-ticularly well illustrated: light fish or dark birds?

mathematics that we shall now, for a change, give preference to the familiar and useful colloquial language. We can outline in a sentence the central problem of this code design: in the encoding of communication it is a matter of making use skilfully of the redundancy which was so much despised in optimal coding. Do testable codes always have to have their full measure of redundancy? Are they 'special tools with superfluousness'? This in fact is so. Here redundancy is by no means superfluous. Verbosity is used intentionally.

What do such codes look like? The first rule is: errors in transmission can only be detected when the amount of information contained in the 'code words' is greater than the average information or doubt-value (entropy) of the information source. In other words: redundancy must be present.

As a simplification we might say that technologists have learnt from the extravagant layout of the written language. We have seen that in most cases misprints in ordinarily worded messages can easily be corrected or else the sequences of signs would not make sense. Or to express it differently: the sequences of sounds which are expressed by these sign combinations do not exist in the repertoire of the familiar language-games. (For example the sequence of signs 'dubidubidadada' could well play some sort of role in private language-games, as perhaps between mother and child or between the pop-music composer and lyric-writer etc. In a normal text, however, one would have to regard it as nonsensical.) With the scripted signs of our alphabet many nonsensical expressions can easily be

formulated like 'hrztlg' or 'aioee' or perhaps less absurd ones like 'repactillible' or 'bastolic'. Only because redundancy is very high distorted or absurd expressions can easily be corrected if there was interference during the transmission of the communication, e.g. 'siturday' to 'saturday' or 'arrile' to 'arrive' or 'Londo' to 'London' etc. If the code is designed with a redundancy similar to that of our natural texts then the artificial code also becomes correspondingly insensitive to distortions. Usually this is a very coarse but effective safeguard: one has then to contend with a sizable subset of absurd sign sequences. Although this renders the code 'error correctable' for the recipient of distorted messages it makes it unfortunately more expensive when, as is usually the case, artificial channels are being used. We have already encountered this not unimportant point when sending a telegram. Redundancy costs money. It just depends on the view one takes: on the one hand redundancy serves to safeguard the message conveyed, on the other it can become an information-deficient deadweight which simply makes the message more expensive.

Another simple method, which also inflates the cost, is the repeated repetition of the message. This way of introducing redundancy guarantees to a high degree the correct selection of the right message by the receiver. The correct message is then received more often than its randomly distorted variants. Redundancy in the form of repeated information becomes the correct and simple information in case the transmission is disturbed; here redundancy is 'potential' information. At railway stations and airports

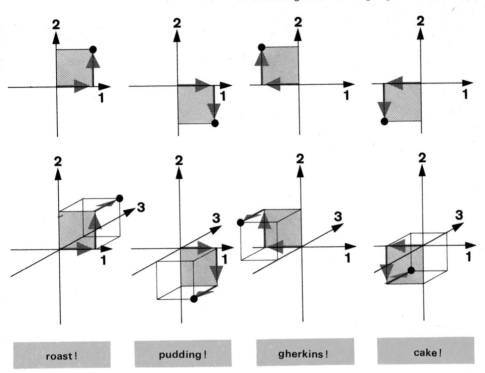

roast!   pudding!   gherkins!   cake!

A code becomes correctable by increasing redundancy. In this example signal pairs of two binary signs are changed to groups of three. If one represents the signal sequences by points in a coordinate system then, in the case of the simple code, these points lie in the plane determined by the axes 1,2, and in the case of the error-correcting code in the space determined by the axes 1,2,3. The distance between the four points is thereby increased; in other words the Hamming-distance of the code words is increased. The larger the Hamming-distance the less prone is the corresponding code (Hamming-code) to disturbances.

important information is always announced several times, even in different languages. Knowing the awful din in large stations or airport buildings one can understand the reason for this. Praise be for good old redundancy!

The repetition of information can, however, become an expensive joke when sending a telegram. Every word which is repeated costs money, and the more so the more often it is repeated. It was precisely the question of cost which was responsible for the telegram style.

Let us go back once more to our instructive fairy tale. The first unambi-

guous, though not optimized, code of the king's culinary wishes was the following (compare page 153).

Roast ⇔ **RR**
Pudding ⇔ **RL**
Gherkins ⇔ **LR**
Cake ⇔ **LL**

Will the king be served according to his wishes if the servant or the cook receives a distorted sequence of signs? The transmission process is certainly simple because the receiver is present in person in the throne room. The natural channel is short. Where could the disturbances come from? The king could, say, be

177

surrounded by some court busybodies and they might well prevent the royal transmitter, the two hands, from being seen. It could then happen that the receiver would not be able to establish whether the king, for instance, raised his right hand six times or whether he raised the left hand once and then the right hand five times. Does the king desire roast three times or gherkins followed by two helpings of roast? Was the message **RRRRRR** or was it **LRRRRR**? Whether the first term of the sequence of signals was **R** or **L** cannot be established subsequently. And the king would certainly not like it if the servant had asked to have the order repeated. The code becomes correctable only if the redundancy is increased. The king would then have to supply an additional 1 *bit* of information per order, i.e. he would have to raise his hand three times instead of twice. The code then becomes:

> Roast! ⇔ **RRR**
> Pudding! ⇔ **RLL**
> Gherkins! ⇔ **LRL**
> Cake! ⇔ **LLR**

Why has this particular code been chosen? A first glance reveals that the original signal pairs have been retained in the first two places of the group of three. And all that has been done was to add a third place. What determined whether **R** or **L** is to be added? Going back to our example of the distorted transmission we had either **RRRRRR** or **LRRRRR**. This problem could not be solved in the old code. In the new code with increased redundancy we have

> **RRRRRRRRR** or **LRLRRRRRR**.

Even if the receiver observed the distorted sequence **RRLRRRRRR** he knows what the king ordered. The first three signals only make sense if they are **LRL**: the other possibility **RRL** means nothing. No corresponding 'code word' exists in the list. A distortion of the second signal of this group leads to similar consequences. The question '**RRR** or **RLR**?' can be answered in favour of **RRR**. A distortion of both the first and the second signals is relatively improbable. But in order to avoid such distortions redundancy would have to be increased even further.

The added third signal in our example merely serves to check the code. It carries no information about the royal wishes and its function is merely one of control. The code has been designed in such a way that the number of the **R**-elements in the group of three signals is always odd. The first signal group contains three **R**'s, the other three only one **R** each.

If we keep this property of the code in mind then we know precisely when planning the new code whether to add an **R** or an **L**. The code has increased redundancy but it is an error-correcting code.

Due to the fact that what is being checked here is an 'equality', a 'parity', this method of safeguarding is also known as a 'parity check'. The introduction of redundancy adds in our case 1 *bit* per signal group. This additional information is called the 'parity check bit'. One speaks of 'Hamming codes' after the American technologist Richard W. Hamming of Bell Telephone Laboratories who systematically developed these methods of code-safety. The probability of error had to be relatively small, however, for these codes to function with safety.

If on the other hand the probability of

error is large then these codes can only be improved one step at a time, and this will make the code fairly intricate. The transmission time increases considerably. The Russian theoretician I. A. Poletaiev gave a witty and pointed description of this procedure:

'The transmission of a telegram with subsequent reduction of errors by means of repeated encoding produces a result only after a certain lapse of time. According to its inventor a transmission of this kind should proceed in perhaps the following way: A telegram which was received with probable distortions is delivered with the accompanying remark: "Error probability per letter ten per cent. Amendment tomorrow." The next day, after having received further telegrams with additional check signs and having located the places needing improvement, the receiver got the following message: "Instead of mouse read house, instead of hive read have. Error probability per word now one per cent. Additional amendments next week." As announced the following message arrives after the appropriate time: "Instead of mist read most. Error probability per letter now one per thousand. Next message in a month." This will continue until the receiver no longer wants to be troubled by continuous messages and emphatically puts a stop to it.'

An 'absolute guarantee' is consequently a very difficult problem in all communications situations particularly if artificial channels have to be used. If one chooses a transmission channel, whatever type it may be, one always has to reckon with disturbances. Even in simple conversations one often meets questions like: 'I beg your pardon?' or 'May I hear that again?' or 'Would you mind repeating that?' etc. If one selects printed matter of any kind one always has to reckon with misprints. In a teleprinter message one finds that, at times, the letters received are

Interference in the reception can always occur in information transport. The source of noise acts as a second transmitter.

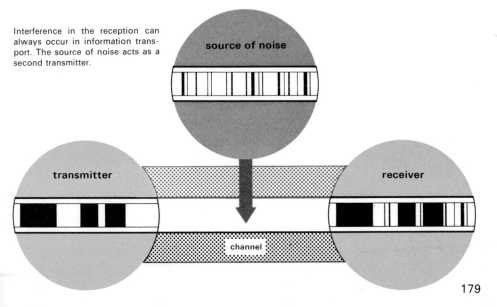

source of noise

transmitter

receiver

channel

different from those transmitted; redundancy permits one to establish this. When listening to the radio one has to reckon with more or less intense sound distortions, with hissing, crackling and whistling. Such interferences could be atmospheric, due to thunderstorms or simply due to the unsuppressed vacuum cleaner of the lady next door. One can also have disturbances which themselves contain information: it is quite easy in the medium-wave broadcast band to receive two stations simultaneously each transmitting different programmes. Both transmit information for different sections of the community. One of these transmissions will always be disturbing. Other types of disturbances occur in television. The picture may be flickering, the image lines may wander, 'snowflakes' may appear on the screen, ghost images make sober people see everything double etc. The more complicated the technical installation transmitter-channel-receiver the more prone it is to disturbances.

The collective noun for such disturbances is 'noise'. Like order, noise is the opponent of information. But it depends entirely on chance. (Every communications engineer is familiar with the dreaded noise-voltages which exist on the output side of receiver amplifiers. Every layman can get a good sound picture of this noise by turning up the volume control of his radio whilst turning the tuner on the FM band.) For our purposes it is sufficient to state that noise is produced by random signals which can occur at random moments in time. The receiver will find them disturbing even if they carry information. The best way so far to study these phenomena is again through Kolmogorov's probability theory: if two or more random quantities occur simultaneously then as shown by the theory the probability of combined events becomes important. This means: if two random events A_1 and A_2 with probabilities $P(A_1)$ and $P(A_2)$ respectively occur simultaneously then the probability of the combined events $P(A_1 \wedge A_2)$ (read: P of A—one and A—two) corresponds to the average $P(A_1) \cap P(A_2)$ (read: the intersection of P of A—one and P of A—two). This sounds more complicated than it is. The diagram shows clearly the meaning of this concept of the theory of sets. (See *Modern Mathematics*.)

What have we learnt about the information transport in a channel susceptible to noise? Briefly it is this: one can't get away without redundancy. The simple and successful recipe of information theory is to make 'pure' information redundant. But to make it redundant economically requires mathematical tools. They help us to treat quantitatively not only the phenomena associated with matter and energy but also information; the letter becomes tangible, measurable, calculable. This is a new aspect of modern technology which was first opened up by communications research and the theory of information. John R. Pierce, the director of the research establishment of Bell Telephone Laboratories, quite rightly explained:

'If a communications engineer had been asked in 1945: "What can one do about distortions and noise?" he would have answered roughly: "One can either increase the transmitter power or try to reduce the inherent noise of the receiver.

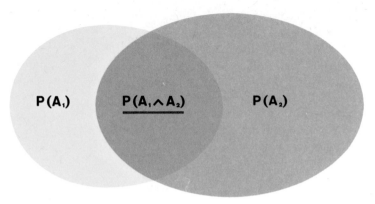

If two random events A_1 and A_2 occur simultaneously they form the event $A_1 \wedge A_2$ (A-one and A-two). If the probabilities of A_1 and A_2 are $P(A_1)$ and $P(A_2)$ respectively then the probability $P(A_1 \wedge A_2)$ equals the intersection $P(A_1) \cap P(A_2)$.

In addition one has to make sure that the receiver is as insensitive as possible to disturbances outside the frequency range of the signals."'

In the meantime new ideas have emerged and very important ones at that. Technologists and mathematicians have developed them and constantly work on their improvement and utilization. And yet the successful recipe for noise in information transport 'force redundancy in!', which was established very precisely by the new technology, has been practised successfully for a very long time in the all too familiar colloquial language. This is in favour of our natural language but is not against technology. On the contrary. With information theory technology began to make an important contribution to the clarification of our surroundings. It takes part in the theoretical construction of the universe.

With this we end our excursion into a young and fascinating region of research which has given a clearer and quantitative meaning to this vague catchword 'information'. This measurable information forms the building brick of our future discussions. It has taken us a long time to isolate it but in the end, by way of redundancy, we have returned to the point at which we began our task: the dependable colloquial language, the 'opaque structure' as information theory sees it, and from which the latter cannot and shall not break away. Carl F. von Weizsäcker warned quite rightly: 'Nobody who talks about information should forget that language as information is only possible in the context of a language which has not been changed into clear-cut information.'

Although we have analysed the language and discovered the 'nucleus' of information we have also seen that this nucleus has to be systematically enriched with redundancy in order to cope with certain situations in communications. The intentional safeguarding of the information transport presupposes a knowledge of the mathematical apparatus. It was the information theory which created the method and showed how to apply it:

similar to modern science it will turn out to be a most useful and significant point of view from which to see our surroundings and the events taking place in it. Together with modern technology it will considerably enrich man's life. Many people may well regret that this information theory cannot tell us anything about the nature of information and language.

But to bar our way because of this would be useless. Just as the 'nuova scienza' long ago started out in the 'old' world on its triumphant journey which eventually was to stretch over the whole world, this young science will do the same by starting out in the 'new' world. Only everything will take place at a much faster rate.

7.2 Thinking with the water tap?
Preliminary discussion on information processing installations

Our book purports to show a way to 'machines that think' or 'intelligent machines', as we called these devices, in a manner reminiscent of advertising (see page 19). But they are intended to be 'machine-slaves' for our thinking. This sounds unusual at first. Yet nobody finds it strange nowadays that human muscular power has been replaced largely by machine power. But when the talk turns to 'machines that think', to mechanical 'thinking slaves', many people cannot rid themselves of certain deep-rooted feelings of discomfort. Some people even whisper about the 'black magic' of machines, the 'work of the devil', and feel a threat to humanity through these synthetic structures. A fear of these intelligent machines cannot be made more convincing than the fear of mechanical looms or of automatic beer bottling plants. If one does not fear a giant milling machine in a workshop—and who does? —then one need not be afraid of machines that think. Let us try to discover the basic ideas behind this multitude of 'intelligent' machines, machines which will soon belong to our familiar technological surroundings.

We started off with an excursion through the landscape of thinking in which machines do not exist. We had a look to see what happens when it is we who do the thinking; and none of us were made to feel like a machine. We have made a few interesting discoveries simply by looking at the 'surface' of our thinking. We found that thinking is done in terms of the familiar everyday language and therefore we turned our full attention towards the latter. All people, unless they happen to be dumb, use this natural language in order to talk to one another. They constantly practise language-games of different types. They communicate by means of speech, they exchange information.

The question of information in the language took us some way through the land of information theory, the mathematical theory of communication. This new field of research is the unavoidable pre-requisite for all considerations about the theme of intelligent machines or cybernetic systems of all kinds. The mathematical tools required for this are necessary but they are very simple. It is impossible straight away to talk of super-clever robots which can play chess very skilfully, of battery-fed mechanical mice which hurry through a maze toward their goal, of electronic brains which play 'war and peace' coolly and relentlessly.

To begin with we shall explain the fundamental ideas of the theoretical, i.e. mathematical, background. Amazement about these fascinating machines will then no longer be boundless. For nothing is so dangerous as the amazement which distracts us from thinking. Even intelligent machines will never be able to take independent thinking away from us. A discussion like this one, which leads to intelligent machines, should always heed Wittgenstein's remark: 'I should not like to spare other people the trouble of thinking, but, if possible, to stimulate someone to thoughts of his own' (page 27). Our book will and can present only selected information and go along only selected ways of thought. This is done according to certain economic reflections. We certainly cannot claim completeness but, what is most important, we can stimulate the reader to have his own thoughts.

To recommend to one one's own thoughts, to think about the future generation of intelligent machines, seems at first glance to be almost oldfashioned and pedagogical. Yet we shall see on various occasions that thinking and intelligent machines definitely belong together; it is only good team play which can solve the most important problems. And since our thinking takes place in the everyday language, in the natural language-games, it will from the outset always be superior to any mechanized thinking that men will invent for their machines. This result will be welcomed by many readers. And it is stressed in Weizsäcker's statement:

'If we were to transfer to a machine all thought operations, which take their course according to a definite pre-conceived scheme, we have by no means transferred all possible thought operations, not even those which we may be inclined to call 'exact'. For instance one can only operate according to a scheme if this scheme has been planned beforehand. The planning of a scheme is a thought process which precedes the scheme. . . .'

'We shall incline to the assumption that what takes place when the scheme is put into operation cannot be more exact than the thought which planned the scheme. Whatever the case may be there is no doubt that the planning of a scheme is a thought process which does not follow this scheme.'

Intelligent machines will and can carry out many tedious thought processes far more precisely, and certainly faster than we would ever be able to. But does this fact perhaps in any form contradict our solid 'day-to-day' thinking? Certainly not. When many millenia ago man invented axes and other tools he did not hit upon the idea of doing away with manual labour. From then on trades were carried on with and without tools. The chances of work were improved and extended. In the technological age modest labour and solid tools were joined by the very useful machine tools. These machine

183

slaves replaced muscular effort by machine power and in this manner the field of human activity became considerably enriched. And what about our thinking? Here too we have a human activity which takes its course according to coarser or finer patterns. Why then should we not think, and even think with 'machines that think'?

This is an important point. Due to the many and varied demands in science and technology it will soon no longer be avoidable for man not to think with intelligent machines. These machines then become familiar instruments. Just as certain devices are as a matter of course being used as tools, intelligent machines are being used as thought tools.

If we examine this often much exaggerated problem of intelligent machines in this matter-of-fact way, then many superfluous pseudo-questions which can bring about unrest and cause discomfort can be by-passed. Thus a list of non-sensical questions can be avoided: 'Can intelligent machines really think for themselves?', 'Can they be more intelligent than their designers?' 'Do these machines relieve us of thinking?' Or even 'Can these machines rule us?' A simple thought which shifts this uncertainty into clearer light, was given by the French linguist Pierre Bertaux: '"Does the machine think or doesn't it?" This is an absurd way of asking a question—a question which is only possible in our inadequate language.' As we have more respect for our natural language we say in this case: It is the thoughtless transgression of a language-game, an enforced assimilation, which is practised here (see page 33). Bertaux argues further:

'In a few years' time language will have developed to such an extent that this question will be quite pointless. Who would think to ask whether a car goes or does not go? A five-year-old child might say: "Yes the car goes but not on its own. Someone has to drive it." This is correct. On the other hand the best driver could not drive if the car were damaged. Just as the car can't go without a driver so the driver can't drive without a car. If one applies this comparison to our discussion then it is practically meaningless to ask whether the machine can think. It becomes only a philosophical question. From the practical point of view it should be sufficient to say that from now on man thinks with the help of the machine and will always do so.'

Now that we are equipped with the slogan 'to think with intelligent machines' we shall return from the border regions of speculation to the matter-of-fact landscape of the exact sciences. Here we may ask quite simply: How does a machine work which can carry out certain thought operations, certain logical processes? What kind of logical processes can be carried out by machines?

In every instance such a machine should be able to process information, to combine, to manipulate it by any means whatsoever. It should be able to operate without information. Now that we have learnt the basic ideas of information theory and know the meaning of measurable information we can easily step into the field of intelligent machines of all types. A more correct but more long-winded name is 'information processing installations'. We know what is to be processed: measurable information. How it can be processed we shall discuss now.

So far we have only roughly outlined the idea of 'artificial languages'. The important thing was that we distinguished clearly between artificial and natural languages. The image of the natural language can be compared with a complicated signal box (compare page 143). Images of artificial languages on the other hand are far simpler. We shall see this when discussing the so-called 'statement calculus'. (See *Modern Mathematics*.) In this context it is sufficient to give a rough outline with the emphasis on the mechanism of transformations within intelligent machines.

All thinking operations which we are going to discuss are limited but they function unambiguously and precisely—and are highly meaningful. They express a sound and basic technique of thinking. This process of thinking can be carried out by a machine. In this context we can adapt one of Wittgenstein's thoughts from *Tractatus Logico-Philosophicus*: What such machines say they say clearly. And 'what they are incapable of expressing they say nothing at all about'. In this way the mechanical thinking tools become useful aids for our thinking which can easily be grasped and controlled. The expression 'statement calculus' implies that the 'game' contains statements and that somehow one can calculate with these structures. The word 'calculate' is derived from the Latin 'calculare'. The ancient Romans managed to calculate very skilfully and quite mechanically with small pieces of marble. And these small stones were called 'calculi'. Can elementary statements in statement calculus be treated just like small marbles? Can we operate with them correctly?

A few tricks will help to do just this. To begin with a few simple structures called 'statements' or 'sentences' are isolated from our natural language. 'It is raining' is such a simple statement, an elementary sentence. Other examples are: 'the sun is shining in Rome', 'Uncle John reads the evening paper', 'seventeen is a natural number', 'triangles sometimes are quadrilateral', 'pepper is a spice', 'the Eiffel tower stands in Stockholm', 'information is neither matter nor energy', etc. If we now mark out with these sentences a definite region of the natural language, that is if we form a system of statements, then we can associate with the elements of this system (the statements) the property of being either true or false, correct or incorrect. In logic such linguistic structures having this clear-cut property are called 'truth definite statements'. It is evident that 'triangles are sometimes quadrilaterals' and 'the Eiffel tower stands in Stockholm' are false statements. But the statement 'seventeen is a natural number' is true.

It should be emphasized that this labelling represents a useful definition. Artificial languages can be constructed only on such a basis. A definite and unique linguistic use has been agreed upon. It would indeed be highly absurd to come up with the argument that 'false' can also mean 'insincere', 'dishonest' etc. Or what is 'really true' is something that we human beings do not know. This fact, as far as logic is concerned, is always connected with a good deal of convention. But when are statements like 'it is raining' or 'Uncle John reads the evening paper' true? The truth criterion in the simplest case could be as follows:

The statement 'Uncle John reads the evening paper' is true only if and when Uncle John reads the evening paper. With such a criterion of truth one can easily show that the sentence 'the Eiffel tower stands in Stockholm' is false. According to our criterion it is true only if the Eiffel tower stands in Stockholm. This is not the case. Thus this statement is not true and is therefore false.

We can therefore make the general pronouncement: a statement of a system is true only if the facts which it asserts actually occur.

This seems to be obvious in every case. But unfortunately first impressions are deceptive. In order to formulate or pronounce such a statement we require our natural language. It was not until the nineteen-thirties that the Polish logician Alfred Tarski, who now lives in the USA,

recognized this clearly. Such a truth criterion is quite impossible for the natural language i.e. for all mother tongues.

It is for this reason that one speaks of the 'statement of a system'. And it is for this reason that the particular statement, referred to in the definition, is placed in inverted commas. The statement which is being discussed then belongs to what is called 'object language'; the language becomes the object of language. Our natural language assumes here an important superior role. In the terminology of the expert it becomes the 'meta language'. The object language can also be formalized and so becomes a calculus or, as in our case, a statement calculus.

Before carrying out the formalization we shall practise a little the use of inverted commas. 'William' is the name of William. The fact that someone, whether man or animal, is William differs quite clearly from the word 'William'.

A statement which can be 'true' or 'false' is truth definite. The statement 'Uncle John reads the evening paper' is 'true' only if Uncle John reads the evening paper. Otherwise the statement is always false.

true   false

'Uncle John reads the evening paper'

The linguistic image is very simple in this case (compare page 27). If we know that William lives in Manchester we can formulate the true statement 'William lives in Manchester'. Another true statement is also '"William" is made up of seven letters.' In the latter case it is the word 'William' and not the object William which is the central point. False statements would be 'William is made up of seven letters' and '"William" lives in Manchester'. Naturally within our colloquial language we can operate less carefully with inverted commas. (At times this is done a little too carelessly.)

Through our safety processes, which are of decisive importance when establishing a calculus, non-'truth definite statements' can be excluded as being 'meaningless with reference to the system'. In the sense of the definition these statements are neither true nor false. If several of such artificial language systems exist then any arbitrary statement can be true in one system but completely meaningless in the other. Truth, falsehood and meaninglessness are established in relation to a certain linguistic system. One can therefore never speak of 'absolute meaninglessness'. Every verbal utterance can be used in any situation as 'tool' even if it is 'only' between two people.

Consider a few examples. 'The time ripens' can be a 'true' statement in the language of the philosopher Martin Heidegger but in an exact scientific system, say in a physical theory, it has to be classed undoubtedly as 'meaningless'. On the other hand the statement 'every ring has exactly one null element' which every mathematician accepts as true will have no meaning to a jeweller. In the

Statements which refer to themselves cannot be truth definite. To describe the statement 'I am lying now' with the words 'true' or 'false' leads to a contradiction in every case. This was already known in Ancient Greece.

latter's jargon this is a meaningless statement, a sentence which is neither true nor false. A similar situation arises in the language-games within our colloquial language (see page 90).

We must therefore be careful not to dismiss rashly any unusual sentences as 'meaningless'. The German philosopher Wolfgang Stegmüller (born 1923) gives the following simple and fitting advice to science: 'Instead of "your statement is a meaningless sentence" it is better to say "your statement belongs to a language which is different from that which I have chosen as the scientific language".'

We will therefore bear this in mind: whether in a linguistic system of elementary statements one of these statements is true, false or meaningless depends entirely on the economically selected truth criteria. It may perhaps be unnecessary to point out that our 'truth definition' does therefore not answer the question 'What is truth?' The logician, insofar as he works along exact scientific lines, does not ask questions about the ultimate nature of things (compare page 118). A

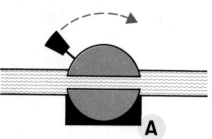

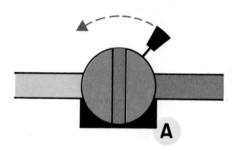

A truth definite statement A, which can be either true or false, represents 1 *bit* of information. This situation can be realized by a water tap which can be opened and closed.

fair amount of convention, of appropriate definition, plays a part in connection with 'truth' in research, at least in the exact sciences. This applies to all the artificial languages of science.

If in statement calculus, non-truth definite sentences have to be excluded as 'meaningless', for reasons of expediency, then this also applies to simple questions like 'What time is it?', polite requests like 'Give me time to think it over', or simple orders like 'Right turn!'. These familiar linguistic structures are all neither true nor false, in other words, meaningless in the selected object-language. To insist that they are 'absolutely meaningless' is obviously grotesque. We simply have a methodically useful demarcation within the language.

One can also say about every system of truth definite statements: every statement which makes a statement about itself, which refers to itself, has to be excluded as meaningless. Such meaningless structures could appear in the following forms: 'This sentence, which is printed here, is false'; 'What I have just

said is not correct'; 'I am lying now', etc. The contradiction in these statements can easily be perceived. If, say, the statement 'I am lying now' is true then what is said is false. If, however, 'I am lying now' is false, then the speaker has spoken the truth. It is a vicious circle which can not be broken. That such sentences lead to contradictions was already know at the time of Plato.

In statement calculus of modern logic such linguistic structures which refer to themselves cannot be admitted. They are definitely considered as being 'meaningless'. The truth criterion clearly brings out their absurdity:

The statement 'This sentence is wrong' is true only when this sentence is wrong. Or:

The statement 'I am lying' is true only when I am lying.

It is obvious that one cannot build up anything sensible on this contradictory basis. If we wish to build up a sound artificial language we must do away with such confusing linguistic structures.

We shall now construct a calculus

188

which will enable us to operate sensibly with truth definite statements. We shall use capital letters A, B, C, D, etc. as statement variables for such true or false statements; we shall use them as 'reserve labels' for blank spaces (compare page 129). True or false; this is only important for the statements A, B, C, D, etc. In the course of operating one can disregard completely the contents of these statements. This has obvious advantages. Although A, B, C, D, etc. are linguistic structures they can, because they are either this (true) or that (false), be treated as technical structures. In other words: they can easily be 'realized technically'.

If two taps A and B are connected in series water can only flow when both taps are open at the same time (top line of diagram). The indicator wheel (on right) revolves only in this case. This combination of the two taps is called an 'And-connection'.

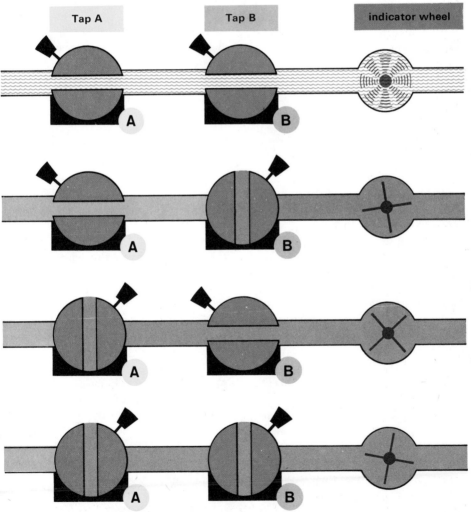

| Tap A | Tap B | indicator wheel |

How would one do this?

Simpler than it appears. If the statement A is either true or false, then as far as information theory is concerned, it represents 1 *bit* of information. True *or* false is thus comparable with yes *or* no, black *or* white, **1** *or* **0**. How can we arrange for a machine to express this?

This will entirely depend on the building elements of the machine. Normally the catchwords 'intelligent machine' are associated with the idea of huge electronic installations provided with electro-technical building elements. Some people believe that the invisible mysterious 'thinking electrons' have something to do with it. For this reason we shall at first not include electronics in our discussions and construct an intelligent machine operated by water. Surely nobody will ever think of 'thinking' water droplets.

Let us then build in our imagination a very simple intelligent machine which has water flowing through its arteries and whose most important building element is a tap. 'Thinking with a water tap?'; this was the polemic question we asked in the title of this chapter. We now have to give the answer. Intelligent machines can process information; and the situation of a statement A being true *or* false represents clearly a quantity of information of 1 *bit*. This situation can be realized with a tap in our machine:

'tap open' means 'the statement is true'
'tap closed' means 'the statement is false'.

We shall incorporate in our installation a small waterwheel as a simple indicating device. If it revolves then the tap is open ('A is true'). If on the other hand the wheel remains stationary then the tap is closed ('A is false'). Thus in our water-operated machine each tap A, B, C, etc, which can be turned on or off represents a two-step (binary digit), i.e. 1 *bit* of information.

If now two taps A and B are connected they can represent 2 *bit* of information, thus four choices:

Tap A open—Tap B open
Tap A open—Tap B closed
Tap A closed—Tap B open
Tap A closed—Tap B closed

But there are various ways of connecting A and B. To start with they can be connected in series as in the water main. Our indicator wheel will tell us what is happening in the four possible situations. The wheel will either revolve or not revolve. From the diagram we see that

A open—B open: the wheel revolves
A open—B closed: the wheel stands still
A closed—B open: the wheel stands still
A closed—B closed: the wheel stands still

Only when both taps A and B are opened simultaneously does the wheel revolve. In all other cases it does not.

We shall now interpret this image by means of the two truth values 'true' and 'false', remembering that 'A open' means 'A is true', 'B closed' is 'B is false' etc. 'The wheel revolves' now means that 'the combination of A and B is true' whereas 'The wheel stands still' means 'the combination of A and B is false'. Thus a pair of truth values always corresponds uniquely to a single truth value. This scheme is referred to as a 'truth table' and takes the following form for the four situations:

(ture—true) → true

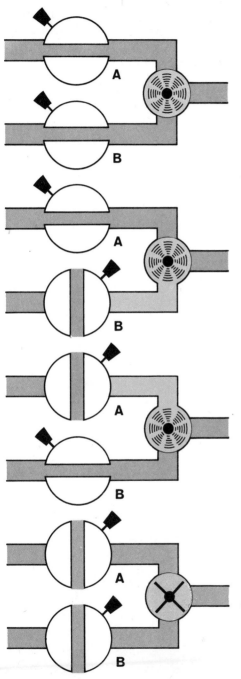

(true—false) → false
(false—true) → false
(false—false) → false

If instead of the words 'true' and 'false' we use the numerical symbols '**1**' and '**0**', then we can define the one-to-one correspondences **1** ⇔ true and **0** ⇔ false. The truth table then becomes:

$(\mathbf{1}, \mathbf{1}) \rightarrow \mathbf{1}$

$(\mathbf{1}. \mathbf{0}) \rightarrow \mathbf{0}$

$(\mathbf{0}, \mathbf{1}) \rightarrow \mathbf{0}$

$(\mathbf{0}, \mathbf{0}) \rightarrow \mathbf{0}$

We have thus related pairs of binary signs uniquely with individual binary signs. But what have these water games got to do with binary signs? Many a reader will say that this has very little to do with thinking. But let us continue.

Two taps A and B cannot only be connected in series, we can also connect them in parallel. The indicator wheel reacts quite differently now. Consider the diagram:

A open—B open: the wheel revolves

A open—B closed: the wheel revolves

A closed—B open: the wheel revolves

A closed—B closed: the wheel stands still.

This time there are more cases when the wheel revolves. It is quite sufficient to open only one of the two taps, A or B. The wheel remains still only when both taps are closed. The simplified truth table with **1** and **0** is as follows:

$(\mathbf{1}, \mathbf{1}) \rightarrow \mathbf{1}$

$(\mathbf{1}, \mathbf{0}) \rightarrow \mathbf{1}$

$(\mathbf{0}, \mathbf{1}) \rightarrow \mathbf{1}$

$(\mathbf{0}, \mathbf{0}) \rightarrow \mathbf{0}$

Two water taps A and B in parallel, only prevent an indicator wheel (on right) from turning when they are both closed (bottom). In order to make water flow only one of the taps needs to be opened. This connection is known as an 'Or-connection'.

What is the difference between the two 'water games for the taps A and B'? In the first case, the series connection, both taps A and B must be open in order to turn the wheel. In the parallel connection, on the other hand, it is sufficient to open A or B in order to start the motion. We see that the important things are the two words 'and' and 'or'. Taps connected in series can be used as 'And-connection' and taps connected in parallel as 'Or-connection'. This picture of a network applies also to the statement calculus. Elementary statements A, B, C, etc are connected by 'logic symbols' to form compound statements. We then have the 'And-connection' $A \wedge B$, which is read 'A and B' and the 'Or-connection' $A \vee B$, which is read 'A or B'. It should be emphasized that A, B, C, etc. in this context are truth definite statements.

Because A, B, C are variables, an expression like '$A \wedge B$' is a 'form', or a 'statement form' as it is also referred to. In our colloquial language the words 'and' and 'or' are used to build up compound structures from simple ones: 'Hansel *and* Gretel got lost in the forest', 'Render therefore unto Caesar the things which are Caesar's; *and* unto God the things that are God's!', 'Would you like tea *or* coffee?', 'To be *or* not to be—that is the question' etc.

Our 'water games' with the 'And-' and 'Or-' connections of two taps A and B have led to two different truth tables. The first one applies to the compound statement $A \wedge B$ ('A and B'). $A \wedge B$ is true only when A as well as B is true. In all other cases $A \wedge B$ is false. If we again substitute '**1**' for 'true' and '**0**' for 'false' then the truth table becomes:

An inverted tap ⌐A behaves in an exactly opposite way to a tap A of normal construction. The knob on the left indicates that the tap is closed, the flow interrupted. In the other state, with the knob on the right, the tap is open and the water can flow. To distinguish clearly between normal and inverted tap the latter is shown with a red knob. By itself it forms the 'Not-connection'.

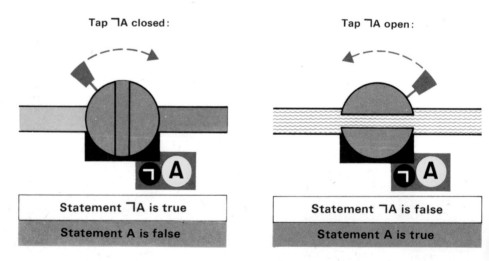

Tap ⌐A closed:

Statement ⌐A is true

Statement A is false

Tap ⌐A open:

Statement ⌐A is false

Statement A is true

A	B	A ∧ B
I	I	I
I	O	O
O	I	O
O	O	O

On the other hand the compound statement A ∨ B ('A or B') is false when both statements A and B are false. In all other cases A ∨ B is true. The corresponding truth table becomes:

A	B	A ∨ B
I	I	I
I	O	I
O	I	I
O	O	O

Let us devote a little time to practise how to use these truth tables: is the statement 'there are yellow *and* red roses' true or false? The word 'and' reveals the compound statement which in full reads: 'There are yellow roses *and* there are red roses'. If we analyse this combination according to the pattern A ∧ B we have:

A: there are yellow roses

B: there are red roses

Both statements A and B are true. After all one can see yellow roses as well as red roses in a flower shop. On the right of the first row of the (A ∧ B)-truth table is 'I'; accordingly the compound statement is true. In the case of our machine the situation assumes the following form: two taps in series are open. The wheel revolves corresponding to 'I' or 'true'.

The statement 'There are yellow roses *or* red roses' is also true: this can be seen

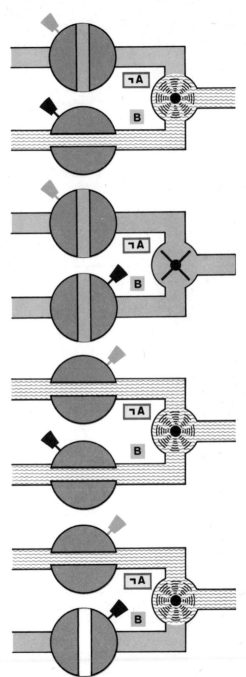

The parallel connection of an inverted tap (¬A) and a normal tap (B) can be regarded as an 'If-then connection'.

193

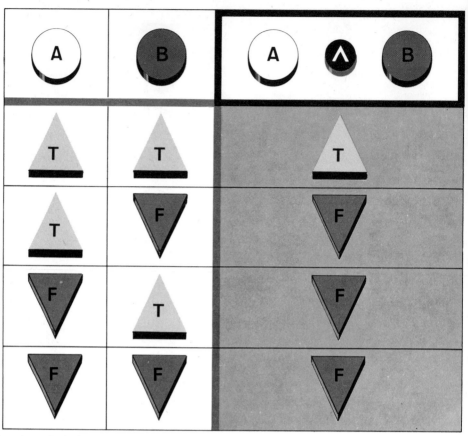

In order to play logic games one does not necessarily require water taps which can be opened and closed. The figure shows a truth table made up with counters (see *Modern Mathematics*).

by glancing at the first row of the $(A \vee B)$-truth table where in the right hand column we also find '**1**' which is supposed to stand for 'true'. Thus $\vee$ is the symbol for 'non-exclusive or'. It must *not* be read as 'either—or'. In full it reads 'either A or B or both A and B'. Note that all explanations are formulated in the 'meta language' which in this case is our natural language.

Is the statement 'Oslo *or* Paris is in France' true or false? 'Paris is in France' is true. The 'Or-connection of a false and

a true statement is true (third row of the $(A \vee B)$-truth table). Also our simple machine with two taps A and B in parallel answers the question of 'true' or 'false' in favour of 'true'. The wheel revolves.

In contrast to this the wheel remains still in the case of the 'And'-connection. The compound statement 'Oslo and Paris are in France' is thus false. A glance at the third row of the $(A \wedge B)$-truth table confirms this; on the right we find '**0**' i.e. 'false'.

Does one need machines for such

childish ideas? Perhaps many a reader may have wondered about this already. To be sure the examples chosen are very simple but somewhere back along the line of development of most sound ideas we find something commonplace. This is so even if they develop into something complicated which cannot be so easily comprehended. Our 'thinking machine' can, however, do a lot more.

In colloquial language we often say something is 'so or *not* so'. We use the word 'not' in order to dispute something, in order to say the 'opposite', in order to formulate the 'negation' of a statement. This is by no means as simple as it appears at first sight. Only truth definite statements present no difficulties. If we use the symbol ⌐ as negation sign then '⌐A' means 'not A'. The truth values in the truth table are then simply reversed: if 'A' is true then '⌐A' is false; if 'A' is false then '⌐A' is true.

A	⌐A
I	O
O	I

Can this case also be realized in our intelligent machine? This is so if we use another type of tap which we shall call 'inverted tap'. We can see from the figure that the black control knob of the taps used so far is always on the left when the tap is open and on the right when the tap is closed. Now we are going to introduce a tap which is constructed in such a way that everything is reversed: knob on left— tap closed, knob on right—tap open. For the sake of clarity we shall colour the control knob red for the inverted tap. The inverted tap as a circuit element forms a 'Not-connection'.

The statement form ⌐A ∨ B (read: 'not—A or B') is very interesting. Let us consider again the truth value distribution in the machine with the help of the circuit diagram for the four possibilities. An inverted tap (⌐A) and a tap made in the normal way (B) are connected in parallel (Or-connection). From the diagram we can see that the control wheel remains stationary only when both the inverted and the ordinary tap are closed ('A true', 'B false'). In all other cases the wheel revolves.

The form ⌐A ∨ B has turned out to be so important that the logician simply writes 'A → B' instead of '⌐A → B'. The expression 'A → B' reads 'If A, then B'. In the case of our machine the parallel connection of two taps of opposing construction can be called the 'If-then-connection'. The four possible connections for the statement form A → B give the following truth table:

A	B	A → B
I	I	I
I	O	O
O	I	I
O	O	I

We have developed the basic equipment for a sound 'intelligent machine' using water taps of normal construction and inverted taps. In fact very many thought operations can be played through and simulated. We obtain similar pictures whether we operate according to certain rules with real marbles A, B, C, etc or with logic signs ∧, ∨, ⌐ and →. This game is described in detail in *Modern Mathematics*. In the following chapters we shall however turn primarily to the mechanical treatment of these problems.

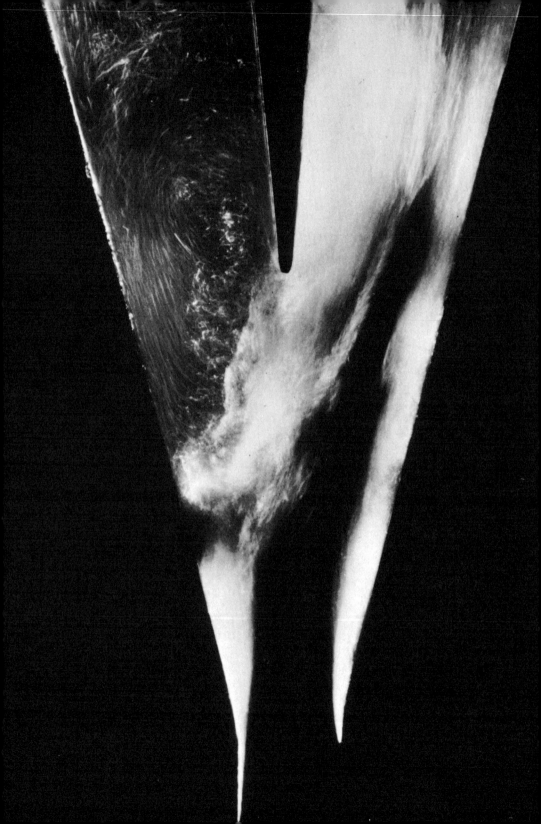

8. BUILDING BLOCKS OF A 'THOUGHT-TOOL BOX'

8.1 When water does or does not flow
Simple mechanical information processing

Our simple 'hydraulic games' with open and closed taps for two different types of construction will have hardly convinced anyone that 'thinking with the water tap' is really a meaningful activity. Our first signpost into this new landscape says 'Thinking with machines which think'. We shall therefore try to construct a few simple 'intelligent machines' or 'mechanical thinking-tools' which will help us to think. We shall use the water taps and the indicator wheel which we discussed in the last chapter.

As usual let us begin with a very simple example which will help us to understand easily the use of such a water-operated thinking tool: mine host of the 'Golden Eagle' is very concerned to maintain the high reputation of his establishment in the small town. He personally sees to it that only a selected clientele is admitted into his hostelry. Let him explain:

'Well, I've got my own strict rules. Trouble with the police does not exist in my place. Take the people who have already had their fill. Let me tell you, drunken customers like that aren't allowed through my door. I make sure of that. If needs be I am quite capable of throwing them out. You know what I mean. My customers could be hungry or thirsty; of course what I would like best

is if they were hungry and thirsty at the same time. But if someone just wants to drink without eating, suits me well enough; and I don't object if he only wants a snack. But the customer has got to pay cash. I don't sell anything on tick— and there are no exceptions. I give credit only to nonagenarians if they are accompanied by their grandparents.'

With this stale joke and the loud laughter of the jovial host we shall 'turn off' the 'redundant source of information'. We have been served the small amount of information, admittedly greatly embellished, which is important to our processing plant. From the account of the host of the 'Golden Eagle' we could deduce that anyone who wishes to be a customer of this pub has to comply with certain requirements. (Mine host reminds one a little of Cerberus of classical mythology who also guarded an entrance.) In order to live up to the requirements the guest does not need to accomplish any feats of thinking but he must know how to behave in the different situations.

What information does the landlord require to define uniquely his reaction towards a guest? Can one define a behavioural pattern? Can this pattern perhaps be simulated mechanically?

When attempting to answer these questions let us proceed step by step. First of all we have to answer the question about the quantity of information, the two-steps or 'bits'. For this we have to extract the 'information kernel' from the

Modern computer technology uses building elements which in fact operate by water flowing through them. These structures are referred to as 'hydraulic amplifiers' (see page 251).

8. Building blocks of a 'thought-tool box'

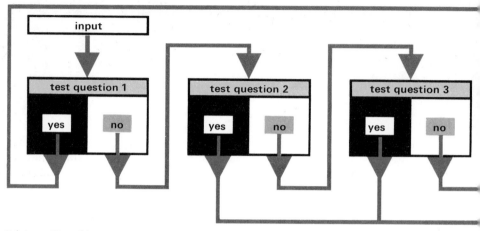

For the problem of how to treat a guest in our example of the innkeeper one can develop a kind of 'route map' for the guest. The expert refers to this as a flow diagram. In this example we are concerned with 4 *bit* of information.

redundant text of the host. We shall find the following bits of information:

> 1st two-step: Is the guest drunk?
> *Yes or no* (1 *bit*)
> 2nd two-step: Is the guest hungry?
> *Yes or no* (1 *bit*)
> 3rd two-step: Is the guest thirsty?
> *Yes or no* (1 *bit*)
> 4th two-step: Can the guest pay cash?
> *Yes or no* (1 *bit*)

(In order not to get lost in technical detail we shall assume again that mine host lives up to the reputation demanded of him by having an eye for these facts. Alternatively by direct and cautious questioning he could sound the guest out. We shall not consider the amount of information which the host supplied for this.)

Our balance sheet, after eliminating redundancy, shows 4 *bit* of information, sixteen possibilities of choosing from the two-steps under discussion. This quantity of information has to be processed in order to obtain a behaviour pattern. For

the landlord this is something like the following: 'If this and that condition is satisfied but not the other, then you have to act in such and such a way.' It is an operating instruction. For the guest it means: 'To be welcome in the 'Golden Eagle' you have to fulfil this and that condition.'

The diagram shows the connections of the two-steps. This kind of diagram is also known as a 'flow diagram'. It does in fact remind one of an irrigation system with water flowing through. On the left in the figure is the inflow (input) and on the right are two outflows (outputs). In between there is a system of ditches and wells through which the water flows. This scheme already points to the construction of the thinking tool with the taps which can be arranged in various ways in order to allow water to flow or not to flow. But we are racing ahead.

A quick glance at the flow diagram is somewhat confusing; but let us study it in detail. It is drawn up as a behaviour

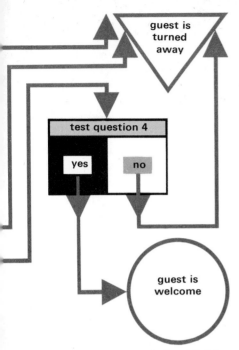

to be hungry or thirsty. If he is not hungry then he has to answer 'yes' to the question about being thirsty in order to remain in the 'yes-channel' of the diagram. If, on the other hand, he is neither hungry nor thirsty then he is out. In the diagram the second 'ditch' from the top takes him to the outflow 'reject'.

The last hurdle in the race to gain the favour of the landlord is the question about the ability of the guest to pay. If he can pay cash then he arrives at the desired goal (bottom right of diagram) but if he cannot pay then he is eliminated from the race and lands amongst the rejects (top right of diagram).

Our flow diagram is drawn in such a way that using it as a plan we can easily construct a thinking tool from our set of water taps and the indicator wheel. Our four binary digits can be represented by four taps each with the possibilities 'tap open'—'tap closed'. The flow diagram also indicates that the taps cannot simply be connected in series. The circuit diagram has to be modified.

In order to arrive at the correct connection we shall apply our modest knowledge of statement logic and its technical realization (see page 189).

The first condition is: 'the guest must not be drunk'. In other words the truth definite statement 'the guest is drunk' is false (see page 185). As a first circuit element an inverted tap with a red control knob (see figure on page 192) would suggest itself. In the 'switched on' state this tap is closed. This means that if the corresponding statement is true, i.e. 'yes' then the inverted tap is 'switched on', i.e. closed. Water cannot flow. But if the statement is false, i.e. 'no', then the

pattern for the guest of the 'Golden Eagle'. The initial situation is this: a guest would like to visit the pub. The situation can be compared with one in which a person wishes to make an application at some kind of government office and is given a form to fill in. The reading of the flow diagram is not really any more difficult than the reading of an official questionnaire or application form. As we shall see the diagram tells us a bit more.

The first test question is: 'Is the guest drunk?' Should this be the case—'if the answer is in the affirmative', as it would be in officialese—then he will unfortunately be refused. The corresponding line in the flow diagram is shown at the top. If, on the other hand, the answer is 'no' the guest is then asked the next question, i.e. whether he is hungry. If his answer is 'yes' then he may by-pass the thirst question (test question 3). It suffices tap is off and water can flow. Water flows only if the guest is not drunk; if he is drunk the water does not flow. In general this can be written as '$\neg A$' (see page 195).

The second condition: 'The guest shall be hungry or thirsty or both'. This forms a clear link with the 'non-exclusive or' of statement logic: 'The guest is hungry *or* the guest is thirsty' according to the general pattern $B \vee C$ (see page 194). The technical realization of this situation is the Or-connection; tap B and tap C are in parallel. Only one of the taps, B or C, needs to be opened in order to let the water flow.

The last condition to be dealt with is: 'The guest has to pay cash'. In other words: 'The guest pays cash' is a truth definite statement which should be true. In general: D is to have the truth value 'true'. The tap D is therefore of normal design. It is open in the switched-on state, the water flows; it is closed when switched off, the water does not flow.

These three conditions have to be fulfilled simultaneously. In terms of statement logic we obtain the following scheme:

$$\neg A \wedge (B \vee C) \wedge D$$

which reads: 'not-A and B-or-C and D'.

This statement form can be realized by connecting an inverted tap ($\neg A$) in series with the two parallel taps B and C as well as with the tap D. This And-connection is also referred to as 'series-connection'; the circuit elements are in series as can be seen from the figure. The indicator wheel is placed at the end of the line.

The four taps ($\neg A$, B, C and D) allow us to select the sixteen settings for the 4 *bit* of information. We shall discuss two of the sixteen possibilities.

(a_1) The guest is drunk $\Leftrightarrow$ Tap $\neg A$ turned on (i.e. closed)

(b_1) The guest is hungry $\Leftrightarrow$ Tap B open

(c_1) The guest is thirsty $\Leftrightarrow$ Tap C open

(d_1) The guest pays cash $\Leftrightarrow$ Tap D open

No water flows in the system, the indicator wheel does not revolve. The reason for this is the closed inverted tap ($\neg A$). And 'stationary wheel' means 'the guest has been turned away'.

Of the fifteen remaining situations we shall now simulate another one chosen arbitrarily:

(a_2) The guest is not drunk $\Leftrightarrow$ Tap $\neg A$ turned off (i.e. open)

(b_2) The guest is not hungry $\Leftrightarrow$ Tap B closed

(c_2) The guest is thirsty $\Leftrightarrow$ Tap C open

(d_2) The guest pays cash $\Leftrightarrow$ Tap D open

The water can now flow through the system and, although B is closed, it can by-pass it through C. The wheel revolves and the guest is made welcome.

Both cases are illustrated schematically in the figures. It would be pedantic and tedious to simulate and explain all sixteen possible cases in this way. Instead we have constructed the truth table step by step with the binary signals **1** and **0** for the general form $\neg A \wedge (B \vee C) \wedge D$. We have used for this the truth tables for the cases $(A \wedge B)$, $(A \vee B)$ and $\neg A$ discussed above (see page 190). Since the letters A, B, C and D are statement variables, 'reserve labels' for any truth definite statements, the truth table for the form $A \vee B$ naturally also holds for the analogous form $B \vee C$ or for $C \vee D$ etc. The arbitrarily chosen letters always indicate

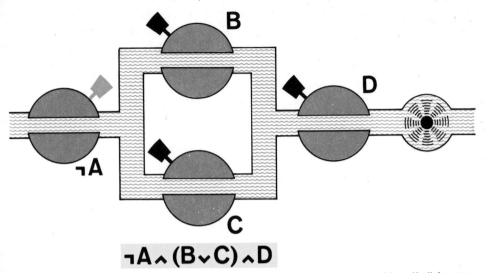

$$\neg A \wedge (B \vee C) \wedge D$$

This connection of water taps simulates the relevant situations of the innkeeper problem. If all four taps ¬A,B,C,D are turned on the indicator wheel does not revolve. One only needs to turn off the inverted tap in order to set the wheel in motion.

blank spaces into which one can place truth definite statements.

In the first few columns of the truth table (white background) '**ı**' means 'tap open' for the normal taps of the thinking tool (or 'tap switched off', i.e. 'open', in the case of the inverted tap) and that, for the corresponding statement, its truth value is 'true'. On the other hand '**o**' has to be interpreted as 'tap closed' (or 'inverted tap switched on') for the installation and 'false' for the truth value of the statement.

In the last column (red background) '**ı**' stands for 'indicator wheel revolves' in the expression ¬A ∧ (B ∨ C) ∧ D and 'true' for the compound statement. '**o**' stands for 'indicator wheel stationary' and truth value 'false'.

The truth table shows that the indicator wheel revolves only in three out of sixteen possible cases, i.e. when the last column

This figure depicts two of the sixteen possible situations of the innkeeper problem. In the second example the indicator wheel revolves; the guest is welcome.

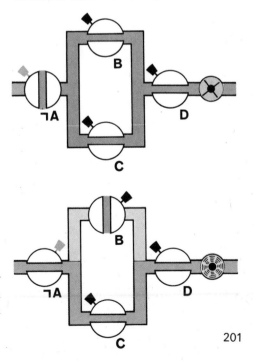

201

contains '1'. This means that the guest is welcome at the 'Golden Eagle' only in these three cases. In the remaining thirteen cases he is turned away. As can be seen the randomly chosen case with the situations (a_2) to (d_2) which we discussed is the entry in the thirteenth row of the truth table.

What we have discussed here was our first 'intelligent machine'. It was of a very simple construction using the simple elements of taps and control wheel. In real life certainly no innkeeper will want to depend on such a machine to select his guests unless, on the basis of such advice, he wanted to develop a 'mechanical chucker outer' which would not be exactly good for business.

Such simple examples demonstrate most clearly the salient points which arise in more complicated situations; this is the interlinking of information. This information processing can be carried out purely mechanically in many cases with the help of a simple machine. Such simple machines are the 'nuclei' of the large and efficient information processing plants which can simulate far more complicated and important situations than the 'guest problem' of the landlord of the 'Golden Eagle'.

No doubt there will be readers who, on the basis of this first example, will think that modern 'intelligent machines' with their 'simplified landlord logic' have nothing in common with the important and respected activity which philosophers call 'thinking': unfortunately we have to reply: our simple water games with the taps connected in parallel and in series, and which can be opened and closed, have a great deal to do with clear and controllable thinking. These thinking tools help us to 'calculate' in a simple way, and also to 'calculate with statements'. This is a perfectly legitimate mathematical activity. As Plato said fittingly: Mathematics was and is the 'awakener of our perception'.

There is another point which is very important and has to be emphasized over and over again. Information processing can be considered as a schematic activity (compare also page 119). The 'material' to be processed can be regarded as something real like a solid play brick or a carved chessman. With these real things one operates according to certain rules, one does 'something' in a meaningful way. If one 'plays' with statements then their contents are of no interest during the game; if anything, they are distracting and disturbing. Also in the course of processing measurable information any thoughts about the contents are quite unimportant. For example in the And-connection, $A \wedge B$, of two statements the contents of A and B are completely unimportant as long as both are truth definite and so represent 1 *bit* of information. It would be quite legitimate if for instance A were replaced by the statement '13 is a prime number' and B by 'Johnny has a toothache'. The combination of '13 is a prime number and Johnny has a toothache' would only be true if Johnny has a toothache otherwise it would be false. (The number thirteen is always a prime number because it can only be divided by itself or by one.) The conscious disregard of reflections about

Truth table for the thinking tool connection for the innkeeper problem. The sixteen possible situations correspond to sixteen possibilities of choice corresponding to 4 *bit* of information.

	A	B	C	D	¬A	B∨C	¬A∧(B∨C)∧D
1	1	1	1	1	0	1	0
2	1	1	1	0	0	1	0
3	1	1	0	1	0	1	0
4	1	1	0	0	0	1	0
5	1	0	1	1	0	1	0
6	1	0	1	0	0	1	0
7	1	0	0	1	0	0	0
8	1	0	0	0	0	0	0
9	0	1	1	1	1	1	1
10	0	1	1	0	1	1	0
11	0	1	0	1	1	1	1
12	0	1	0	0	1	1	0
13	0	0	1	1	1	1	1
14	0	0	1	0	1	1	0
15	0	0	0	1	1	0	0
16	0	0	0	0	1	0	0

the contents is difficult for most people. Only too quickly does one have at the ready the argument about 'scholarly sophistry'. We shall consider a typical example which at the same time will show us why the representatives of the exact craft feel insulted. The If-then connection has been based on the linkage $A \rightarrow B$ (see page 195). In logic $A \rightarrow B$ is in fact often read as 'If A then B'. Other ways of reading are simply 'A arrow B' or also 'A implies B'.

We have regarded the expression $A \rightarrow B$ at first merely as an abbreviation for $\neg A \lor B$ (read: 'Not-A or B'), as a purely formal link which can be realized technically in the corresponding connection (inverted tap and ordinary tap in parallel). If such a connection is built into 'intelligent machines' then naturally any appraisal concerning its content is excluded. In the thinking tool the statements A and B are after all not 'read' or 'understood' as regards their contents but the possibilities of a linkage of their truth values is simulated. We shall explain this with a simple example.

'If it rains then the road is wet'. This is an If-then connection of two statements which is used constantly in everyday life. The formal view is that this situation is simply a 'coupling' between two statements according to the scheme '$A \rightarrow B$' which stands for $\neg A \lor B$. In this example the variable A is replaced by 'it rains' and B by 'the road is wet'. It is clear that both statements are truth definite. It may rain or it may not rain. The road may be wet or it may not be wet. (The various intermediate steps between these states will not be considered here.) Thus each statement has an information value

1 *bit* with the truth value of either 'true' or 'false', '**1**' or '**0**'. As we know the following truth value table (truth table) applies to the connection $A \rightarrow B$:

A	B	$A \rightarrow B$
1	1	1
1	0	0
0	1	1
0	0	1

For example the third line of this table could be read as follows: 'If A is false and B is true, then A-arrow-B is true.' We can characterize the truth table in one sentence: 'The connection A-arrow-B is false only if the conditional clause (A) is true and the consequent clause (B) is false; in all other cases it is true.'

The conventional linguistic usage in this case is concerned not only with formal reasoning but also with content: the sentence is often regarded as an answer to an unspoken why-question; the If-then connection is then used 'causally'. 'The reason why the road is wet is because it is raining.' There are many such If-then statements which express causal connections: 'If the road is icy then the driver has to be particularly careful.'—'If William is not colour blind, then he can become an engine driver.'—'If we are 18 years of age, then we are entitled to vote.' etc.

The customary use of the If-then connection is far too vague for exact science. It embraces not only a causal use but also a conditional and a deductive one, e.g. 'If Peter does not drink his soup, then he is not allowed to play football' or 'If there is a lot of rain in April, then the harvest will be good'. Very popular in colloquial language are also abstract sentences like: 'If the third goal had not been recognized then Germany would still have had a chance to win the world football championship'. Exact science can't do anything with this sort of sentence.

In a mathematical science, linguistic usage has to be defined unambiguously. If a If-then connection of two statements occurs then it has to be agreed upon that there is no doubt that it means this and nothing else. This agreement which feels a little artificial can be defined quite easily when constructing an artificial language. In contrast to the natural language we can simply agree on the linguistic use. If this or that sign recurs in the text then it means this and that and nothing else.

This is what logicians do when compiling a truth table for any connection of statements. We will now consider the truth table for A → B using our simple example:

First row of the truth table: 'If it is raining, then the road is wet'. The conditional clause is assumed to be true (the road is wet). With regard to purely formal reasoning as well as with regard to content, this composite sentence is accepted as 'true'.

Second line of the table: 'If it is raining, then the road is not wet'. Both, the formal reasoning as well as the content lead to the result 'false'. We do remember, however, that the logician does not look at the content of the statements but merely to the co-ordination of the signals $(1, 0) \to 0$ in the truth table. The reaction within the thinking tool is

similar: inverted tap A on (i.e. closed) and tap B, connected in parallel with A, closed, means: indicator wheel remains stationary.

Third row of the table: 'If it is not raining, then the road is wet'. Leaving the content aside the truth table and the connections of the thinking tool decide that the complete statement is 'true'. This is the case where the usual linguistic use deviates most clearly from the formal scientific one. Ordinarily one would, in this case, search desperately for any kind of criteria in order to establish 'true' or 'false'. No doubt one will say 'this is nonsense' or 'this is a meaningless and nonsensical assertion'. At best one might admit that this statement could be 'true'— it is possible that it is true. A burst water main could well be involved, or a melted layer of snow, or a turned-on stand pipe, or a water sprinkler etc. It is not possible colloqually to make a clear decision of 'true' or 'false' for every case. Such a decision is only possible through an appropriate definition within the framework of an artificial language.

Fourth row of the table: 'If it is not raining, then the road is not wet'. The formal decision is clear and unambiguous. Conditional clause false, therefore the combination is true. $(0, 0) \to 1$. When considering the content the total statement leads in this case mostly to 'true'. But, as in the previous example, certain restrictions cannot be dismissed: 'Although it is not raining, it is still possible ...' The decision within the natural language is by no means unique, and cannot be so.

Uncertainties of this type are avoided in the artificial languages of the exact sciences and technology. This is indeed a point in favour of these artificial structures as efficient special tools. But this does not imply that a negative judgement has been made against the 'universal tool', the coloquial language. Have we not constantly praised the usefulness of this unviersal 'instrument' in the first part of this book?

Artificial languages, calculi, thinking tools, these are highly specialized instruments which can be used very effectively; but one can get into trouble if one uses them carelessly. We shall return to this point later on. Special tools, let us remember, have a well-defined but often very narrow field of application.

The logician Gottlob Frege (1848–1925) compared the artificial structures of his science in its relation to natural language with the relation between the microscope and the human eye. This comparison can be extended: every efficient carpenter's shop these days contains a variety of machine tools for specialized purposes. Which sensible carpenter would therefore entertain the idea of throwing away his simple planes, files and pliers? No biochemist would presumably smash his reading glasses because there is a far more efficient electron microscope available at his institute. No woodwind player would dream of throwing away his clarinet just because he could also produce sounds with comb and paper. Accordingly, no scientist can do without thinking tools just because he himself is capable of thinking; no mathematician can do without calculating machines or computers simply because he can calculate without them. In the same way that every mechanic should have his well-equipped tool box, every efficient member of the exact craft should have his well-equipped 'thinking-tool box'.

Precise spade work for such sound thinking tools had already been done in Ancient Greece. Logicians of Ancient Greece then transformed logic, the philosophical discipline, into logic the 'tool' of philosophy. 'Organon' was the Greek word for tool. Philo of Megara, the 'tool maker' of philosophy, who lived in the fourth century BC established the complete 'table of values' for the If-then connection. We have already met the expression 'A implies B' (see page 204). The classical thinkers called this connection 'implication'. In this context one still speaks nowadays of 'material implication' or 'Philonian implication'. It has been hotly disputed, even by logicians, ever since the time of Philo. So many alternative definitions had been proposed that Callimachus, the librarian of the famous library of Alexandria, poked fun at it: 'Behold even the crows upon the roof are croaking which of the implications is more correct.'

Modern logicians are much more modest and find that, even without the croaked agreement of the crows, the Philonian implication does not need to be 'correct' or 'true'; it is only a definition. Such definitions are neither true nor false but simply useful or not useful. The history of logic has confirmed over and over again the appropriateness of the Philonian definition of the If-then-connection. Incidentally his implication was also known in the apparently 'dark' Middle Ages. In the scholasticism of the time, of which excellent examples of the literature of logic have survived, two rules which referred to the Philonian table of values were used.

First rule: The true follows the true or the false. ('Verum sequitur ex quodlibet.') This rule refers to the first and third lines of the truth table A → B.

Second rule: The false can be followed by the true as well as the false. ('Ex falso sequitur quodlibet.') This rule refers to the third and fourth lines of the table.

Thus the two rules express the correspondences $(1, 1) → 1$ and $(0, 1) → 1$ or $(0, 1) → 1$ and $(0, 0) → 1$ of the truth table A → B. Incidentally examples for the third and fourth lines of the truth table A → B (i.e. for the scholastic rule 'ex falso sequitur quodlibet') can be found in colloquial language. Admittedly these statements have an 'air of sophistry': 'If white horses were black, and black ones white then the greatest scoundrels would pay their debts' or 'If Easter and Whitsun coincided then Mr Miller would buy his wife a mink coat.' Despite the incorrect conditional clause in each of the two examples the compound sentences do contain a 'truth' which makes sense. Yet the 'great scoundrels' will not pay their debts and Mrs Miller will have to wait in vain for her expensive fur coat. From the formal point of view these two sentences are 'true' by definition; there is no need to discuss this. A → B means nothing else but $\neg A \vee B$. For our second example we could also read: 'Easter and Whitsun do *not* coincide *or* Mr Miller will buy his wife a mink coat.' The truth of this Or-connection is already certain when *one* of the two clauses is true (compare page 193). The first clause, which states that Easter and Whitsun do not coincide, is definitely true. In order to make sure that the compound statement has the truth value 'true' Mr Miller ought not to have to pay out for his wife.

In order to illustrate the use of an If-then-connection in a thinking tool we shall discuss another example. Again, to avoid an over-complicated situation, we shall keep it relatively simple:

It used to be the custom of the Hooper family to visit the cinema round the corner quite often. Father, mother, the son Albert and daughter Sally often spent a few pleasant hours in front of the large silver screen. But things have changed since the Hoopers acquired a television set. Mr Hooper spends his evenings in in the television chair, his beer within easy reach, and smokes his pipe when it pleases him. He likes to watch everything that comes over the little screen but particularly football matches. Mrs Hooper only takes time off for popular plays and operettas; and she does not miss a single one of the latter. Albert is there whenever a thriller is on and Sally is particularly susceptible to pop programmes.

And so it happens only very rarely that a member of the Hooper family goes to the cinema. Albert goes only when there is an operetta on television. As he says, he can't stand this old fashioned stuff. Mother on the other hand, will never go to the cinema if there is an operetta to be watched on television. When mother does go to the cinema then Sally always goes with her. Sally, like her brother, can't stand operetta either and so, whenever one is shown on television she accompanies her brother to the cinema. Father never visits the cinema because he spends all his free time in front of the television screen.

All these conditions have to be satisfied when Mrs Hooper, Albert and Sally go to the cinema. Can it ever happen that these three are in the cinema together? Can it happen that one of the three goes by him—or herself? If so, who could it be? In which cases are all the rules of the game satisfied for the Hoopers' visit to the cinema?

One could certainly re-read the above lines and think about them or one could take pencil and paper and analyze this problem. After a while one will find that this problem is only simple in parts and that it is no easy task to represent the situation clearly and completely. To be sure this problem is not insoluble. But a simple thinking aid can be of great service and yield clear and unambiguous answers. We shall proceed as in our first example and extract the two-steps which are decisive for further processing. We shall proceed as economically as is possible and only look at those 'bits of information' which are definitely being used to answer the questions. Since all questions refer only to the cinema visit the following two-step is superfluous for information processing: Does the father go to the cinema? Yes or no. We know that the father never goes. If we were to represent this by a tap in our circuit it would have to remain closed all the time. This would be highly inexpedient. Therefore we shall leave it out. Similarly a whole lot of other superfluous binary digits can be avoided. Finally we are left with the following list:

First two-step: Is an operetta being

shown on tv? Yes or no (1 *bit*).
Second two-step: Does Albert go to the cinema? Yes or no (1 *bit*).
Third two-step: Does mother go to the cinema? Yes or no (1 bit).
Fourth two-step: Does Sally go to the cinema? Yes or no (1 *bit*).

Again we end up with a relevant information of 4 *bit* which represents sixteen possible choices. The next step is to carry the connections through. Since it is usual in statement logic to link truth definite statements with the truth values 'true' (i.e. '**1**') or 'false' (i.e. '**0**') we shall first of all transform the above Yes-No-questions into such true or false statements. They then become:

'An operetta is being shown on television'. This sentence is true if the television station transmits an operetta; otherwise it is false.
'Albert goes to the cinema'. This statement, like the two following ones, is truth definite; it is true if Albert goes to the cinema and false if he does not go.
'Mother goes to the cinema.' Again this statement can be true or false.
'Sally goes to the cinema.' Again this statement can be true or false.

We can now connect according to the rules:
(a) 'If there is an operetta on television then Albert goes to the cinema.' The general case is $A \rightarrow B$ ('If A, then B'). We know that this connection is only false if there is an operetta being shown on television (conditional clause true) and Albert does not go to the cinema (consequent clause false). Otherwise this con-

Thinking tool connection for the cinema problem.

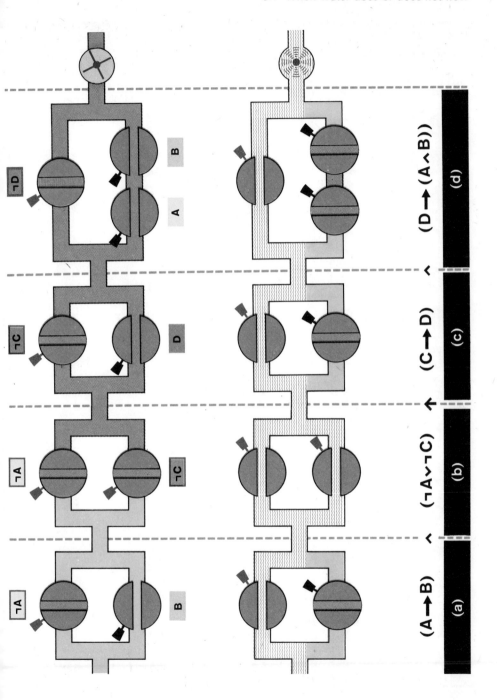

8. Building blocks of a 'thought-tool box'

	A	B	C	D	A→B (a)	¬(A∧C) (b)	C→D (c)	D•(A∧B) (d)	a ∧ b ∧ c ∧ d
1	1	1	1	1	1	0	1	1	0
2	1	1	1	0	1	0	0	1	0
3	1	1	0	1	1	1	1	1	1
4	1	1	0	0	1	1	1	1	1
5	1	0	1	1	0	0	1	0	0
6	1	0	1	0	0	0	0	1	0
7	1	0	0	1	0	1	1	0	0
8	1	0	0	0	0	1	1	1	0
9	0	1	1	1	1	1	1	0	0
10	0	1	1	0	1	1	0	1	0
11	0	1	0	1	1	1	1	0	0
12	0	1	0	0	1	1	1	1	1
13	0	0	1	1	1	1	1	0	0
14	0	0	1	0	1	1	0	1	0
15	0	0	0	1	1	1	1	0	0
16	0	0	0	0	1	1	1	1	1

nection is always true, e.g. if there is no operetta and yet Albert goes to the cinema.

(b) 'It is false that an operetta is being shown on television and mother goes to the cinema.'

Here the general case is being satisfied: ¬(A ∧ C), read 'not A-and-C'.

(c) 'If Mother goes to the cinema, then Sally goes to the cinema.' General case: C → D ('If C, then D'). The connection is only wrong if Mother Hooper goes to the cinema but not Sally.

(d) 'If Sally goes to the cinema then an operetta is being shown on television and Albert goes to the cinema.' General case: D → (A ∧ B) ('If D, then A and B). This linkage is false only when D is true and the A-and-B connection is false. And such an And-connection is true only when A as well as B is true. (This may sound confusing in a verbal formulation but, when considering the possibilities of what follows in the truth table, becomes relatively clear and distinct.)

The four conditions (a), (b), (c), (d) can be combined in an And-connection to form the generalized scheme

$$(A → B) ∧ ¬(A ∧ C) ∧ (C→D) ∧ [D → (A ∧ B)]$$

We can now construct the truth table, step by step, for this formula. This time we only require the tables of the connections A → B, A ∧ B and ¬A. The four terms (in brackets) of the And-connection are shown coloured in the diagram for the sake of clarity. This 'And-connection' is called 'conjunction' in

Truth table for the thinking tool connection according to the relation (A → B) ∧ ¬ (A ∧ C) ∧ (C → D) ∧ [D → (A ∧ B)].

logic. One also speaks of the connection being 'conjunctive'. For the conjunction of the four terms in the brackets to be 'true' (**1**) all four terms must be true. As the last column of the truth table shows (dark red background) this happens only four times; the binary symbol **1** occurs only four times.

We are now going to play through the family history of the Hoopers between the cinema and the television screen on the thinking tool. The first four columns of the truth table (A, B, C, D) define line by line our 'repertoire'. Looking for instance at the seventh line we find the coordinations A → **1**, B → **0**, C → **0**, D → **1**. As regards our machine game this means:

tap A on (possibly 'inverted tap ¬A off').

tap B off (possibly 'inverted tap ¬B on').

tap C off (possibly 'inverted tap ¬C on').

tap D on (possibly 'inverted tap ¬D off').

Instead of 'tap A on' we could equally well have written 'tap A is on'. In this context let us recall Wittgenstein's remark: 'Every instruction may be regarded as a description, every description may be regarded as an instruction' (see page 143). From this point of view every truth table can be regarded not only as a description of a system of relations but also as an instruction of how to act.

Before we can think of the game, before the 'going to and fro' of the Hoopers between film and television can be simulated with water taps, we shall have to build our thinking tool according to a definite 'circuit diagram'.

211

This complete circuit diagram is already laid down; it is the three If-then connections (a), (c) and (d). They each occur in their simplest form (parallel-connection of inverted and normal taps) in (a) and (c): A → B is technically realized in the form ¬A ∨ B and C → D in the form ¬C ∨ D. The if-then connection (d) D → (A ∧ B) is realized in the form ¬D ∨ (A ∧ B): the inverted tap (¬D) lies in parallel with the series connection of two taps (A-and-B).

A few explanations are required to realize the situation (b) in the thinking tool. The circuit diagram shows two inverted taps in parallel. In statement logic this means ¬A ∨ ¬C (not-A or not-C). We had, however, expressed the general case for (b) by the form ¬(A ∧ C) (not-A-and-C). Is it possible, therefore, that we can write ¬A ∨ ¬C instead of ¬(A ∨ C) and vice versa? We have already met a similar case: The expression A → B can always be replaced by ¬A ∨ B and vice versa. Why can this be done?

We know that such statement connections must be seen purely formally: The connections are defined exclusively by the particular appearance of the truth table where pairs of truth values correspond uniquely to individual truth values (see page 190). And just as the connection A → B—by virtue of definition—leads to the same truth table as the connection ¬A ∨ B, so ¬(A ∧ C) and ¬A ∨ ¬C also lead to the same truth table. In other words: the associations of pairs of truth values with single truth values are:

(1, 1) → 0
(1, 0) → 1
(0, 1) → 1
(0, 0) → 1

Let us first compile the truth table for the connection ¬(A ∧ C) in two stages:

A	C	A ∧ C	¬(A ∧ C)
1	1	1	0
1	0	0	1
0	1	0	1
0	0	0	1

The table for ¬A ∨ ¬C can be constructed as follows

A	C	¬A	¬C	¬A ∨ ¬C
1	1	0	0	0
1	0	0	1	1
0	1	1	0	1
0	0	1	1	1

The scheme
$$(A \to B) \land \neg(A \land C) \land (C \to D) \land [D \to (A \land B)]$$
which we developed above can be realized in our thinking tool in the form
$$(\neg A \lor B) \land (\neg A \lor \neg C) \land (\neg C \lor D) \land [\neg D \lor (A \land B)].$$
Therefore the four switching stations (a) to (d) are in series (And-connection). The indicator wheel, placed at the outflow of this circuit, revolves only in four out of sixteen cases as is shown by the truth table. This happens when:

(1) an operetta is being shown on television and Albert as well as Sally goes to the cinema.

(2) an operetta is being shown on television and only Albert goes to the cinema.

(3) no operetta is being shown on television and only Albert goes to the cinema.

(4) no operetta is being shown on television and no member of the family goes to the cinema.

The truth table and the use of the thinking tool tell us that neither the head of the family nor Mrs Hooper ever manage to go to the cinema now. Therefore the question whether Mrs Hooper goes to the cinema accompanied by her two children has to be answered in the negative. On the other hand the question of whether one of the members of the family goes to the cinema by himself can be answered with 'yes'. By virtue of the conditions (a) to (d) Albert can go by himself whether an operetta is being shown on television or not (fourth and twelfth line of the truth table).

The following are two points which one has to bear in mind if one wants to play meaningfully through all situations. (I) Taps which stand for the same statement variables have always to be placed in the same switch-position. Example: if tap B in the circuit branch (a) is closed then the tap B in the circuit branch (d) also has to be closed. We know that the truth table is the 'repertoire', the operating instruction for the meaningful realization of the situation by means of the thinking tool. Hence, if there is an '**o**' in column B then as far as the thinking tool is concerned this means: 'All B-taps in the circuit are to be turned off'. Thus, in this situation, the black control knobs of the B-taps are on the right.

(II) If the normal tap for a statement variable is on (open), then the corresponding inverted tap must also be on (i.e. closed). If the normal tap is off (closed) then the corresponding inverted tap must be off (i.e. open). Example: If the tap A is on in part (d) of the circuit then the inverted tap ($\neg A$) must be on in each of the circuit elements (a) and (b):

If the (black) control knob of a normal tap is on the right then the (red) control knob of the corresponding inverted tap must also be on the right. Our detailed circuit diagram shows first of all the normal situation of the installation which is formulated in the first row of the truth table. All black levers point to the left and so do all the red ones. Thus all normal taps are open and all inverted taps are closed. The indicator wheel does not revolve.

The drawing underneath shows however that the indicator wheel revolves when all normal taps are closed and all inverted taps are open. This corresponds exactly to the situation expressed by the last row of the truth table.

8.2 A little game of logic with an 'intelligent machine'
The mechanical solving of a brain teaser

Ever since exact science came into existence, that is since the time of ancient Greek mathematics and logic, there always were some people who invented brain teasers or puzzles—however one may wish to call these structures which make you rack your brain, if you will let them. This amusing border region of the exact sciences, which offers a 'precise pastime', is recreational mathematics. In our day the credit goes particularly to the American Martin Gardner for having cultivated and enriched this fascinating panorama. Through his puzzles Gardner managed to acquire a large circle of 'sharp-witted and punctilious' readers for the *Scientific American,* the high-standing popular science periodical.

Such games in logic began already in the pre-christian era. As an example we only need to mention the 'dog syllogism' of the Greek logician Chrysippus of whom Cicero wrote: 'Chrysippus says that the dog, having arrived at the crossing of three roads and having sniffed two roads which the deer did not use, immediately ran along the third road without sniffing it. Chrysippus says that the dog possibly draws the conclusion "Either the deer ran along here, *or* here, *or* here; but *neither* here *nor* here; *therefore* here."

Also the fallacy of the 'liar', which was discussed earlier (page 187), fits very well into this context; it was already known to the ancient Greeks. Medieval scholarship has presented us with a formidable collection of such amusing puzzles. Leibniz, Euler, Einstein and Turing also occupied themselves with such 'precise delights'. In a poetic sense the zenith was no doubt reached during the last century by the Englishman Charles L. Dodgson, who under the pseudonym of Lewis Carroll, published the now world-famous *Alice in Wonderland* and by the American Edgar Allan Poe whose tale of *The Gold Bug* fascinated not only mathematicians.

Many of the most intricate puzzles can however be solved by means of a thinking tool. The solution can then be found purely mechanically. Perhaps this fact may help to convince many a sceptic about 'thinking with the water tap'. To begin with we shall select one example from the large number of products coming from the logical and mathematical 'thought-factory'. The most expert of the connoisseurs will no doubt recognize the pattern according to which our problem is woven. Our little game in logic is based upon the relatively well-known story about the peasant who wants to transport a wolf, a goose and a sack of corn across a river.

Let us put this problem in a different way: the Taylors have two children, Charlie, who is three years old, and Mary who is two. Mrs Jones, the neighbour, has come baby-sitting and in return for this kindness Mother Taylor has made a large trifle for her. Mrs Jones was delighted with it but now she finds she has problems on her hands. Little Mary who is usually a good girl is irresistibly attracted by the trifle. On such an occasion she becomes a compulsive nibbler. Mrs Jones must never leave Mary alone with a trifle.

In the matter of the trifle the baby-sitter is luckier with Charlie; he can't stand it and eats it only against his will under the strict supervision of Father Taylor. But he makes Mrs Jones' life miserable in different ways. He always likes to play the superior villain before his sister and no sooner are the two children left alone than little Mary starts to cry. As far as Mrs Jones is concerned it means that the two children must not be left alone together.

Everything seems to go according to plan when suddenly the telephone rings; it is Mrs Taylor the mother of the two children. She says that her car has broken down and will not be able to get back until an hour later than originally planned. What is Mrs Jones to do now? She must be at home in time to prepare her husband's supper and so she mentions this to Mrs Taylor who simply replies: 'Well then just take the children with you for an hour or so'; and being extremely grateful and in a great hurry she says goodbye and hangs up.

Mrs Jones is now alone with this problem: how can she transport the two children and the trifle to her own house on the opposite side of the busy road? Charlie is such a lively fellow that she needs both hands free to get him safely across the road. On the other hand little Mary naturally has to be carried. And the huge bowl of trifle also requires two hands. So Mrs Jones can only transport one 'object' from house to house, either Charlie, or Mary, or the trifle.

On top of this are the problems mentioned previously: Charlie and Mary must not be left alone together, neither in the Taylor's nor in the Jones' house.

Is there a way out in spite of all this, to transport Charlie, Mary and the trifle without any difficulties? The experienced puzzle solvers will wrinkle their brows and say 'this problem can be solved by hard thinking. First of all Mrs Jones takes…' This is all right until someone interjects 'yes, but…' and it is realized that this particular way does not lead to a solution and so one has to go back to the beginning. We might even think that we have to employ a trick to get to the solution. In the end one will take pencil and paper because this may be the most sensible thing to do. For a systematic approach these are indeed the best tools to use; with them one can simulate the

problem. An American scientist quite rightly referred to such a case as a 'paper-and-pencil-operation'.

We shall make our task simpler by using the thinking tool. Many a reader will probably be quite eager to see how such a problem can be solved with open and closed water taps. This time however we shall program our machine in a different way from usual. On many devices a red warning lamp lights up when some kind of dangerous situation develops. Thus 'red warning light on' means 'danger': 'red warning light off' on the other hand means 'no danger' or 'everything is in order'. Instead of the red warning light, which obviously could not be operated easily in a water operated device, we shall again use our indicator wheel. When the wheel revolves it means there is danger. When it is stationary everything is in good order.

We shall now design the circuit for the water taps representing this situation. Our first question is: when will the indicator wheel revolve thus indicating danger? The answer is: when Mary and Charlie are together without Mrs Jones, no matter whether in the Taylor's house or in the Jones' house or anywhere else. The wheel will also revolve (danger) when we find Mrs Jones in either of the two houses without Charlie and Mary.

A similar situation arises also with Mary and the trifle and the presence or absence of Mrs Jones. Danger exists when Mary and the trifle are left together and Mrs Jones is not there. In this case the water flows and the wheel turns. Danger exists also if we encounter Mrs Jones whereas Mary and the trifle are conspicuous by their absence.

8. Building blocks of a 'thought-tool box'

The list of relevant yes-no decisions shows again two-steps.

1. Is Mrs Jones there?
   Yes *or* no (1 *bit*)
2. Is Mary there?
   Yes *or* no (1 *bit*)
3. Is Charlie there?
   Yes *or* no (1 *bit*)
4. Is the trifle there?
   Yes *or* no (1 *bit*).

Our next task is to channel these 4 *bit* of information into the right lines and to interlink them correctly. We have already agreed that the wheel should revolve whenever 'danger' is to be signalled to Mrs Jones. We call this an error detection routine because our indicator wheel revolves only when in the game with the thinking tool Mrs Jones makes a mistake.

Again we shall transform the yes-no decisions into truth-definite statements, which can be true or false, and place behind them, within brackets, the statement variables A, B, C and D which indicate the position of the statement:

Mrs Jones is there (A)
Mary is there (B)
Charlie is there (C)
The trifle is there (D)

Hence whilst for example A indicates the presence of Mrs Jones $\neg$C represents Charlie's absence, etc.

We have already asked when the indicator wheel revolves, thus indicating a warning. For Mary and Charlie this question can be answered by the statement form

$$(\neg A \wedge B \wedge C) \vee (A \wedge \neg B \wedge \neg C).$$

The reader may perhaps like to read this 'shorthand' expression for himself; the correct wording is given on page 345

For Mary and the trifle we can formu-

late the following 'danger situation' when the wheel revolves:

$$(\neg A \wedge B \wedge D) \vee (A \wedge \neg B \wedge \neg D).$$

When the one *or* the other situation prevails, the wheel has to revolve. Therefore both circuit elements have to be linked by the Or-connection, i.e. they have to be in parallel. The final expression then becomes

$$[(\neg A \wedge B \wedge C) \vee (A \wedge \neg B \wedge \neg C)]$$
$$\vee [\neg A \wedge B \wedge D) \vee (A \wedge \neg B \wedge \neg D)]$$

This statement form could be somewhat simplified according to the rules of statement logic but we shall use this scheme as it stands to design the circuit of our thinking tool. (After all we don't want to do more logic than is absolutely necessary and therefore we don't need to economize with taps 'on paper'. Moreover the linking of the statements is quite clear although admittedly a little long.)

The truth table has again been built up step by step. In this case, however, we have chosen a more useful presentation of columns so that the respective truth value for the complete circuit can be found in the middle of the table, underneath the ∨-sign of the decisive Or-connection of the two double-bracketed expressions, and not in the last column as was done so far. This important column is again shown with a red background. If the 1-signal occurs in this column this means mistake or danger in our connection. This occurs for the first time in the sixth row where in the first four columns we have the sequence of binary signals **1 0 1 0**. This tells us that Mrs Jones is there, Mary is not, Charlie is there, the trifle is not. In other words Mary and the trifle have been left alone together.

The binary sign **1** occurs in the control

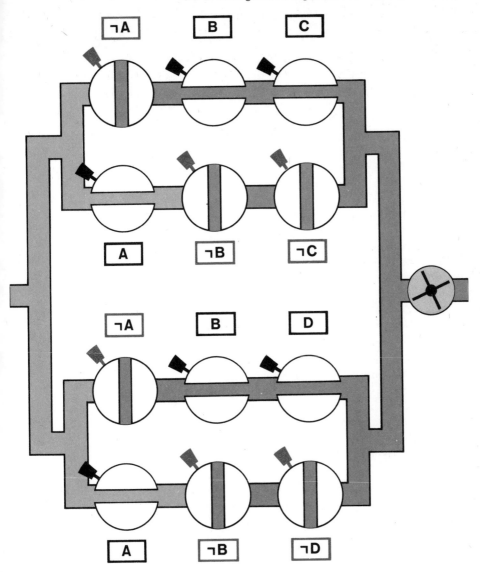

Thinking tool connection for the transport problem.

column in the middle of the truth table in six out of sixteen cases. These six situations of our 'object' distribution must not appear in our transport program. Only if Mrs Jones were to follow the top five instructions (yellow background)

and the bottom five (blue background) of the truth table would the warning wheel not revolve. The red middle column (control column) shows the binary sign **o**, i.e. the wheel is stationary.

If we now compare the permissible

rows at the top of the table (yellow) with those at the bottom (blue) we can establish a definite relation between them. Each of the top rows has a 'negative' at the bottom. Just as a white area in a photograph appears black in the negative and vice versa we find here that the signals **1** and **0** stand in a similar relationship to one another. For instance the first row **1 1 1 1** has its negative in the last row of the truth table **0 0 0 0**, the third row **1 1 0 1** has its counterpart in the third row from the bottom with **0 0 1 0**, etc.

Corresponding pairs of 'positive-negative' signal sequences can now be coupled; they reflect the situations in the two houses. As an example we pick out a sequence of signals and its counterpart which we shall place underneath

1 0 1 1

0 1 0 0

We can read this as follows: in the Taylor's house ('T-house') are Mrs Jones, but not Mary, but Charlie is there and the trifle (upper sequence of binary signs). Therefore in the Jones' house ('J-house') Mrs Jones is not there, but Mary is although Charlie and the trifle are not there (lower sequence of binary signs).

The next step is to design a program which will make it possible to take all four subjects from the T-house to the J-house. In other words the program has to start with

1 1 1 1

0 0 0 0

and end with

0 0 0 0

1 1 1 1

But what is the program between these stations? We shall proceed mechanically.

The first signal value (A) has to be reversed step by step. The instruction for the machine is therefore: the A-taps (and their opposites the ⌐A-taps) have to be turned on and off alternately. If they happen to be on for a particular step then they have to be off in the following step and vice versa. This simulates the toing and froing of Mrs Jones between the T-house and the J-house.

In addition to this only one further signal value, can change from step to step; Mrs Jones can take only one 'object' (Mary or Charlie or the trifle) from the T-house to the J-house and vice versa. This clearly lays down the first step in the program. These conditions therefore allow only the following transition:

1 1 1 1

0 0 0 0 (start of program)

0 0 1 1

1 1 0 0 (first step in program)

The imposed conditions don't permit any other combinations for the situations in the lower part of the truth table. Translating the 'machine language' into concise colloquial language this first step in the program can be read: 'Mrs Jones takes Mary from the T-house to the J-house.' The next step: 'Mrs Jones goes back to the T-house' is

1 0 1 1

0 1 0 0 (second step)

Mrs Jones again has to go to the J-house but now she is free to take either Charlie or the trifle with her. If we decide that she takes Charlie then the third step is:

0 0 0 1

1 1 1 0 (third step)

In the fourth step—Mrs Jones returns with Mary to the T-house—the following

Truth table for the transport problem.

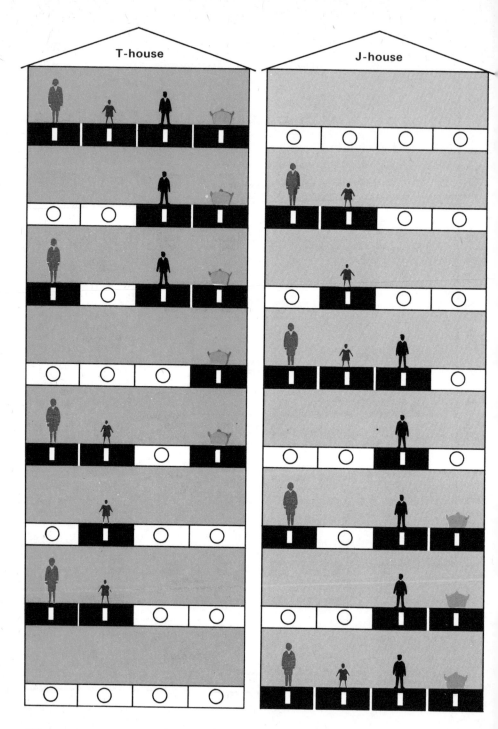

transition takes place.

$$\frac{\text{I I O I}}{\text{O O I O}} \quad \text{(fourth step)}$$

Mary now remains alone in the T-house whilst Mrs Jones, with trifle, proceeds again to the J-house:

$$\frac{\text{O I O O}}{\text{I O I I}} \quad \text{(fifth step)}$$

Charlie can safely be left alone in the J-house with the hated trifle. Mrs Jones now returns empty handed to the T-house to fetch Mary. And with these two steps the 'transport' problem is finally solved. The last two pairs of signal sequences are:

$$\frac{\text{I I O O}}{\text{O O I I}} \quad \text{(sixth step)}$$

and finally

$$\frac{\text{O O O O}}{\text{I I I I}} \quad \text{(seventh step, end of program)}$$

In order not to make things too dull we have included verbal explanations of the program. On the machine these are naturally superfluous, indeed they are disturbing. The problem can be simulated by the machine purely according to rule without any consideration about the content. It is only a matter of turning taps on or off, step by step, according to a definite pattern. Our machine helps us to link statements to which it can only say 'yes' (I) or 'no' (O) in terms of open or closed taps.

We can now write down the program for our thinking tool as a clear and unambiguous instruction of how to connect the taps A, B, C and D with their corresponding inverted taps. This can be done without any comments about the

content and without writing down the 'negative' sequence of signals which, in fact, only serves for control purposes.

I I I I (Turn on all taps)

O O I I (Turn off A- and B-taps and also the corresponding inverted taps. Leave C- and D-taps on and also the corresponding inverted taps)

I O I I

O O O I

I I O I

O I O O

I I O O

O O O O

This program describes the systematic clearing of the T-house. It can be seen that step by step the A-tap is alternately turned on and off; this is shown by the first binary digit of the sequences. Hence going down the first column we have I-O-I-O-etc. Of the three remaining signals at least two remain the same between one step and the next. At most only one of the variables B, C, D changes its value from one step to the next.

Of course the unambiguous 'negative' of this program which begins with O O O O and ends with I I I I reports on the population of the J-house. What does it look like? The reader is asked to write down the pattern of the binary signs. Compare with answer on page 345.

In the following chapter we shall continue to 'think with our thinking tool'. We shall, however, somewhat modernize our equipment by electrifying the water operated device. Instead of water flowing through our installation it will be electric current. And after this we shall use electronic information processing which so often is viewed with astonishment.

Schematic representation of the events in the transport problem.

221

9. MACHINES THAT 'LIKE TO MAKE DECISIONS'

9.1 From the And-connection to the 'black box'
Bistable circuit elements, link boxes, black-box-theory

In the course of reading this book some readers may have wondered from time to time at the lack of excitement with which the fundamentals of a completely new branch of the exact sciences have been described. Discussions about our 'exalted' thinking turn here into discussions about language, a seemingly natural subject. And the information is suddenly turned into mathematics, alongside with language, and yet everyone knows how 'tedious' mathematics is. But there is no field of the modern sciences, be it physics or chemistry, biology or information theory, that one can write about without including at least the basic truths of mathematics; not even pop-science can be presented without it. An author who promises his reader to introduce them to any part of the exact sciences without numbers, without formulae, in a completely non-mathematical way, is either doomed to failure right from the start or just pulls wool over their eyes.

And if this dull collection of mathematical formulae were not enough—one might perhaps continue to object—to make matters worse, the artfulness of logic had to be brought into play. But there was a very good reason for this. Clear and controllable thinking must take place on 'solid rails', as G. Frege once put it, and an 'intelligent machine' has to be able to 'calculate' with statements and with sentences. In the case of a system consisting of many, but always a finite number, of clearly distinguishable discrete states the machine can only 'say' either 'yes' ($\mathbf{1}$) or 'no' ($\mathbf{0}$). In other words it is capable of describing in binary form, a system which under certain conditions can be very complex and, as a whole, can hardly be taken in by us at a glance.

Unfortunately this does not sound terribly exciting. Yet it is always said that such a 'logical machine' is capable of making decisions. As we shall see this again is a linguistic misunderstanding. The technical term 'decision procedure', used in logic and in mathematics, has been given a completely wrong meaning. How can this happen?

Well, there have always been people who—consciously or unconsciously—have brought about and exploited linguistic misunderstandings. There are many writers, in the broadest sense of the word, be they philosophers, poets, or journalists, who make use of the natural and artificial wealth of our language-games in a more or less uncontrolled and uncritical way. Ingeborg Bachmann, the Austrian writer, once made the valid point: 'In order to make a point one sacrifices truth, and something well said is half a lie.' And Wittgenstein saw his philosophizing as a 'fight against the bewitching of our intelligence by means of language'.

Who then are these 'bewitchers'? There are first of all the 'serious authors of essays who cultivate the exciting sound

Small lights, on the control panel, which are on or off, help to express electronic information processing.

of the words 'intelligent machines' or 'machines that think' to create uneasiness about one's existence. According to them the technological demon has finally taken control of the human spirit and undermines the traditional foundations of man's existence. The outlook is frightening. 'Electronic brains' rule the world and are the slave-owners of man. Guillaume Apollinaire's despairing question 'What will become of the world when machines begin to think?' has been thought over carefully by the essayists and the alarming results put down on paper predicting the decline of culture and the downfall of civilization. A lack of factual knowledge is covered up by a delicately chiselled verbiage and a dark and nebulous torrent of words. Were one to apply to these pleasantly sounding structures the critical tests of linguistic analysis these resonating soap bubbles would burst straight away. One is then confronted with something that has not been thought out and that leads to nowhere and is only apparently unsuspected; the uneven chasm of rumours and surprise opens up before us.

Much easier to see through, but presumably far more dangerous, are the literary hacks who write about science 'for everybody' in the exaggerated jargon of the more popular press. But this stunt-like and spectacular nonsense is certainly no help to the men and women who carry out their scientific work sincerely and calmly. The teams of these scientists, all over the world, are not football-elevens. There may well be wizards on the field like Pele, Eusebio and Beckenbauer but mathematical wizards don't exist. It is easier to show off with the football than it is with an information processing installation. An unlucky shot is of lesser consequence on the football pitch than it is in the workshop of the exact sciences. Here the mathematician, the information-theoretician, the physicist and the molecular biologist work with formulae 'which are constructed from signs, in a way not dissimilar to that of the joiner who uses timber and plane, saw and glue'. This is how Hermann Weyl once put it so strikingly. We can extend this a little to meet present day situations. Just as the workshop of the joiner is fitted out nowadays not only with planes and saws but also with machine tools so the workshop of the scientist requires also information processing machines, 'intelligent machines'. This sober view of scientific research does not permit sensational reports which are aimed at open-mouthed ignorance. If scientists really wanted this kind of admiration they might just as well take their equipment and move to the fair-ground. A thinking tool, tailor-made to work like a robot, would fit in very nicely with the ghost train and the 'talking electronic brain' would not be out of place next to the lady without an abdomen. Who wants 'cybernetic wax-works'? One has to use a different approach in order to understand scientific work. Information theory is not a fair-ground. Unfortunately even among the academics at times there are people who use this kind of approach to make science glamorous and attractive.

Popular science has one clear and vital task and that is to avoid misunderstandings and not to create them. Exact science constantly changes our surroundings, the world in which we have to live. It changes the job of the instrument mechanic, who one day might be faced with an automatic lathe and similarly it changes the job of the accountant, who one day might have to use a 'data processing unit'. Methods and problems of business-and-management studies have changed due to the development of efficient thinking tools. 'Intelligent machines' can simulate the turn-over of merchandise in shops and stores; in fact the information processing installation thus becomes an essential tool of the manager. The detective uses it as a quick and reliable means in criminal investigations. The less glamour these instruments have for the user and the outsider the easier they can be used and understood; they finally become a matter of course. Why should we show more respect towards a data processing unit than does a housewife towards her automatic washing machine? 'In any case it is a peculiarity of progress that it appears much bigger than it really is.' Wittgenstein used this profound remark by his fellow countryman Nestroy as the motto to his *Philosophical Investigations*, observations which, with extreme precision, analyse our thinking and our language in which this thinking is done. Nestroy's remark could well head observations on intelligent machines.

Following these occasional and useful asides about the apparently so disquieting theme of 'intelligent machines' we can once more return to the unpretentious, unsensational facts. To begin with we shall carry out the 'electrification' of the plant. This can be done in a very simple way. The heart of our thinking tool was the water tap which could be opened or closed. 'Tap open' or 'tap closed' are two simple and clearly distinguishable states. There is no third state which might have to be considered. (It is much simpler for the scientist than it is for the plumber who has to take into consideration the by no means unimportant state 'tap drips'.) The two clearly distinguishable states 'tap open' and 'tap closed' place the tap into the class of 'bistable circuit elements' which are employed in modern technology. Each bistable element represents 1 *bit* of information.

We are of course well acquainted with one of the electrical bistable elements, namely the light-switch. This circuit element as we all know permits us to switch on or switch off electric light. Here again we have two clearly distinguishable states of the switch: the switch makes contact *or* the switch does not make contact, or briefly 'contact' *or* 'no contact'. This corresponds again to 1 *bit* of information.

If we want electric current to flow through the channels of our thinking tools we have first of all to replace the supply pipes by electrical conductors, in the simplest case by wires. The water reservoir is replaced by an electric generator, in our case a simple dry battery. A simple switch which permits us to make or break the circuit is the bistable element which replaces the water tap. Instead of the indicator wheel we now have a little indicator lamp which lights up only when the switch is on, i.e. contact is made, and the current flows in the circuit. If the circuit is broken, no current flows and the lamp does not light up.

The inverted tap too can be replaced simply by the equivalent electronic in-

9. Machines that 'like to make decisions'

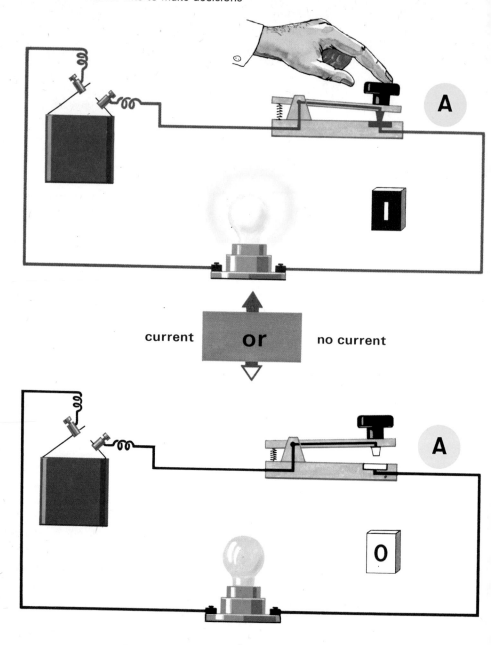

current **or** no current

A simple switch which makes (top) or breaks (bottom) an electric circuit acts as a bistable switching element. An indicator lamp signals the states 'current' (lamp on) or 'no current' (lamp off). In addition the normal switch is also characterized by its black knob (compare figure on page 188).

verted switch whose construction and operation is exactly opposite to that of the normal switch. If it is switched on (red knob down) the circuit is interrupted; when it is switched off (red knob up) the circuit is closed.

In the language of the technologist a 'closed circuit' means 'current flows'. (As is so often the case in science and engineering this is another example of a linguistic use differing from colloquial language. If in everyday life we find that something is 'closed', e.g. the notice 'closed' on a shop door, this usually means that there is nothing going on.)

As simple examples the figure illustrates the And-connection of two ordinary switches and the If-then-connection (parallel connection of an inverted and an ordinary switch). It can be seen that the arrangement is similar to that of the water-operated installation (see pages 188 and 192). These equivalent technical realizations are referred to as 'isomorphous'. This is again a very apposite definition of a linguistic use which can be applied to many other situations.

A detailed discussion of when two systems of elements are isomorphous is given in chapter 7.2 of *Modern Mathematics*. But even without a detailed mathematical treatment of isormorphism it is not difficult to see that the two arrangements—the water operated one on page 189 and the current operated one on page 228—are isomorphous, that they have the same structure. They only represent different technical realizations of one and the same problem.

Having dealt with the electrification of the 'intelligent machines' which was carried out very simply, we shall now

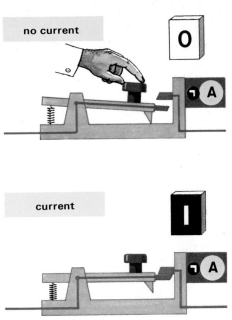

The inverted switch breaks the circuit when it is on (top) and makes the circuit when it is off (bottom). In order to distinguish it clearly from the normal switch it is shown with a red knob (compare figure on page 192).

turn to the question of the misunderstood 'eagerness' of these machines 'to make decisions'. Contrary to what one might assume this discussion will still not lead us directly to 'intelligent machines', to the 'robot who thinks as quick as a flash' but into those regions of the exact sciences where the problems of modern fundamental mathematical research are important.

Decision procedures by machines in modern mathematics have nothing whatsoever to do with the 'prerogative of the machine to make decisions'. On the contrary; they have to be instructions which permit the process of proof or of a contradiction to run its whole course uninterrupted and consistent right to the last detail. The important mathematical field of 'decidability' and 'undedicability' is covered nowadays, with precision, particularly by 'Turing machines' (see *Modern Mathematics* Chapter 11.2). The decision procedure of the mathematicians leaves not the slightest margin for a free choice.

In addition to these 'proof machines' of fundamental mathematical research there exists also an enormous collection of machines which we have called 'intelligent machines', 'machines that think' or 'thinking tools'. To some of these one also ascribes a 'freedom to make decisions'. The following statement, taken from a German newspaper, is characteristic of thousands of others similarly absurd: 'Electronic brains will make the most important decisions in politics and will decide about war and peace.' There are some scientists working in this field who don't object to such journalistic exaggerations simply because their work is then at least talked about. We shall, however, proceed along a different path and deny ourselves that kind of publicity.

Show-off tactics by scientists are quite unnecessary in order to achieve a meaningful understanding with the general public (see page 224).

To make this possible it is advisable to start from the field of statement logic. Our thinking tools are after all technological realizations of structures formed from connections of truth definite statements. Such machines have to be regarded as real, taken so to speak as materialistic in a sense which for philosophers is 'out-dated' and 'overtaken'. Even the philosopher, mathematician and logician Gottfried Wilhelm Leibniz (1646–1716), who must be considered immune from the accusation of downright materialism was of the opinion that it was precisely this logic which should represent the 'perceptible Ariadne's thread of thinking'. And when Gottlob Frege, who definitely was not materialistically inclined, spoke of 'solid rails' in logic we don't need to protest overmuch about the association with a solid system of rails on which a truck can move only in one way.

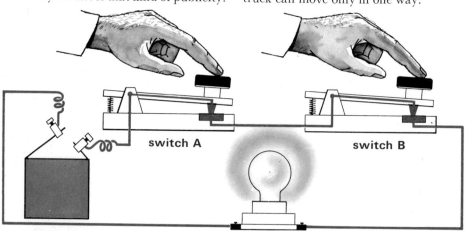

Two switches A and B in a series circuit form an 'And-connection' (or And-gate). The indicator lamp lights up only if both switches are on.

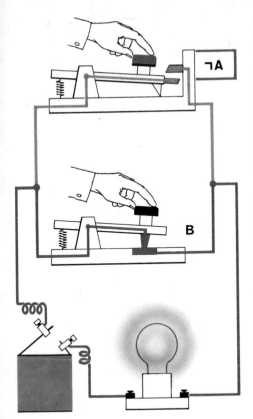

An 'If-then-connection' is formed by an inverted switch and a normal switch in parallel. (Compare with figure on page 193).

i.e. their truth value is either 'true' or 'false'; a third possibility does not exist. The construction of more or less complex statement connections from elementary truth definite statements can be compared with the chemical synthesis of molecules from atoms. As is well-known, here too one can demonstrate the linking of the building blocks by means of material ball-models.

Let us return to the building set of statement logic. Whether a statement connection is 'true' or 'false' depends entirely on the truth values of the truth definite individual statements. Any thoughts about the contents don't enter into the problem. The appropriate column of the truth table—which is always depicted in the diagrams with a red background—shows quite clearly when the particular connection is associated with the truth value 'true' (**1**), or 'false' (**0**). In all examples of connections discussed so far the values occurring in this column were both **1** and **0**, i.e. according to the distribution of the truth value of the individual statements A, B, C, D, etc. the statement form was either true or false. The compound statement is in every case truth definite just like the individual statements.

In the truth table the truth values of the basic building blocks A, B, C, D, etc. of the connection have always been arranged according to the same pattern

The 'calculus figure', the sign sequence A → B (A arrow B) is just as real, just as material, as a parallel connection of two bistable circuit elements with opposite characteristics (normal and inverted switch). As the mathematician says both material structures are isomorphous. Their totality forms the structure.

We have seen that the simple building blocks of the truth definite statements A, B, C, D, etc. can be combined into larger units which we have called 'statement connections' or 'statement forms'. These structures too are truth definite,

1	**1**
1	**0**
0	**1**
0	**0**

This table shows the arrangement which

occurs automatically in all truth tables if only two statements A and B are combined. For the sake of simplicity we shall write the pairs of truth values next to one another:

I I, I 0, 0 I, 0 0.

If there are three variables A, B and C then the usual scheme at the beginning of the table is

I I I, I I 0, I 0 I, I 0 0, 0 I I, 0 I 0, 0 0 I, 0 0 0

If four statements A, B, C and D are interlinked then the truth values in the table occur in blocks of four according to the following scheme:

I I I I, I I I 0, I I 0 I, I I 0 0, I 0 I I, I 0 I 0, etc.

If one always adheres to this kind of distribution of the truth values at the beginning of the table then the only thing that is important is the characteristic distribution of the **I**- and **0**- signals in the main column of the truth table. Taking an example for the And-connection of two statements A and B it looks as follows:

For the sake of simplicity we shall again write the binary signs of a column next to one another: **I 0 0 0**. The Or-connection of two statements (A ∨ B) is then represented by the column **I I I 0** and the If-then-connection (A → B) by **I 0 I I**. Of course we know already that these sequences of binary digits do not form a one-to-one correspondence with the appropriate calculus figure; they are not like fingerprints. The logic connections

¬A ∨ ¬C and ¬(A ∧ C) both lead to the same column of truth values **0 I I I** (see page 212). They represent equivalent connections which could be interchanged under suitable conditions in statement logic.

Such equivalent statement forms occur very frequently. For example the connections A → B, ¬B → ¬A (If not B, then not A), ¬A ∨ B and ¬(A ∧ ¬B) (Not-(A and not-B)) lead to the same main column in the truth table, **I 0 I I**: this could be proved quite easily.

In this way one can speak of a '**I 0 0 I I**-', a '**I 0 0 0**-' and a '**I I I 0**-connection', etc., factually, uniquely and without any reference to content. In the simplest case this means either the If-then-connection, or the And-connection, or the Or-connection. But the other notations are more general and more precise. What can we deduce from them?

Since the columns always consist of four binary signs we are concerned in every case with the linking of two truth definite statements A and B. The appropriate mode of expression can simply be applied to the thinking tool. The And-connection becomes the general **I 0 0 0**-connection, the If-then-connection becomes the **I 0 I I**-connection, etc.

The decisive thing is what comes out at the end for an equivalent 'feed in' to various connections. To put it more clearly: the simple If-then-connection of two variables A and B for example possesses two inputs (A and B) and one output (A → B) just like the And- and

This diagram of And- and Or-connections of bistable switching elements shows different outputs for the same inputs. In the first case one spaks of a '1000-connection' and in the second case of a '1110-connection'.

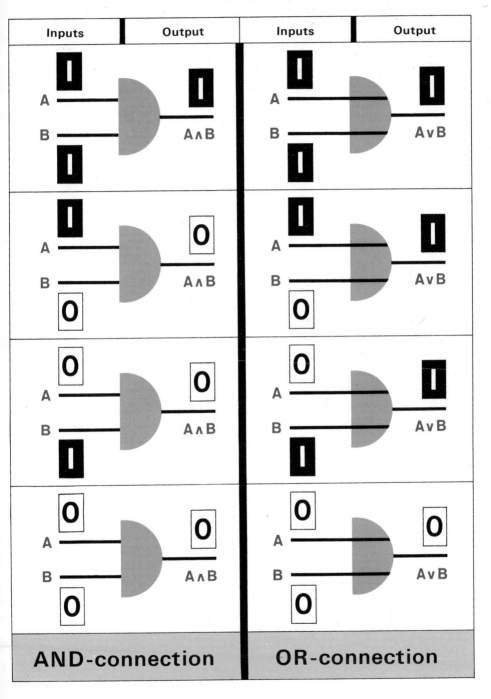

the Or-connection. If now input A gives the binary value **1** and input B simultaneously the value **0** then the value **0** must appear at the output. In the remaining cases the output has to give the value **1**. If these interconnections are electrical in nature then we can read for example '**1**' as 'current' and '**0**' as 'no current'. And because in all the interconnections of two terms A and B the two inputs are always fed in in the same stereotyped way (**1** and **1**, **1** and **0**, **0** and **1**, **0** and **0**), what interests us really is what appears at the output for these same inputs. Is it **1 1 1 0** or **1 0 0 0** or **1 0 1 1** or **0 1 1 1** etc.?

How many of such outputs of blocks of four binary digits are possible if we feed the two inputs to the circuit always with pairs of binary signals? At the two inputs we always have the four pairs of binary signs with which we are quite familiar: **1 1, 1 0, 0 1, 0 0**. Each of these pairs can again be associated with either **1** or **0**. This yields sixteen possible output signals which may appear at the output

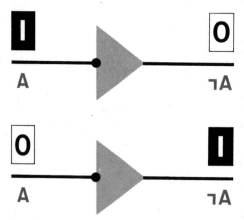

In a Not-connection (Not-gate, 01-connection) the input signal (1 or 0) is simply reversed giving an output of 0 or 1.

because of sixteen different interconnections.

Not all of these sixteen connections can be grasped colloquially as easily as the And-, the Or- or the If-then-connection. For example, let us consider the **0 1 1 0**-connection. It can be realized technically by placing a normal and an inverted circuit element in series and placing this series connection in parallel with a similar series connection of an inverted and a normal switch. Symbolically this can be written as: $(A \wedge \neg B) \vee (\neg A \wedge B)$ which reads '(A and not-B) or (not-A and B)': or we can say somewhat more briefly 'either A or B but not both'.

One can still find a fairly plausible linguistic description for the sixteen different connections of two objects A and B with binary characteristics (e.g. 'true' or 'false'). The situation becomes considerably more difficult when linking three truth definite statements A, B and C. Here we have at our disposal 256 columns of truth values or output signals from one interconnection; each of these is always made up of eight binary terms. What else could we call an interconnection of A, B and C yielding a sign sequence **0 1 1 0 1 1 1 0** but simply a '**0 1 1 0 1 1 1 0**-connection'? In this case our colloquial language fails us already; it is not the right tool for such specialized requirements. We would be helpless without the special instruments of the artificial language when considering the connection of four statements, A, B, C and D, each of which may be true or false. We have a choice of 65536 possibilities of constructing truth tables. There are 65536 different output signals or columns of truth values, each of which is made up of sixteen binary signals.

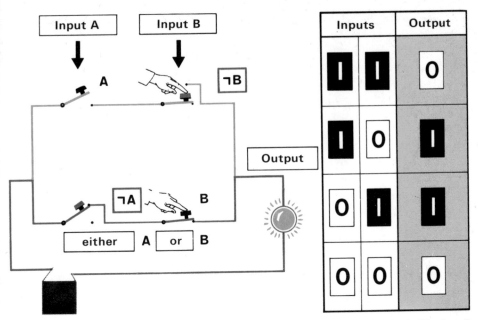

Diagrammatic representation of a 0110-connection according to (A ∧ ¬B) ∨ (¬A ∧ B) (read either A or B but not both). The figure represents the case when the A-switches are off and the B-switches are on (third row of table).

The possibilities of interlinking five, six, seven etc. different truth definite statements grow like an avalanche; the corresponding number of output signals from the network naturally grows at the same rate. If the variable x represents the number of these signals and a the number of truth definite statements which are to be linked then

$$x = 2^{2^a} \quad \text{(x equals 2 to the power 2}$$
to the power a).

Thus with two basic binary signs (**1** and **0**) a network with a inputs can produce 2^{2^a} output signals. We have already met the term 2^a (which is part of 2^{2^a}) when we discussed the formation of figures from binary symbols (see page 129). We have referred to these figures as communications. These artificial structures of binary signs could also be called 'messages' or 'code-words'.

Let us now compare the number of input signals in an arbitrary selected network with the number of output signals. Since the particular type of connection (And-, Or-, If-then-connection or any mixture of the basic connections) is quite irrelevant to our problem we shall consider quite generally a box containing a network with a inputs and one output. As regards the a inputs to the network box, each of which receives the binary signals **1** and **0**, we can speak of an 'a-digit input' which is fed with code words of a binary signs. A four-digit input, with the inputs A, B, C, and D, accepts only code words of the form '**1111**', '**1110**', '**1100**', etc., nothing shorter and nothing longer. The corresponding output signal from such a box is there-

233

fore only one of the 256 possible sixteen-digit expressions.

To the expert all these formulations which we have used here are still too colloquial and not sufficiently unambiguous. He sees only a box with an input and which consequently produces an output. We know that, as far as this discussion is concerned, it is quite immaterial what the inside of the box looks like and what connections it contains. It is simply a 'black-box' which, for a systematically given input, produces an output. This is a process which is typical of the creation of an artificial language by simply ignoring certain things that may be important to us in everyday life and shifting the emphasis to something quite different. Artificial languages are simply special tools.

For the connections which we have investigated so far we can use this vocabulary to make quite a general statement:

A black box can react to an input of 2^a a-digit codewords of binary signals (e.g. 1 and 0) by producing an output of 2^a-digit codewords in 2^{2^a}-fold ways.

Such a general statement is the concluding step of a more or less lengthy abstracting discussion. But modern mathematics, theoretical scientific research and technology are nowadays already in a situation where such abstract statements are used as the starting point of further ideas. This is by no means surprising if we remember that science has been practised by man for more than two thousand years. Lancelot Hogben, the English mathematician, whose books have contributed greatly to the popularization of this science, once remarked that

the best cure for depression, which befalls many highly intelligent people when face to face with the concentrated statements of mathematics, is the realization that what has taken men hundreds or thousands of years to grasp, is taught us nowadays in a matter of a few hours or even minutes.

What use is this 'confounded' abstraction, this 'troublesome mathematization'? No doubt some readers will ask this question. Water taps which can be opened and closed, which can be connected according to certain patterns and where one can always check whether water flows or not—well this is something to do with meaning. But now, suddenly, these familiar structures have simply become special kinds of bistable circuit elements. Moreover, the circuit diagram has vanished into a black box which reacts with different outputs to definite inputs. What use is all this? In the course of our discussion we were in the rather advantageous position of being able to build up our circuit structures, step by step, from simple building elements. This situation generally prevails in technology. The technologist, but especially the scientist, is however often placed in a situation in which a structure, either natural or artificial, can simply not be 'taken to pieces' in order to see what it contains. He then treats it just as a black box with an 'unknown inside'. He tries to find out whether such a structure reacts somehow or other to its surroundings, particularly to systematically applied inputs. He carries out an experiment.

Let us suppose that we were to supply an engineer with a black box, containing two inputs and one output, which he cannot take to pieces without damaging it. Yet he wants to find out what this box contains and what the circuit is. Is it possible that the engineer can satisfy his curiosity simply by observing the behaviour of the box from outside? Or ought he to be content with the words from one of Lehar's operettas: 'But what goes on inside is nobody's business'?

By no means. The engineer can apply binary signals to the two inputs to the box. The type of signal, its physical, material 'body', will depend entirely on the 'input material' which the box accepts, and which material it is capable of processing. If the box contains some kind of electrical device then it would be senseless and useless to pour water into it. This would only ruin the circuit of the box. If, for instance, it only accepts small wooden balls or cubes then it would be pointless to feed in current pulses. Thus the technical realization of the unknown connection is of decisive importance.

For instance let us assume that the black box can accept only the binary signals wooden cubes (**I**) and wooden balls (**o**); it could well be some kind of 'fruit machine'. As we have two basic signals for the two inputs the following input combinations are possible:

Input I	Input 2
cube	cube
cube	ball
ball	cube
ball	ball

According to its input-output relation this black box, which can process the binary signals 'cubes and balls', turns out to be an 'If-then-box'. In other words this device operates according to a 1011-connection.

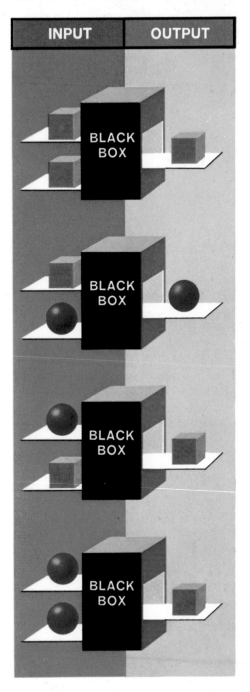

235

9. Machines that 'like to make decisions'

We further assume that the 'fruit machine', the black box, produces one of the two signals at the output for every one of the four input situations. If, for example, the output is as follows:

Output
cube
ball
cube
cube

the engineer would know from this output sequence that he has an If-then-circuit box, a **1011**-connection or a **1011**-circuit. Of course he still won't know what the inside of the box is like but in our case this is of no consequence. What is important, though, is that the output follows the sequence cube-ball-cube-cube or, what amounts to the same thing, the sequence **1011**. The box, therefore, contains a circuit which corresponds to the **1011**-connection, which is isomorphous with the equivalent statement forms $A \rightarrow B$, $\neg A \vee B$, $\neg(A \wedge \neg B)$, etc. We could of course write down the input-output list in form of a truth table where the binary signs **1** and **0** are replaced by 'cube' and 'ball'. The structure of the tables does not change:

Input 1 (A)	Input 2 (B)	Output $(A \rightarrow B)$
cube	cube	cube
cube	ball	ball
ball	cube	cube
ball	ball	cube

If the engineer is well-versed in the use of logical and mathematical tools then he will be able to solve this simple problem quite easily. If, on the other hand, he is not so well trained in the theory then he will be puzzled, perhaps unnecessarily, why, when feeding in two balls, the machine should 'spit out' a cube. But this is a consideration that refers to the contents of the box and does not concern us here.

In a second example let us consider what type of box we are dealing with when we apply current pulses to the two inputs, current pulse or no current pulse or briefly 'current' or 'no current'. These are the two binary input signals. To the usual pairs of input signals, current-current, current-no current, no current-current, no current-no current, the box, let us assume, replies with the following output signals: no current, current, current, no current, or in terms of the binary signs **1** and **0**: **0110**. This means that the box contains a **0110**-connection. We could also call it an 'Either-or-box' (see page 233). Of course if we liked tinkering and if we were not bogged down by theory, we would be curious to know what sort of structure the box did contain which could produce a current-pulse output when current is fed into only one of the inputs, but not when current flows through both inputs simultaneously; especially so if the current is an 'ordinary' d.c. Meanwhile, in view of our problem, such superfluous brooding about the contents can extract only a tired smile from us.

We shall only be able to carry out such theoretical discussions if we acquire a certain familiarity with the underlying mathematical apparatus. Every scientist, every technologist and soon even every businessman requires or will require a knowledge of modern mathematics. It is common knowledge that nobody can study physics these days without a sound and up-to-date training in mathematics. That an engineering student must be taken beyond the mathematical knowledge of the eighteenth century sounds nowadays like an absurd requirement. The increased emphasis on modern mathematics should apply also to courses in economics. Modern operational research demands modern mathematical methods. Even those sciences which, as the outsider believes, have nothing whatever to do with mathematics can no longer do without formal knowledge of the subject. As examples we may quote biology and medicine, psychology and linguistics, philosophy and law, sociology and political journalism.

All these branches of knowledge are nowadays in much closer contact with each other than they used to be at one time. The unifying bond is formed by modern mathematics with its large number of special tools. It is precisely the idea of this special tool which is so decisive for the drawing together of the various branches of science. Admittedly at one time the process of mathematization was often considered to be a very one-sided one, indeed almost short-sighted. Philosophical works, as was fashionable, were inappropriately written in the manner of geometry, or certain facts from other branches of science were forced into the straight-jacket of infinitesimal calculus.

But since then many a change has come about in mathematics. Geometry has become a small specialist subject within modern mathematics and has considerably changed and expanded from the twenty-three century old model of Euclid's *Elements*. Differential and integral calculus too did not stand still from the time of Newton, Leibniz and Euler; but it also forms only a small part of the enormous tool box of modern mathematics. And although differential equations may be extremely useful in the description of a small part of science they may be useless, even ridiculous in other parts. Let us stay with the image of the tool: one should use the razor for shaving but not for peeling potatoes. Of course one could use it for potatoes but we have to ask ourselves 'what in that case are potato peelers for?' The tool box of modern mathematics contains not only 'razors' but also 'potato peelers'.

Modern mathematics forms the cross-link between the various branches of science. In more or less complex abstracting processes it uncovers patterns, structures, schematic operations, games-rules which, when applied to other scientific areas, can assume a new meaning. Take the black box as an example. Although the words 'black box' were coined in electrical engineering, the underlying method, however, has been practised for as long as the exact sciences have existed. In physics we only need to remember, say, the experimental methods used in the investigation of the atomic structure which was described in detail in the companion book on *Modern Physics*. But the development of a 'black box theory' is really a matter for mathematicians. That it can then be used in different ways as a tool in psychology, biology and medicine is something about which the mathematician will no doubt be pleased. For instance the chemist Richard Kuhn (1900–67) has drawn a nice image for the black-box method used in the investigation of cell-metabolism: the scientist uses the methods of an industrial spy who has not yet managed to penetrate into the works ('cell factory') but nevertheless can gain important information by examining, registering and controlling the 'incoming and outgoing trucks' in other words the inputs and outputs.

But for the time being let us stay with the theory which we developed through a series of abstractions. Experiments on the black box, by systematically feeding in inputs and noting the corresponding outputs, tell us something about the pattern of information links inside the box without having to look in—in certain cases without being able to look in—and to find out what goes on there. Although we won't be able to discover all the details of the circuit by this method we can find out all about its structure which can be made tangible by an isomorphous set-up (see page 227). This of course applies only to the case when the system within the box has a structure at all which is certainly the case for our connections of truth definite statements. If the terms which are to be connected are truth definite (always **1** or **0** at the input) then the corresponding circuit is also truth definite (**1** or **0** at the output).

If we consider the box containing the switch circuits as a black box, and so know nothing about the types of circuits inside, then all we do know is that, for a certain input from the collection of all possible inputs, the output can be '**1**' or '**0**', 'true' or 'false'. But we won't know in advance whether we shall get the value '**1**', whether the connection is 'true' in this special case. It might equally well be 'false', i.e. the output would be '**0**'. This compound statement, the statement connection, which is built up of truth definite statements, may be 'true'. Its truth is possible, accidental. It is a 'chance event' in Kolmogorov's sense (see page 160). The probability of the chance event comes into play.

'Accidental truth'? To some readers this may sound rather sinister. But if one remembers the fact that we are dealing here with the vocabulary of an artificial language, if one is still familiar with Tarski's sober truth definition, the almost bookkeeper-like definition of a truth definite statement, one does definitely not feel nervous. We could just as well have spoken of the 'accidental **1**-value' and the grim forebodings would not have occurred in the first place.

Having thus returned to the fold of probability theory we shall now define the two 'extreme values' of probability for our black box game. Kolmogorov's theory defines the 'certain event' as one which occurs with the probability $P(E) = 1$, one which occurs in every case. If, therefore, in the case of a statement connection the output from a switch box always represents the value **1** then 'truth' becomes a 'certain event'. The output could be as follows: **11**, **1111**, **11111111**, etc. But what is the corresponding **11**- or **1111**-connection of truth-definite statements like?

Before searching for an answer to this let us note the other extreme value, the 'impossible event' having a probability $P(0) = 0$ for the occurrence of the **1**-signal at the output. This is precisely the case when the output consists of nothing but **o**-values: **oo**, **oooo**, **oooooooo**, etc. As we have not encountered such truth columns so far the question about the corresponding **oo**- or **oooo**-connection arises again.

According to our discussion there is no doubt that such connections must exist. But what are they like? Is there only one, or several or even a large number of such connections which always yield the value **1** or the value **o**? In every conceivable case these connections have to be only 'true' or only 'false'. Do these extreme values play a special part?

So far we have met only connections which are partly 'true' or partly 'false' according to the truth value distribution of the link elements. These statement connections could be 'true'. Their 'truth' was purely accidental. The value **1** occurred by chance. This chance of a composite statement being true, the possibility of it also being different (i.e. false), was called 'contingency' by mediaeval philosophers. Statement forms which are sometimes 'true' and sometimes 'false' are called 'contingent statement connections'. $A \rightarrow B$ is one of the simplest connections which we have met. On the other hand a more complex contingent statement form was

$$(A \rightarrow B) \wedge \neg (A \wedge C) \wedge (C \rightarrow D) \wedge$$
$$[D \rightarrow (A \wedge B)].$$

In the following chapter we shall deal with connections which are always 'true' or always 'false'; they play a special part.

9.2 Connections which always say 'true'
A mechanical decision procedure for statement connections

Up to now we have been concerned with contingent connections, statement forms, which, like the statements from which they originated, were defined in a sober categorized way as 'true' or 'false'. Our examples have shown that these statements and statement forms which can be associated with the values '**1**' or '**o**' can refer to quite ordinary day-to-day matters. In the simplest case they may say 'it rains', or 'Albert goes to the cinema', or, in simple connections, 'it rains *and* it snows' or 'Albert goes to the cinema *and* Sally does *not* go to the cinema', etc.

The associations of contingent statements and statement forms with the truth value 'true' (or '**1**') are accidental. If one were to play through all possibilities with the black box by varying the inputs systematically then the outputs could be **1**- as well as **o**-signals. In the truth value columns of the truth tables of contingent connections we find '**1**' as well as '**o**' values.

We have already raised the problem of the always 'true' and always 'false' connections. They have to be meaningful, regularly constructed statement forms which are not contingent and where chance (whether or not it rains, or whether or not Albert goes to the cinema) plays no significant part. From the purely technical point of view this means: the output of a particular switch box should always produce only **1**-signals or only **o**-signals.

239

Consider first of all the always 'true' connections. The simplest case is the one giving an output of '**II**', i.e. two **I**-signals.

Input	Output
I	**I**
o	**I**

What would the appropriate **II**-connection look like? As there is only one input to the box (a single input column) the only possibility is a connection in which a single type of variable (A) occurs. Were we to use only one bistable circuit element with normal characteristics (A-normal tap, A-normal switch) then the normal input **I**, **o**, would yield an output **I**, **o**. But we want the output to be **I**, **I**. On the other hand an inverted tap or switch reacts to the normal input (first **I**, then **o**) with the inverse output **o**, **I**. Thus a single inverted bistable element inside the switch box would also not lead to the desired result; for an input signal **I** the

output would be **o** and conversely for an input signal **o** the output would be **I**. Therefore in order to obtain the desired output of **II** we will have to combine the normal box with an inverted box.

There is nothing simpler than this. All we need to do is to put the normal element and the inverted element in parallel. A parallel connection of two bistable elements with opposite characteristics will always operate according to the motto: 'If you say "**I**" I shall say "**o**". If you say "**o**" I shall say "**I**".' One or the other of the two elements will always yield the value '**I**'. In the calculus of statement logic the corresponding scheme is A ∨ ¬A (A or not-A). The input-output table of this parallel connection is identical with the truth table for the statement form A ∨ ¬A.

A	$A \vee \neg A$
I	**I**
o	**I**

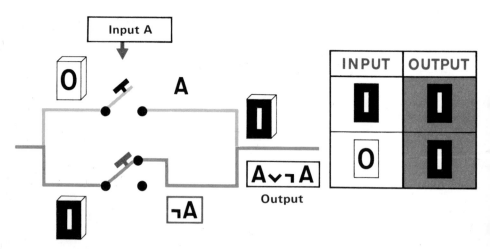

Two bistable switching elements with opposite characteristics are connected in parallel form a circuit which always yields 1- signals(current). The diagram represents the lower line of the input-output-table.

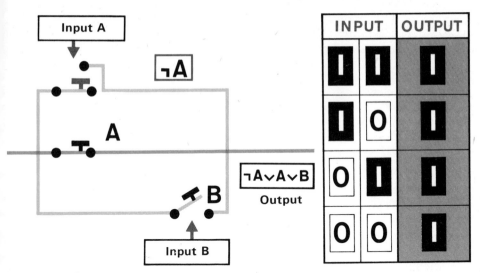

A tautological or redundant connection ⌐A ∨ A ∨ B. The arrangement corresponds to the second row of the table on the right.

Here again the variable stands for truth definite statements, i.e. for linguistic structures which can be either 'true' or 'false', which can be represented by the values '**I**' or '**o**'. We shall consider the most obvious example for the form A ∨ ⌐A, replacing A by the statement 'it is raining'. 'It is raining or it is not raining'.

It is obvious that this statement and other similar connections of this form are always true. In this way chance does not come in at all. It has lost in this case the leading part which it had for contingent connections. One can say with certainty that it is raining or that it is not raining. By definition another possibility just cannot exist. In a way we may consider this as a 'law' the 'law of the excluded third'. A or not-A; there is no third possibility. In Latin this is referred to as 'tertium non datur' and as such has been known for centuries.

Statement connections which by virtue of their form are 'true', i.e. are always 'true', are referred to as 'logical laws' or also as 'tautologies'. As Wittgenstein wrote in his *Tractatus* such structures of classical statement logic are 'unconditionally true'. But in contrast to the contingent forms they don't tell us anything about the processes taking place in our surroundings. As Wittgenstein said 'they are not images of reality'. 'I learn nothing about the weather when I know that it does rain or it does not rain.'

Yet for methodological reasons these laws of statement logic cannot be ignored. It is advantageous to be acquainted with connections of truth definite statements which by virtue of their form only always have the value '**I**'. A ∨ ⌐A is a very simple but at the same time a very important example of such a tautology. The fact that there are large regions in logic and mathematics in which this law

241

does not apply is a relatively recent discovery. This is dealt with in detail in chapter 1.2 of *Modern Mathematics*.

Let us consider a few more examples of 'classical' tautologies: $A \rightarrow (A \vee B)$, 'If A, then A or B'. This situation, in the form of a circuit, can be realized by connecting three bistable elements in parallel of which the first element must be of the inverted type. For we know that $A \rightarrow (A \vee B)$ is equivalent to $\neg A \vee (A \vee B)$ and by omitting the brackets (which strictly speaking ought to be proved first, as indeed it can) is equivalent to $\neg A \vee A \vee B$. Incidentally the isomorphous circuit diagram makes it clear that brackets are not required for a translation back into the artificial language.

One way of satisfying the form $A \rightarrow (A \vee B)$ which is always true is through the simple statement: 'If it rains, then it rains or it snows'. The layman who is inexperienced in formal science will probably not see the validity of this form right away. The experienced logician, however, sees the connection $A \rightarrow (A \vee B)$ purely formally as a toning down of an assertion A by the Or-connection $(A \vee B)$.

If someone were to assert that it rains then he may also assert that it rains *or* snows. The Or-connection is false only when both assertions are false. The If-then-connection on the other hand is only false when the conditional clause is false. But if we were to link the two connections according to the pattern $A \rightarrow (A \vee B)$ then this connection can never be false. If A in the conditional clause is true then the final clause can never be false.

The truth table illustrates this situation very clearly.

A	B	$A \vee B$	$A \rightarrow (A \vee B)$
I	I	I	I
I	0	I	I
0	I	I	I
0	0	0	I

If we consider the connection in the equivalent form $\neg A \vee A \vee B$ then the facts become still clearer. $\neg A \vee A$ is (classically) always true and when linked with B, which can be true or false, the total expression is also always true. The statement form is also a tautology (or redundancy) if A and B are truth definite building blocks: 'If A or B and not A, then B.' Example: 'If Peter is hungry or thirsty, and he is not hungry, then he is thirsty.' This connection is obvious. We know, however, that statement forms which refer to the contents are incapable of making a precise decision as to whether the form is always true. In order to show that in fact they are always true it is advisable to construct a truth table.

The following example shows how problematical the discussion of a tautology, taken from colloquial language, can become if it refers mainly to its content:

$$(A \rightarrow B) \rightarrow [(C \rightarrow A) \rightarrow (C \rightarrow B)].$$

Even the colloquial interpretation of this figure represents considerable difficulties. Your head would start spinning before you could get to the point of the question ('always true?'): 'If A, then B, then if, if C, then A, then, if C, then B.'

A bystander, who is not bogged down by formal science would in all probability take us for mad when hearing this sentence form—or at least break out into resounding laughter. Yet the fact of the matter is that we are dealing with a 'logical law'. Both, the truth table as well as the appropriate circuit of an 'intelligent machine', can tell us all about it. Both represent decision procedures for tautologies.

We could ask the truth table and the thinking tool whether or not a tautology exists. A connection of truth definite statements becomes a tautology if the truth-value column consists only of '1'-values, i.e. if the output of the circuit is always a 1-signal no matter what the input.

The following statement form shows us that it is always more reliable to consult the table or the thinking tool, even in simple cases, as to whether or not a tautology exists:

$$(A \to B) \to (\neg A \to \neg B).$$

Does this represent a tautology? It seems so at first sight: 'If A, then B is valid, then if not-A, then not-B is also valid.' We can give a convincing example: 'If the following holds: if Jean is allowed to dance then she is happy, then we also have: if Jean is not allowed to dance then she is not happy.' For Jean and for all young ladies who are crazy about dancing this connection is logical in every case. But does this represent a law of statement logic?

It is best not to embark on discussions concerning the contents but to construct a truth table step by step. We have to assume of course that the statements 'Jean is allowed to dance' and 'Jean is happy' are truth definite, that is that they assume

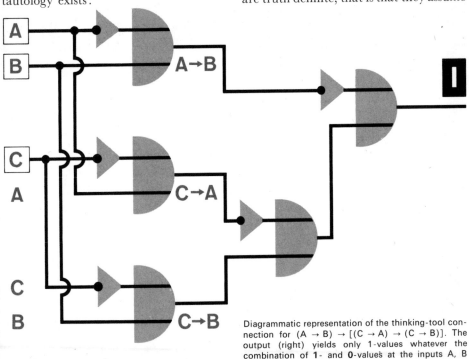

Diagrammatic representation of the thinking-tool connection for $(A \to B) \to [(C \to A) \to (C \to B)]$. The output (right) yields only 1-values whatever the combination of 1- and 0-values at the inputs A, B and C.

A	B	C	(A→B)	→	((C→A)	→	(C→B))
1	1	1	1	1	1	1	1
1	1	0	1	1	1	1	1
1	0	1	0	1	1	0	0
1	0	0	0	1	1	1	1
0	1	1	1	1	0	1	1
0	1	0	1	1	1	1	1
0	0	1	1	1	0	1	0
0	0	0	1	1	1	1	1

Truth-table for $(A \rightarrow B) \rightarrow [(C \rightarrow A) \rightarrow (C \rightarrow B)]$. This statement form yields only **1**-values.

the values '**1**' or '**0**' as the case may be:

A	B	A→B	¬A → ¬B	(A→B) → (¬A → ¬B)
1	1	0	1	1
1	0	1	1	1
0	1	1	0	0
0	0	1	1	1

We see that the truth table is not of the same opinion as the young ladies. Because the truth value column shows **1101** this does not represent a tautology. The same result can be obtained from the circuit of the 'intelligent machine'; it shows the following input-output table:

Input 1	Input 2	Output
1	1	1
1	0	1
0	1	0
0	0	1

The circuit diagram (see figure) represents the technical realization of the expression

$$(A \wedge \neg B) \vee (A \vee \neg B)$$

which is equivalent to the form discussed here. The reader can easily prove that this equivalence holds simply by constructing the appropriate truth table. The truth value column is again **1101**.

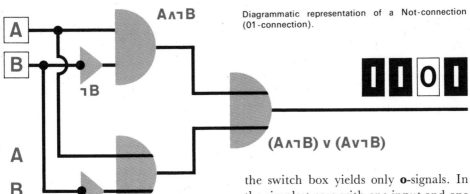

Diagrammatic representation of a Not-connection (01-connection).

On the other hand, the truth table as well as the thinking tool circuit confirm that the connection $(A \to B) \to (\neg B \to \neg A)$ is a tautology. The truth value column and the output from the switch box yield only **1**-values. The circuit follows the pattern $(A \wedge \neg B) \vee (B \vee \neg A)$. In this case the expressions $(A \wedge \neg B) \vee (B \vee \neg A)$ and $(A \to B) \to (\neg B \to \neg A)$ are equivalent.

And now let us consider the other extreme value of connections of truth values. Statement forms which are always false are called 'contradictions'. To put it loosely, they are statement connections which contain naturally contradicting building elements. In more precise terms the truth value columns of contradictions contain only **0**-values and the output of

the switch box yields only **0**-signals. In the simplest case with one input and one output the input-output table is:

Input	Output
1	**0**
0	**0**

What would a simple connection be like for this case? In view of the fact that the simplest circuit for a tautology was realized by the parallel connection of bistable elements of opposite types $(A \vee \neg A)$, we could try to realize the contradiction connection by placing these elements in series. If, for example, the normal switch is closed then the inverted switch must be open and vice versa. If both switches are in series than a **1**-signal cannot get through; the output is always **0**. In fact $A \wedge \neg A$ (A and not-A) is a

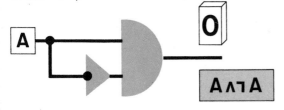

The And-connection of a bistable normal element and an inverted element forms the simplest contradictory connection. The output consists only of 0-signals.

INPUT	OUTPUT
1	**0**
0	**0**

simple but important contradiction. A statement and its opposite are asserted together. As examples we have: 'It does rain *and* it does not rain', 'Jack goes to the cinema *and* does not go to the cinema', 'seven is a prime number *and* is not a prime number', etc.

Every tautology becomes a contradiction by mere negation and vice versa. Example: $(A \lor \neg A)$ is a tautology. Therefore $\neg(A \lor \neg A)$ which is read as 'not: A or not-A', or 'it is false that A or not-A' must be a contradiction. This can easily be checked with a truth table.

An analogous situation exists also with the thinking tool. The expressions $\neg(A \lor \neg A)$, $\neg A \land \neg \neg A$ (not-A and not, not-A), and $\neg A \land A$ are equivalent. We already know the corresponding connection of normal and inverted elements in series.

In many transformations of this kind we find expressions like $\neg \neg A$ or $\neg \neg (A \lor B)$. These are 'double negations'. In the field of classical statement logic these doubly negated expressions can always be replaced by a non-negated expression as for example $\neg \neg A$ by A, or $\neg \neg (A \lor B)$ by $A \lor B$, etc. The validity of this process can always be checked by means of the corresponding truth table. We can see this easily for the case of bistable circuit elements of the thinking tool: an element which is doubly inverted must correspond to the normal element. If, say, the normal element gives an output $\mathbf{1}$, $\mathbf{0}$ then the double inversion of the values, because of the double negation ($\mathbf{10}$ to $\mathbf{01}$ and $\mathbf{01}$ to $\mathbf{10}$), leads again to the original output. This holds for each 'not-not-box' or 'doubly inverted box'. The output $\mathbf{1100}$ first becomes $\mathbf{0011}$

and then again $\mathbf{1100}$; the output $\mathbf{1111}$ first becomes $\mathbf{0000}$ and then again $\mathbf{1111}$, etc.

When discussing the connections of truth definite statements we have met three types of statement forms, the contingent forms, tautologies and contradictions. Would it be possible to see straight away to which of the three types an arbitrarily constructed fairly complicated connection belongs? Our discussion has shown that thinking, which is primarily oriented towards the content, is not able to do this even if the forms in question are built in a relatively simple manner.

But when several variables A, B, C, D, E, etc occur in a lengthy and incomprehensible connection, in which each of the variables may appear repeatedly and also inverted, then we are completely helpless without technical aids. The truth table, which we can construct as a paper and pencil operation, is admittedly a very reliable tool provided the form does not contain too many variables. Although, in principle, the truth table is a valid tool it becomes far too involved and incomprehensible for more complex connections. Who would ever think of using a fretsaw to cut through a tree trunk of several feet diameter even though it is possible in principle? Surely one would use a power driven saw which will make this job easier and faster.

In our case the power tool corresponds to the thinking tool, to the 'thinking machine'. The truth table is a safe 'mechanical' decision procedure telling us whether a statement form is a tautology, contingent or contradictory; but it remains just a sound 'manual tool'. We have to resort to pencil and paper. On the other hand the machine tool corresponds to the thinking tool. It is a mechanical decision procedure which operates reliably and fast. With the right kind of connection and systematically fed input signals we can arrange for the outputs to consist either of **1**-signals only (tautology), or **1**- and **0**-signals (contingent forms), or **0**-signals only (contradiction). The decision is made mechanically and with amazing speed by the thinking tool.

In order to get a clearer understanding of the technical aspects the following chapters will deal with the technology of 'intelligent machines'. So far we have worked with water taps, in rather an old-fashioned way and only spoken generally of bistable circuit elements. This was quite sufficient for the problems encountered up to now. Had we concentrated more on technical details we would not have been able to see the wood for the trees.

'Intelligent machines' have helped us, by means of contingent connections, to play through or to simulate everyday situations or puzzles. Their advantages lay particularly in the mechanical decision procedure regarding truth definite statement connections. In the case of a properly formed connection, no matter how complicated, the machine can 'decide' whether one is dealing with an always true, contingent, or always false form. This must sound disappointing to someone who believes that these machines can take decisions away from us, that they can tell us in any situation to act in this or that manner or to decide one way or the other. We are again faced here with a linguistic confusion. A machine which represents a decision procedure can make no decision by itself. This is in no way different from an automatic machine tool by means of which one can manufacture a cylinder block but which by itself does not decide whether or not the block is to be made.

A machine which makes decisions, and which man has to follow blindly, does not exist. It is a very poor invention of saying that 'intelligent machines' are reliable tools and valuable aids to people who have to make decisions. He who makes decisions should be well informed. And 'intelligent machines' do process information. This is done according to certain rules, mechanically, soberly, precisely and rapidly.

Therefore 'intelligent machines' can only help to suggest or advise, through their logical action, a certain course of action to people who have to make decisions. Their strength lies in the dispassionate mechanical presentation of information obtained through the processing of input data. In a way one could think of them as being in an advisory capacity. But as far as the making of decisions is concerned this can only be done by man.

This ends our admittedly narrow discussion about the theme 'decision problems'. But we have created a solid basis which will enable us to make a few additional comments about machines which 'like to make decisions'.

10. FROM THE THINKING TOOL TO THE COMPUTER

10.1 Switching quicker than a 'flash of lightning'...
Transistor—the building element

In the field of modern technology there exists a wealth of fascinating products of human inventiveness which we can justly admire. Without exaggeration, we can speak of the 'creative art of engineering', because it is the creative fantasy of technologists which formed this landscape. The meaning of the Ancient Greek word 'techne' points to the field of 'artistic or technical skill'. In the context of our discussion these words refer to the technical ideas of an inventor, or his conception of design and the ability and possibility of technical realization. This applies particularly to the varied electronic thinking tools which are manufactured by numerous firms in many technically developed countries. The fact that these machines are made up of electronic building elements is, at first, only important to the expert.

In order to demonstrate the fundamental action of such devices we have selected an apparently primitive and unusual starting situation, a game with open and closed taps which can be connected in a variety of ways. This was done for reasons which we have already explained at least in part. But there is one important point which we have not yet mentioned. Normally, the power of creation in technology shows itself in two successive steps: first in the mental concept and then in the possibility of its

These spiral stairs for a caterpillar are formed by npn-silicon transistors.

technical realization. (Generally one speaks here, in a somewhat solemn manner, of a dream for mankind which will be realized when the time is right.) Thus, it became possible, only at the end of the nineteen-fifties to send satellites into orbit round the earth. It was only by that time that technology had advanced sufficiently far to make realization of this centuries' old idea a possibility. In the development of 'thinking machines' we find exactly the opposite behaviour. The technical possibilities had existed for a long time before the idea was conceived. This applies particularly to our primitive water game but also to electrical and electronic thinking devices. The technical building elements for 'thinking machines' had existed before man developed the idea of building such instruments. This is one of the reasons why, in our discussions, the mental concept, which could be realized in the simplest manner through the machines described in the examples, was placed in the foreground. The point of our discussion is not the narration of the 'history of intelligent machines'; this has already been done by other authors, sometimes in an impressive manner.

Our much-quoted water taps could render the idea of the thinking tool comprehensible, though perhaps in a somewhat old fashioned way, and without the glamour of the jet world but sound and clear like the good old Junkers-52 (to continue the comparison with

The cockpit of a Ju-52 of the year 1935.

aviation). Walking through the aviation section of the German Museum in Munich one is shown first, and not without good reason, the control centre of this foolproof propeller-driven plane. In an article in the German Weekly *Zeit*, Manfred Sack notes the reason for this.

'The cockpit: yellow, blue and red levers and knobs, two huge joysticks, taps—like at home—on the water gauge. Next to the captain's seat I can see a large wheel and I think: cosy like a brake-van's cabin. Never before has it become so clear to me in which way a jet-plane differs from an (early) propeller plane. I think it lies in the difference in the relation between technology and the way it is used. If the pilot of a Junkers-52 pulls on a lever he can follow the effect of his action over hinges, joints, pins, rods or tow ropes. If the pilot of a Boeing-727 presses a button he can only imagine the transmission of his command; he can't see it. Here is mechanics, here is electronics.'

Our water tap connections represent so to speak the simpler thinking tools 'à la' Junkers-52. Two-coloured knobs, traceable connections between the circuit elements. Every situation which was simulated could not only be imagined but it could be clearly seen.

But the hard facts about the world of 'thinking machines' are that these basically sound and logical water games are not known there. The devices which are used are thinking tools à la Boeing-727.

Our archaic water tap building-set which, at least, is instructive and sound is of no use in the modern development of thinking tools. And yet students at the Massachusetts Institute of Technology (MIT) developed a hydrodynamic thinking tool, which carries a liquid in its plastic tubes, and which can solve logical and mathematical problems according to the motto 'tap on', 'tap closed'. This instrument is named 'Flunivac' and operates without electrical or mechanical drive. The word is again a contraction of 'fluid' and 'Univac' the name of a well known thinking tool made by Remington Rand. In contrast to the mechanically adjustable taps of our primitive device, Flunivac, which also thinks with water, operates through cunningly constructed fluid switches without moving parts. This increases the speed of working enormously. And this is the central problem of modern thinking tool technology—the working rate of the machines.

The water tap connections, which are of great help when explaining the basic rules of this modern development to the layman and to the beginner in electronic information processing, would be hopelessly slow in practical use. It would require precious minutes before one could accomplish the appropriate switching of the system. To run through the relevant tap adjustments corresponding to the different situations would again require far too much time. To actually work with such an instructive thinking tool would be completely impractical and in fact highly uneconomical from the point of view of time. So far we have intentionally disregarded this time aspect. If one wants to learn something new and unusual then one must not grudge time. Haste is the arch-enemy of all learning and understanding, especialy when mathematics and logic are involved.

But in practical science, politics and economics other factors control the course of events. Economy, rationalization, optimization are the headings of more and more closely linked fields of activity of human society. Nowadays scientists have to consider the economical, economists the political and politicians the scientific aspects of their work. But the sound basis of all their activities is the readily available information and the precise and rapid processing of information.

Ferdinand Martin (Technical Univer-

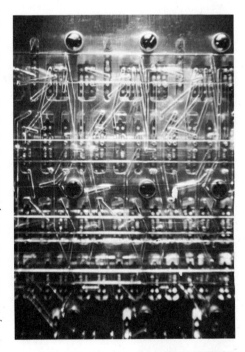

The hydrodynamic circuit system 'Flunivac'. In contrast to electronics one speaks here of 'fluidics'.

sity of Graz), an exponent of modern economics once explained the catchword 'optimization' as follows: 'Optimization means to "be an enemy" of any kind of extreme. Optimizing means "to search for the most meaningful agreement between extreme requirements". War against waste, war against delay, timely information, prompt reaction, these are the basic requirements—the optimum behaviour, however, is the object of the exercise.'

Thus, timely information forms part of the basis of such useful behaviour. So far, we have laid emphasis on the word 'information' which is to include also what was said on information processing. In practice, however, the word 'timely' is also important and we shall therefore

like to note a few points. In order to elucidate this we shall give a few examples. A weather forecast which contains a storm warning is obviously useless when the storm arrives before the forecast. The precise calculation of the correction for the orbit of a space probe which has to be carried out at the time t_1 is of no value when the result of this calculation does not become available until some later time t_2. The management of a commercial firm will hardly be satisfied with a detailed report giving precise information about the possibilities of losing a vital market when the report appears after the market has been lost. In all these situations information must be available in time otherwise it is of no value.

The simple thinking tools which we

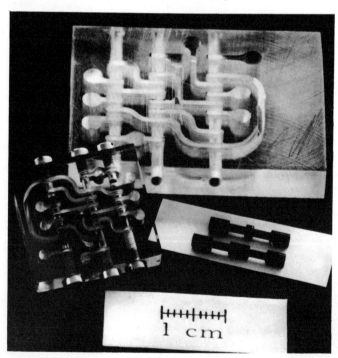

A typical building block of 'fluidics'. The channels in a plastic plate form controllable paths for the liquid. This water-operated building element is used in hydrodynamic thinking tools.

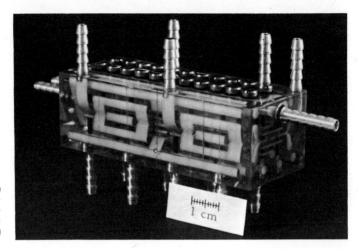

Several plastic plates with flow channels can be combined to form various connections. The figure represents a fluidic adding device.

have described so far, have operated with truth definite statements. With appropriate connections such instruments can also calculate with numbers. How this can be done will be described later. What is important is to know that such information processing plants are computers in the widest sense of the word. These instruments may be called computers rather than intelligent machines or thinking tools. The water game is equivalent to a small computer built up with logic

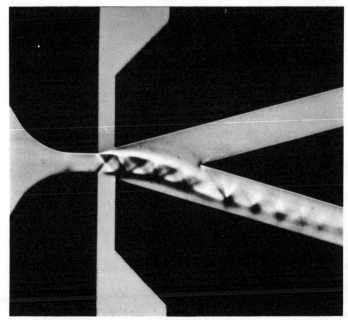

Schlieren-photograph of a bistable circuit element operated with compressed air. The control link (vertical channel) directs the air flow coming from the left into the one or the other channel forming the V on the right.

circuits. This book is thus a book about computers although the approach to this field was a somewhat unusual one.

How fast do such computers work if they are built from appropriate and up-to-date building elements instead of water taps which have to be operated by hand? Back in the middle of the nineteen-fifties electronic circuit elements of a computer had a response time of milli-seconds (thousands of a second). Of course if one considers that an exposure of this length of time is sufficient to produce a picture with a good camera then this short period of time is not quite so impressive. (In this comparison it may well be the shutter mechanism of the camera which is more impressive.) At the beginning of the sixties the speed with which the circuit elements worked was, however, raised to microseconds (mil-lionths of a second). Since the mid-sixties computers operate in the nanosecond range. A nanosecond is a thousandth of a millionth of a second, an inconceivably short time interval. The expression 'as quick as lightning' becomes quite mean-ingless here because natural lightning lasts for milliseconds.

Computer technologists are already talking in terms of picoseconds, a mil-lionth of a millionth of a second. A beam of light which covers 300000 km in one second will only cover 0·3 mm in a pico-second and 300 mm in a nanosecond.

This unimaginable and breathtaking speed of working can presumably be increased further. The theoretical limit corresponds to considerably shorter times; it is determined by the principles of relativity theory and quantum theory. There is first of all the barrier of the velocity of light which an ordinary moving body cannot exceed. This follows from Einstein's theory of relativity. Sec-ondly another limitation is provided by Heisenberg's uncertainty principle. We shall meet this quantum mechanical principle later in a different context; a detailed discussion was given in *Modern Physics*. What is important in this con-nection is that in time intervals of the order of 10^{-23} seconds (a hundred thousandth of a millionth of a millionth of a millionth of a second) time becomes blurred.

What does this mean? Within such unimaginably short time intervals time can be 'jerky'. In the so-called strong interactions between elementary particles in time intervals of the order of 10^{-23} seconds time reversals can occur. That is to say that for extremely short periods of time certain processes take place backwards. The effect of this would be similar to showing a film of the collision of two billiard balls, if at the moment of impact the projector were to run back-wards for a bit and then continue its normal run. The investigation of this startling time reversal belongs to the most fascinating and exciting problems of modern science.

Keeping these theoretical barriers in mind the operating speed, which some experts think will be reached within the next few decades, lies at around 10^{-20} seconds. It is amusing to carry out some order of magnitude calculations, as is done by many a popularizer; for example such a fast computer will be able to do as many calculations in one second as a present day one can do in millions of years.

Another point which is of decisive importance is the systematic widening of the field of application of such computers, and this means that the machine has to cope with several different programmes at the same time. F. Martin remarked in this connection: 'An electronic unit (of the computer) can simultaneously, for example, compute the wages for 10000 workers, as well as solve a scientific-technical problem, print out bills to customers and control a rolling mill.' This formidable work-load for a computer can already be tackled nowadays and is no longer 'music of the future'.

No less imposing than these startling prospects about the increased speed of

The control panel of the veteran computer ENIAC appears oldfashioned and primitive nowadays.

The American computer ENIAC built in 1946 with 18000 valves could heat a medium sized gymnasium. Nowadays, ENIAC has become a veteran of the pioneer days of computer technology.

machines is also the tackling of the size problem. The keyword here is 'miniaturization'. Hand in hand with the increasing efficiency of information processing plants, by reducing the time required to carry out the work, goes the reduction in the size of the instrument. Whereas in 1946, eighteen-thousand radio valves were required which, assembled in huge racks in the space of the size of a ballroom, produced heat equivalent to about fifty electric fires, nowadays there are cool-running, compact sets of the size of sitting room furniture available. Efficient table models have been developed which look like a large typewriter. And there are computers for rockets which are no larger than a flowerpot and which contain batteries of thin insulating silicon wafers of millimeter dimensions, each carrying half a dozen or so bistable circuit elements. The only too familiar mass of cables and flex has gone. The conductors are replaced by thin metallic bands evaporated on to the insulating sheets; these are known as 'printed circuits'. No matter whether they are of the size of confetti or postcards they can be exchanged as easily as files in a filing cabinet.

All these amazing developments in computer technology (incidentally also in space technology) began with the development of electrical semiconductors. They are solid-state materials which are neither good conductors nor insulators. This hybrid as regards electrical properties is being used very effectively in

The complicated and dreaded wiring of the pioneer days of computer technology no longer exists. An appropriate construction technique ensures easy inspection.

Modern information processing installations look like simple drawing room furniture...

modern technology. As long ago as the nineteen-twenties semiconductor crystals (mainly copper oxide) were used as rectifiers (current valves). (A rectifier allows the current to pass in one direction and blocks it in the opposite one. In this

...or like a large built-in wardrobe.

257

'Miniaturization' is the key word of modern computer technology. The picture shows several circuit elements (transistors, condensers, resitors) mounted on a silicon plate of about 2 mm² area surrounded by six contact points.

crystals was not properly understood until after the Second World War. In the late nineteen-forties the semiconducting magic tool the 'transistor' was developed in the Bell Telephone Laboratories by the physicists Walter H. Brattain (born 1902), John Bardeen (born 1908) and William B. Shockley (born 1910). In recognition of their work on semiconductors and the discovery of the transistor effect they were awarded the Nobel prize for Physics in 1956.

Without transistors there would be no efficient thinking tools (transistorized computers) today nor would space research have been able to develop by leaps and bounds. All the amazing advances in working speed and the miniaturization of equipment is due mainly to these tiny components. For our discussion the transistors interest us only as bistable circuit elements. In principle they operate exactly like our

way alternating current can be changed into direct current.) The mechanism of electrical conduction in semiconductor

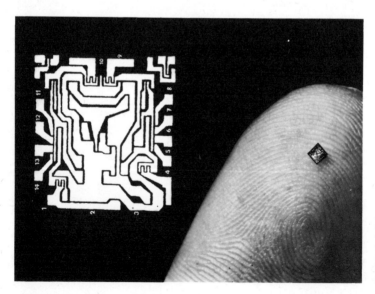

A square base with sides of 1·8 mm length carries fifteen transistors and thirteen resistors connected by a subtle etching—and diffusion process.

In connection with the technical development of information processing devices one often speaks of different computer generations. The third generation is characterized by micro building elements. Relays and valves have been replaced by transistors which are no larger than an ordinary salt crystal.

The three American scientists (from left) John Bardeen, William B. Shockley and Walter Brattain shared the Nobel prize for physics in 1956 for their discovery of the transistor effect.

water taps. With response times of nanoseconds they can be switched on to 'current' (**1**) or 'no current' (**o**). In all other respects the circuits are isomorphous (see page 227). Transistors control current impulses (**1** and **o**) almost without delay. Whilst all that happens inside the transistor is that electrons are being slightly displaced and stopped by 'potential barriers'; no mechanical levers have to be moved and no switches have to be turned on and off. An ordinary electrically controlled relay, which by means of an electro-magnet can open and close a circuit through a contact, takes as long as a tenth to a fiftieth of a second to perform this operation. (Although there exist faster relays with response times of milliseconds, compared with transistors even these are left well behind.)

As mentioned already the electrons in the transistor move over minute distances only. These 'switches', which are of the size of the head of a matchstick, are made up of three layers of crystals. The control current causes the electrons to play a kind of musical chairs. Sandwiched between two layers of crystals, where conduction electrons are always available, is a crystal layer which is so to speak electronically perforated, so that vacant places exist for electrons. These freely moving vacant places or holes are electrically positive and can be filled by the negatively charged electrons. Semiconductors of this type, that is those with *positive* holes, are known as *p*-type semiconductors or hole conductors. Because they accept electrons the *p*-type crystals are also referred to as acceptors. The two outer crystal layers supply the negative charges to the electron-depleted layer; they are referred to as donors and because they release *n*egative charge carriers they are called *n*-type semiconductors. The finer details of the interplay between donors and acceptors in a transistor is outside our line of discussion. It represents such a large field of physics that anything except this brief explanation would take us on a very long detour.

We know now why modern computers can think so logically and so unbelievably fast with current pulses. They operate, like their old-fashioned cousins the water taps, with binary signals **ı** (current) and **o** (no current). But here, in the technical realization of the bistable switching elements, the transistor effect of semiconductors is being utilized. The input signal coming over the control lead causes donors and acceptors to interchange electrons. The normally constructed transistor reacts to the control signal **ı** with an output signal **ı** i.e. the current flows. The transistor as an inverted switch reacts to the control signal **ı** with an output signal **o** (no current can flow) and vice versa. And when transistors are connected into the circuit of a computer in the form of And-, Or-, If- then-, and Not-connections we get the same type of input-output pattern that we know so well from the water tap connections. For instance two transistors A and B in an Or- connection ($A \vee B$), in other words connected in parallel, show the familiar picture of binary signals where in our scheme '**ı**' means current and '**o**' 'no current':

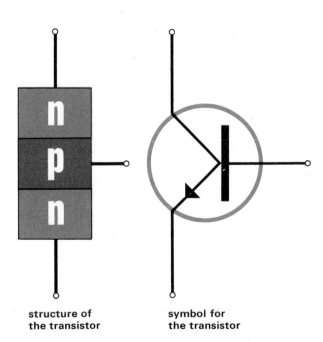

Schematic representation of a npn-type transistor. Transistors of different structures form the most important bistable switching elements in modern technology.

**structure of
the transistor**

**symbol for
the transistor**

261

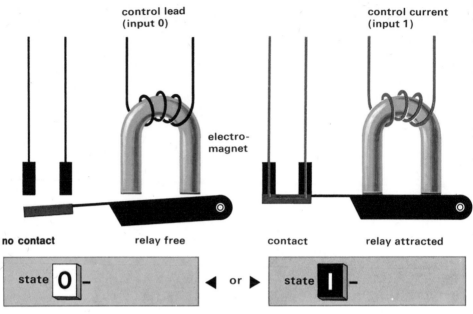

control lead
(input 0)

control current
(input 1)

electro-
magnet

no contact   **relay free**   **contact**   **relay attracted**

state **0** –   ◀ or ▶   state **I** –

An electrical relay is a bistable switching element which receives its input via the control lead: current (**1**), no current (**0**).

A	B	A ∨ B
current	current	current
current	no current	current
no current	current	current
no current	no current	no current

For the same input pattern the If-then connection of two transistors will produce the following output sequence: 'current-no current-current-current'. When does a current flow for a series connection of two transistors A and B? What are the control impulses like in this case? What type of connection is this? The answers can be found on page 345.

The teeth of this comblike structure carry npn-silicon transistors each 2 mm in length. The head of a match is shown for comparison.

10.2 'Flip-Flop' game with zero and one
Computing circuits

'To be a computer means to be a calculator.' This is presumably how advertisements might be formulated, in order to draw our attention to the fact that a machine called a computer does not only work with statements which are either 'true' (**1**) or 'false' (**0**), but above all also with numbers. 'Calculating' with truth-definite statements is after all not nearly as obvious and widespread as ordinary numerical calculations with which the man in the street is familiar. So far we have regarded computers exclusively as thinking tools i.e. we have built up logical connections. Typical examples of such connections were the And-, Or-, Not-, and If-then-connections which could be realized by bistable circuit elements. These building blocks can, however, also be used to produce circuits for calculations. And then we shall be able to think with thinking tools and calculate with calculators. For the sake of simplicity we shall limit our discussion to the addition of natural numbers; this is a sensible methodical limitation. It will highlight the important problems without leading us astray in technical details which are

Micro unit of transistors seen through a magnifying glass.

For obvious reasons Mickey Mouse counts with his eight fingers. He prefers the octal system.

important only to the expert. The field of computer technology has already reached such dimensions that the maxim of the Göttingen educationalist Hartmut von Hentig becomes topical to the interested layman: 'what matters is to learn how to guard against knowledge'.

The first important question we ought to ask ourselves is: How is it possible to count numbers or calculate with them with the aid of a machine which can merely say 'yes' ($\mathbf{I}$) or 'no' ($\mathbf{o}$), 'tap on' or 'tap closed', 'current' or 'no current', etc? If one wants to calculate one has to be able to count. This also applies to the computer. As far as counting is concerned this is purely a question of suitably encoding the sequence of numbers (see page 146). We have already spoken of coding in great detail. If a hungry king can put his culinary wishes into binary code then the same ought to be possible for the sequence of simple numbers like one, two, three, four, etc. We have successfully operated several times with the sign store $\mathbf{o}$ and $\mathbf{I}$ (or · and -, or $\mathbf{R}$ and $\mathbf{L}$) i.e. with binary signs and therefore we expect it to work this time as well.

Counting is associated with the sequence of numbers one, two, three, four,

etc. In the simplest case one could represent counting by strokes |, ||, |||, ||||, ... where each figure evolves from the previous one by adding one stroke. What is important here is the 'carry one', a process which the machine could accomplish just as well as man and, what is more, it could do it far, far quicker, particularly if the computer is transistorized.

We have been trained since childhood to count and calculate in the decimal system. This is based on 10 and we use a sign store of ten digits 0, 1, 2, 3, 4, 5, 6, 7, 8, 9. But this is a mere convention and habit which presumably is due to the fact that we have ten fingers. According to this convention, the wise horses of Jonathan Swift's *Gulliver's Travels*, the Houyhnhnms, use the binary system if they look at their forelegs when counting or calculating. Walt Disney's delightful Mickey Mouse would, for obvious reasons prefer the octal system which is based on the figure 8 (see figure). We don't however have to take our examples from the field of fantasy. In the same way as we count on our ten fingers the Mayas, in pre-Columbian South America, based their counting on twenty, by taking fingers and

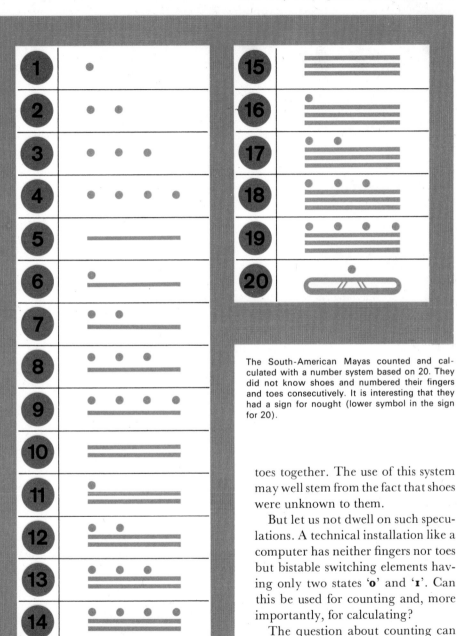

The South-American Mayas counted and calculated with a number system based on 20. They did not know shoes and numbered their fingers and toes consecutively. It is interesting that they had a sign for nought (lower symbol in the sign for 20).

toes together. The use of this system may well stem from the fact that shoes were unknown to them.

But let us not dwell on such speculations. A technical installation like a computer has neither fingers nor toes but bistable switching elements having only two states '**o**' and '**1**'. Can this be used for counting and, more importantly, for calculating?

The question about counting can be answered straight away in the affirmative. It is quite immaterial in which of the possible systems we count.

265

10. From the thinking tool to the computer

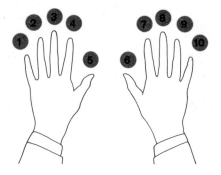

We have been trained from childhood to count and calculate in the decimal system. Simple mathematical problems can therefore easily be solved by using one's fingers.

What is important is that we should always be able to continue counting by successively adding one. In the binary system we can count with the signals **o** and **1** in the following manner: **1, 10, 11, 100, 101, 110, 111, 1000, 1001, 1010**…which should be read as: one, one-zero, one-one, one-zero-zero, etc.

How can we recognize that we are operating here to the base of 2? We have come across this base two before and that was in our block-doubling game (see page 125 f). There the 'block numbers' were exponents of 2 e.g. 2^1, 2^2, 2^3, etc. The following relations apply between the numbers of pieces in a block and the powers of 2:

$$2 = 2^1$$
$$4 = 2^2$$
$$8 = 2^3$$
$$16 = 2^4$$
$$32 = 2^5$$
$$64 = 2^6$$
$$128 = 2^7 \text{ etc.}$$

Let us select the fifth number of the counting sequence which is written 'five' in the natural language, '5' in the decimal system and '**101**' (read: 'one-zero-one' and not 'one hundred and one') in the binary system. Five can be written as four plus one or in a different way $5 = 2^2 + 1$ or even $5 = \mathbf{1} . 2^2 + \mathbf{0} . 2^1 + \mathbf{1}$. If we omit the powers of two (i.e. 2^2, 2^1) we can abbreviate to **101**. This three figured number can be realized for example in a parallel type computer by three bistable elements. Each digit has its own input connection

transistor 1 : 'current' (**1**)
transistor 2 : 'no current' (**o**)
transistor 3 : 'current' (**1**)

What number would be realized if all three transistors were to produce current pulses simultaneously? In the binary system this would be **111** (one-one-one). What is its equivalent value in the decimal system? As discussed above the abbreviation **111** is only a shorthand note for $\mathbf{1} . 2^2 + \mathbf{1} . 2^1 + \mathbf{1}$ which is the same as $4 + 2 + 1 = 7$. We therefore have the one-to-one correspondence **111** ⇔ 7.

The shorthand way of writing binary numbers with the binary symbols **o** and **1** (which, in order to avoid confusion with decimal numbers, are often replaced by **o** and **L** or **Q** and **L**) seems unusual to most people, in fact very odd and confusing. They ought to consider perhaps why the number one hundred and fifty four is written 154. Is this the most natural way of writing this number? Certainly not, but we are so used to it that we regard it as natural. 154 is similarly an abbreviation but in this case one omits the powers of ten. The longhand way of writing would be

$$154 = \mathbf{1} . 10^2 + \mathbf{5} . 10^1 + \mathbf{4}$$

This three-digit coding of the number 'one hundred and fifty four' with the figures 1, 5 and 4 taken from the sign-store 0, 1, 2, 3, 4, 5, 6, 7, 8, 9 is familiar to us but not the eight-digit way **10011010** of writing this number with binary signs. And yet here things are not very different from quoting the price of an article in American dollars one day and in Swiss francs the next. The different numerical systems are so to speak the different currencies of counting. We shall discuss this in more detail now by evaluating the number one hundred and fifty four in different numerical systems

(a) Binary system (base 2, sign store **0, 1**)
$$1. 2^7 + 0. 2^6 + 0. 2^5 + 1. 2^4 + 1. 2^3 + 0. 2^2 + 1. 2^1 + 0 \ (= \mathbf{10011010}).$$
This reads 'one-zero-zero-one-one-zero-one-zero'.

(b) Ternary system (base 3, sign store **0, 1, 2**)
$$1. 3^4 + 2. 3^3 + 2. 3^2 + 0. 3^1 + 1 \ (= \mathbf{12201}).$$
This reads 'one-two-two-zero-one'.

(c) Quinary system (base 5, sign store **0, 1, 2, 3, 4**).
$$1. 5^3 + 1. 5^2 + 0. 5^1 + 4 \ (= \mathbf{1104}).$$
This reads 'one-one-zero-four'.

(d) Octal system (base 8, sign store **0, 1, 2, 3, 4, 5, 6, 7**)
$$2. 8^2 + 3. 8^1 + 2 \ (= \mathbf{232}).$$
This reads 'two-three-two'.

(e) Decimal system (base 10, sign store **0, 1, 2, 3, 4, 5, 6, 7, 8, 9**)
$$1. 10^2 + 5. 10^1 + 4 \ (= \mathbf{154}).$$
The latter is the form that we are used to.

The sequence of counting in different numerical systems is shown in the large coloured diagram. And it turns out that counting in the decimal system, as we learnt it in school, does not need to be the most natural method by any means; it may be just as appropriate to use the

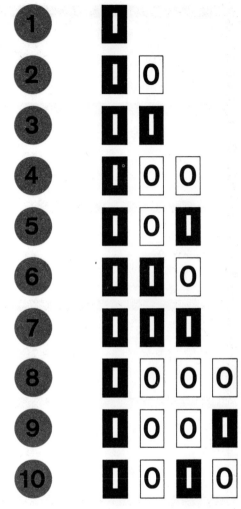

The simplest thing in the binary system is always to add one: one, one-zero, one-one, one-zero-zero, one-zero-one, etc. The binary system forms, so to speak, the 'basic currency' of counting.

binary system. After all our ten fingers are shared between two hands and there is no reason why we should not count 'right, right-left, right-right, right-left-left, right-left-right, right-right-left, etc.'

We could even denote this counting

| 1 | 10 | 11 | 100 | 101 | 110 | 111 | 1000 | 1001 | 1010 |

| 1 | 2 | 10 | 11 | 12 | 20 | 21 | 22 | 100 | 101 |

| 1 | 2 | 3 | 10 | 11 | 12 | 13 | 20 | 21 | 22 |

| 1 | 2 | 3 | 4 | 10 | 11 | 12 | 13 | 14 | 20 |

| 1 | 2 | 3 | 4 | 5 | 6 | 7 | 10 | 11 | 12 |

| 1 | 2 | 3 | 4 | 5 | 6 | 7 | 8 | 9 | 10 |

In any number system we can add one. This figure represents the sequence of numbers in the systems based on two (binary), three (ternary), four, five, eight and ten (decimal).

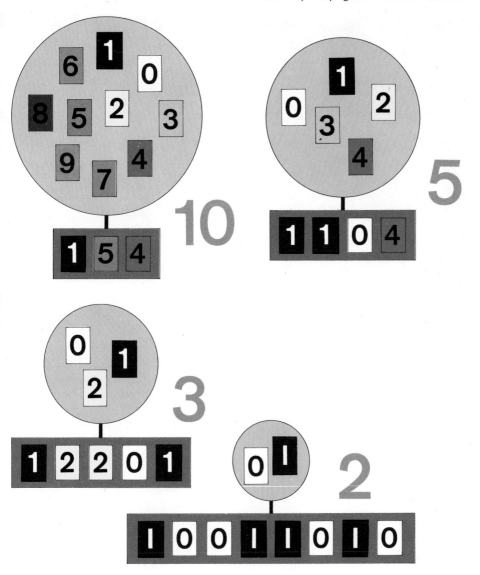

The various number systems are, one might say, the 'currencies' of counting. They are distinguished by differently sized sign stores. Of the usual currencies the decimal system has the largest store with ten basic signs and the binary system has the smallest with only two signs. The figure shows the values of the natural number one-hundred-and-fifty-four in various systems.

sequence with the binary signals **R** (right) and **L** (left) (see page 148):

R, **RL**, **RR**, **RLL**, **RLR**, **RRL**, **RRR**, **RLLL**, **RLLR**, **RLRL**...

But because we have become accustomed to counting in numbers 'one, one-zero, one-one, one-zero-zero, etc.' we shall not change it now. But why don't we stick to

269

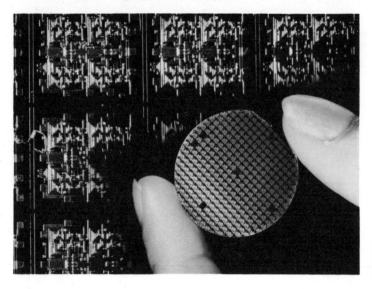

This silicon disc, of the size of a German five mark piece, provides space for 300 logic connections. An area of 2·4 mm² always carries 40 building elements.

the old and familiar decimal system when counting and calculating? This has reasons which are mainly economical. No technologist wants to build a machine which cannot be used to its utmost capacity. In order to use the decimal system one would have to translate into practice ten possibilities of choice for the figures o to 9. How can these possibilities be provided? There are no insuperable difficulties with a simple mechanical system. One could, for instance, use cog wheels as building elements with ten equidistant places. In electronic computers, which are built from bistable switching elements (transistors), this choice of ten can only be realized by linking such elements, with each one having two stable states. A successful realization of the required ten possibilities is by no means to be taken for granted. The coupling of three bistable elements would only yield eight, whereas the coupling of four such elements already

yields sixteen possibilities. This is too small a number in the first case and too large a one in the second.

A possible way out of this peculiar situation would be a combination of bistable elements to blocks of four and wasting six out of the sixteen possibilities of choice. If one would be willing to make this sacrifice then one could retain the decimal system in a computer. But computers should also be profitable. Because of their complex building elements they are expensive enough as it is. And this solution would represent a waste of 37·5 per cent. The decimal system is therefore of no use for a computer.

As we said above a computer should not be able to count but should primarily be able to calculate. Or, more precisely we want to use this tool to calculate; this is, after all, what their name implies. In fact calculating is child's play to these machines. They complete long calculations with large numbers in next to no time, calculations which would take man days and even months to carry out.

What does such a computer circuit look like? To begin with there are two possibilities. Either a computer circuit could be entirely different from a logic circuit which we used in the thinking tool. Or we could combine our familiar And-, Or-, Not-, and If-then-connections to form computer connections. The latter would be preferable particularly as we would not have to deal with completely unknown fields. So, let us try our luck in this direction.

First of all let us try to add two binary numbers. We shall try the simple problem of adding three and four. In the familiar decimal system this presents no problem—the result is seven. Yet, let us proceed systematically:

$$3$$
$$+4$$
$$\overline{7}$$

Can we transfer this simple scheme to binary numbers? In the binary system three becomes **11** and four **100**. In contrast to the two single-digit numbers of the decimal system we have here a two-digit and a three-digit number. Let us add the corresponding figures in the same way as for the decimal system. We start with the last digit:

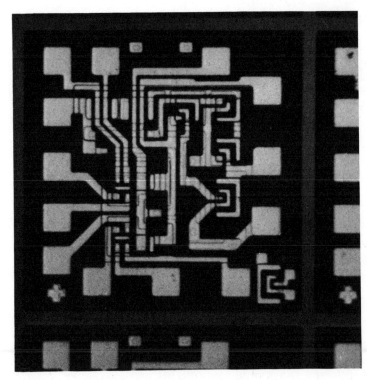

An area of 1 mm² contains an 0111-box.

$$II$$
$$+\,\mathbf{100}$$
$$\overline{}$$
$$III$$

III is in fact the binary expression for seven. $3+4 = 7$ is equivalent to **II**+**100** = **III** (one-one plus one-zero-zero equals one-one-one). In order to derive as much as possible from this addition we shall rotate the whole by 90 degrees. Counting the digits from left to right we have

	first number	second number	first number + second number
first digit	**0**	**I**	**I**
second digit	**I**	**0**	**I**
last digit	**I**	**0**	**I**

Again the two binary numbers **100** and **II** (or **011**) make a new binary number **III**. It seems that the operation of addition works with binary numbers. (The fact that we wrote **011** instead of **II** is of course permissible because the adding of **0** in front of a number does not alter its value. Actually what we have done is to add the term **0**. 2^2 which, of course, equals zero. Any number multiplied by nought makes nought, e.g. a.**0** = **0** or **0**.a = **0**. In the decimal system instead of 7 we can equally well write 07 or 007.)

In the above scheme the numbers are read from top to bottom in each column (**011**, **100**, **III**). The values of corresponding digits are next to one another. We know that when adding numbers made up of several digits the rule is to add the values of corresponding digits. This can clearly be seen in the first row and in the second or third rows where we have two different simple additions:

$$0+I = I$$
$$I+0 = I$$

The other two possibilities are equally elementary:

$$0+0 = 0$$
$$I+I = 10$$

(one plus one equals one-zero). The latter is the most difficult operation which a computer with bistable building blocks has to perform. 'One plus one makes two' means, in the binary system, $I+I = 10$. We shall now collect these four basic additions in an input-output-scheme which will give us a lead how to construct the corresponding switch box (black box).

input a	b	output c
I	**I**	**10**
I	**0**	**I**
0	**I**	**I**
0	**0**	**0**

Comparing this table with our input-output table of logic interconnections we notice one difference, namely the two-digit output signal in the first row of the table. This can be put right if we remember the following: The characteristic of logic connections is that a single binary signal (a 'truth value') corresponds uniquely to a pair of binary signals ('truth values'). In other words logic connections with two inputs always have only one output. But why can a computer connection not have two outputs? Surely

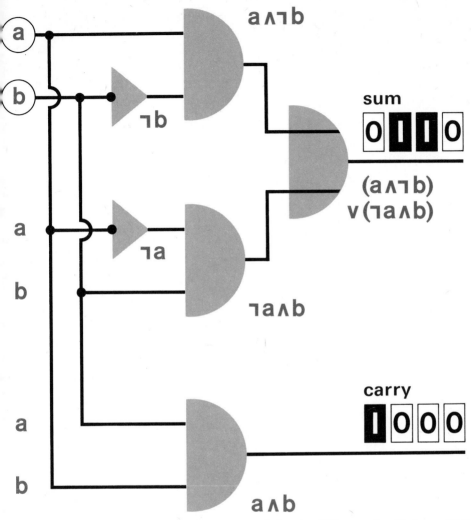

The combination of an 0110-connection (Either-or-connection) and a 1000-connection (And-connection) represents a half-adder.

it is possible that a single-digit number a, added to another single-digit number b, could result in a two-digit number c, made up of the figures c_2, c_1; and this could apply to any numerical system. Just as in the binary system we have

$1+1 = 10$, the decimal system for instance gives

$5+6 = 11$ or $4+9 = 13$.

For two inputs a and b and two outputs c_2, c_1 we get the following input-output table

273

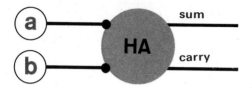

Symbol for a half-adder (HA-box).

| input | | output | |
| a | b | c | |
		c_2	c_1
I	I	I	O
I	O	O	I
O	I	O	I
O	O	O	O

In the output $c = c_2, c_1$ we shall call c_1 the sum and c_2 the carry. A carry is that value which one adds to the next higher column–and this applies also to the decimal system. At the moment it does not concern us how the computer carries these figures. What is important to us just now is: Given the inputs **I** and **I**, **I** and **O**, **O** and **I**, **O** and **O**, what type of circuit would produce simultaneous output signals of **OIIO** (sum) and **IOOO** (carry)?

The output columns of the table suggest that one should simply combine a **IOOO**-connection with a **OIIO**-connection in such a way that both, in their own characteristic ways, should react synchronously to the same output. We are already familiar with the two connections which are to be synchronized. The **IOOO**-connection for the carry is our familiar And-connection and the **OIIO**-connection for the sum is the Either-or-connection (see page 233). The diagram clarifies the combination of these two.

This synchronization of two logic connections forms a basic building block for computing circuits. It is designated by its own schematic symbol (see figure) and is known as a 'half-adder'. We shall refer to it in the text as 'HA-connection' or 'HA-box'.

This HA-connection is the synchronous combination of a logic connection according to the schemes $(a \wedge \neg b) \vee (\neg a \wedge b)$ for the sum and $(a \wedge b)$ for the carry. The variables a and b may be replaced by the values **O** and **I**. We can use this HA-connection as a computer element to construct a so-called simultaneous (or parallel) unit which will be able to add several multidigit binary numbers at the same time. The larger the number of digits of the numbers to be added the more half-adders have to be incorporated into the computer circuit.

We shall now consider the connection for adding two two-digit binary numbers $a = a_2 a_1$ and $b = b_2 b_1$ in a simultaneous system. The appropriate circuit diagram is shown in the figure. In a manner similar to the schematic summation with paper and pencil, the corresponding pairs a_1 and b_1, a_2 and b_2 are in pairs connected to the inputs of the two half-adders (HA-I and HA-2). If a figure has the value **I** then the appropriate input receives a current pulse; if the value is **O** nothing happens.

We shall now trace out step by step the mechanics of this addition. The values of the last two digits a_1 and b_1 are combined in the HA-I-box. Their sum c_1 goes to the output of the box. The HA-I-carry goes to the half-adder HA-I2 (read 'HA one two'); it moves up by one digit. At the same time the HA-2-box

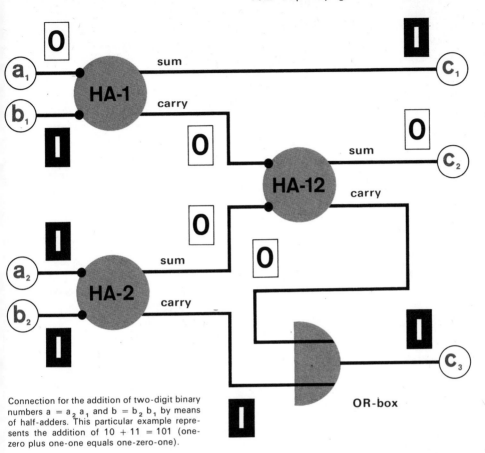

Connection for the addition of two-digit binary numbers $a = a_2 a_1$ and $b = b_2 b_1$ by means of half-adders. This particular example represents the addition of $10 + 11 = 101$ (one-zero plus one-one equals one-zero-one).

adds the values of the first pair of digits a_2 and b_2 the sum of which goes to the HA-12-box. This box now forms the sum c_2 of the HA-2 sum and the HA-1-carry; this also goes to the output forming the next digit c_2. Finally the carry from HA-12 and the carry from HA-2 are combined in an Or-box. The output c_3 gives the highest value of **1** if a pulse arrives from HA-2 *or* from HA-12.

This description, which was kept quite general, may not appear at first sight to be as simple as it in fact is. Our natural language is not yet quite suited to the

needs of computer mechanics; the technological field is still too new. If we were to consider the example 'two plus three makes five' the mechanics become far simpler:

$$\begin{array}{r} \mathbf{10} \\ + \mathbf{11} \\ \hline \mathbf{101} \end{array}$$

which reads 'one-zero plus one-one makes one-zero-one'. The input of the HA-1-box consists of a pair of pulses $a_1 = \mathbf{0}$ and $b_1 = \mathbf{1}$. This yields the sum $c_1 = \mathbf{1}$ and

275

the carry $\mathbf{o}$. At the same time the HA-2-box receives the input $a_2 = \mathbf{1}$ and $b_2 = \mathbf{1}$. This makes the HA-2-sum $\mathbf{o}$ which together with the HA-1-carry $\mathbf{o}$, yields the digital value $c_2 = \mathbf{o}$. The HA-2-carry $\mathbf{1}$, however, forms the input pulse for the Or- box which responds even though the HA-12-carry is $\mathbf{o}$. Thus the output of the Or- box is $c_3 = \mathbf{1}$. Hence the final result $c = c_3 c_2 c_1$ is $c = \mathbf{101}$.

We can now build up computing circuits systematically with the aid of half-adders for three-, four- and multiple-digit binary numbers. The diagram depicts the circuit for the addition of two three-digit numbers. This requires five HA-boxes and two Or-boxes. It can easily be seen that for the addition of two ten-digit binary numbers such a parallel machine is built up of as many as nine-teen HA-boxes (HA-1 to HA-10 and HA-12 to HA-9 10) and nine Or- boxes. The equivalent installation for twenty-figure numbers requires thirty-nine half-adders and nine Or- boxes.

A large binary machine calculator can work with thirty- to forty-digit numbers, that is in the giga- and tera ranges (10^9 and 10^{12} respectively) of our decimal system. It is important that such a super installation should operate according to the same scheme and equally fast as do the mini-circuits which we have discussed here. After all the large machines are built from the same basic building blocks (half-adders and Or- boxes) except that there are more of them. It is said in computer circles that 'speed is not witch-craft'. This certainly holds when transistors are being used.

Another important building block for computing circuits is the 'adder'. It is a bistable flip-flop switch. In the flip-flop circuit a pair of opposite bistable states are technically realized; they carry out a simple but meaningful interplay. If one state is $\mathbf{1}$ then the neighbouring state is always $\mathbf{o}$ and vice versa. And every time a pulse appears at the input of the flip-flop box the system flips over, thereby revers-ing the states. This new situation will remain in existence until the next impulse arrives and triggers off another reversal. The flip-flop has only one input.

We will now consider an example of the simple flip-flop game. In a little box

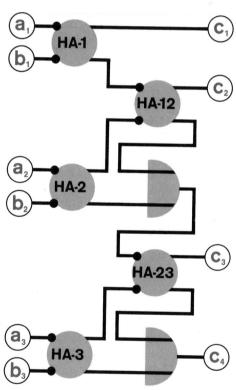

Circuit of half-adders for the addition of the two three-digit binary numbers $a = a_3 a_2 a_1$ and $b = b_3 b_2 b_1$.

there are two lamps mounted one above the other. If the upper lamp is lit (**1**) the lower one is dark (**0**). If, on the other hand, the lower one is lit (**1**) then the upper one is dark (**0**). The input to the box receives current pulses (**1**), for example by pressing a knob. Every time the knob is depressed a signal travels to the input of the flip-flop (**1**). Every input reverses the flip-flop state. If the signal arrives when the upper lamp is on, then it is switched off and the lower one comes on. If, however, the impulse arrives when the upper lamp is off then it will be switched on and the lower one switched off. We add the further condition that, whenever the lower lamp is on, the signal **1** appears at the output. The flip-flop game then goes as follows:

First situation: Upper lamp on (**1**), lower lamp off (**0**), hence output **0**. An input **1** causes the system to flip over. Second situation: the upper lamp is now off (**0**), the lower lamp is on (**1**), hence output gives off a pulse (**1**). After a while, pressure on the knob releases a new input pulse **1**. The system reverts back (flops) to its original state. The upper lamp is on (**1**), lower lamp off (**0**) and output **0**. This corresponds to the third situation. A renewed input pulse (flip) brings about the fourth situation: upper lamp off (**0**), lower lamp on (**1**) output **1**, etc.

This simple 'snap-action' between two states **0** and **1**, which in practice can be done extremely fast with transistor circuits, has also earned the flip-flop the name 'bistable multivibrator'. (Incidentally the simplest member of the family of multivibrators is surely the little rascal who persistently keeps pressing the bell push, on-off-on-off etc.) No matter whether we speak of a flip-flop, a bistable multivibrator, a toggle or a bistable Kipp circuit we are dealing with meaningful devices, switch boxes, which flip over after receiving an input signal. Such devices can be realized by electromagnetic relays, radio valves or transistors (see diagrams).

With the help of the schematic diagrams we shall now see how a computing circuit of flip-flops can be used to add binary numbers. This time we shall straight away consider as an example the addition **110** + **111** = **1101** (six plus seven makes thirteen).

Since the result is a four-digit binary number we shall construct a circuit from four flip-flops, the boxes FF-4, FF-3, FF-2, FF-1. Each of the four boxes has an input (the control lead) which accepts **1**-signals (pulses). The respective main output, which gives the corresponding digital value **1** or **0** of the sum, is always shown below. The sum $c = c_4 c_3 c_2 c_1$ (in our case $c = $ **1101**) is therefore determined by the four outputs c_4, c_3, c_2 and c_1. The normal situation of the flip-flop is indicated by upper square black, lower square white that is output **1** and **0** respectively.

We feed in the first binary number **110** into the four inputs of the flip-flop. Since only the inputs of FF-3 and FF-2 receive **1**-signals the states in these two boxes are reversed. The black squares move down and the upper squares are now white. The flip-flops FF-4 and FF-1 don't change. We note that the output $c = c_4 c_3 c_2 c_1$ of the circuit registers the first binary number **110** in the form of **0110**. But we have not finished yet. We now have to add **111** which should give us the

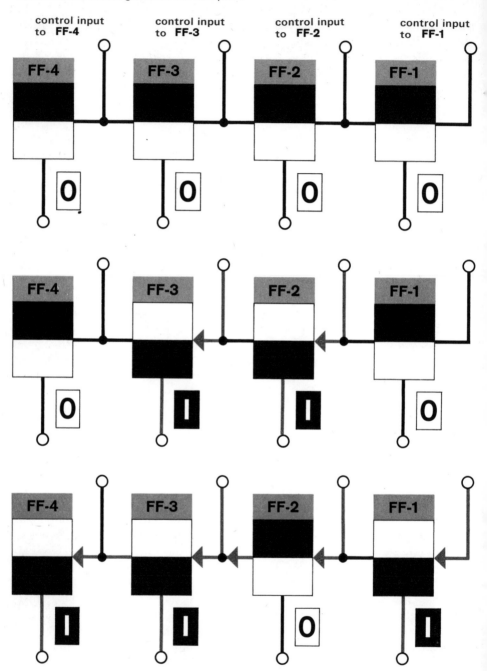

Flip-flop circuit for the addition of the binary numbers 110 + 111 = 1101.

final result $c = \mathbf{1101}$. What is going to happen?

We shall start again with the last element FF-1. As the input to this element is $\mathbf{1}$ it flops over. The top square becomes white, the bottom one black and the output is $\mathbf{1}$. This is the last digit of our sum.

In the adjacent FF-2 box the complimentary process takes place. This circuit had already flipped due to the previous number therefore receiving the signal $\mathbf{1}$ it now reverts back to the initial situation. In other words the top becomes black and the bottom white and the output c_2 is $\mathbf{0}$. This however leaves a carry and as the diagram shows this carry is fed into the input of the next box FF-3 via a secondary output. What happens at FF-3? This carry obviously activates the circuit but the input had also received a pulse from the binary number $\mathbf{111}$. Therefore the element reverts back to the state before the second number was fed in that is top white, bottom black, output $c_3 = \mathbf{1}$ and the carry is fed into the input of FF-4.

FF-4 has neither received a direct pulse from the first number nor from the second number but only the carry from FF-3. It therefore flips, the top becomes white, the bottom black and the output is $c_4 = \mathbf{1}$. We have accomplished the addition $\mathbf{110} + \mathbf{111} = \mathbf{1101}$ step by step. These words 'step by step' are rather important. The various processes don't all take place in parallel as was the case with half-adders (see page 273). To compute with a flip-flop circuit simply means first flip, then flop, then flip again, etc. In order for the machine not to get out of step pulse generators are built in which perform the same sort of task as the metronome for the piano player, the drummer for the beat group, or the conductor for the orchestra.

We have seen that the flip-flop circuit can be used in computing machines. The flip-flop element is a building stone for the computer. It can be used in a variety of ways and, as we shall see, not only in the arithmetic unit of the computer. The arithmetic unit may be the heart of every computer but a great deal more happens in such a machine which is worthy of attention. We shall discuss this in the next chapter.

1. A,B,C OF COMPUTER TECHNOLOGY

1.1 'Modelling' specialists
The analog computer

The goal of our discussion is to calculate with computers, and in the course of this we have met the basic units of computing circuits. We have learnt to look at computers as efficient specialist instruments. We have to bear in mind that the toolbox created by man has become considerably larger and that man's inventive genius constantly creates new devices which usefully enriches his collection of instruments. Tools in the usual sense of the word have to be supplemented by a 'thinking tool' and a 'computing tool' which by themselves, are as incapable of thinking and calculating as a motor car is of going on its own initiative or a machine tool of turning or drilling by itself.

All these machines take over routine work which is basically a chore or even degrading. In subjects like weather forecasting, surveying, elementary-particle research and x-ray crystallography scientists are confronted with a flood of data which they would be incapable of mastering without some kind of data processing unit. Substances no larger than dust particles yield an enormous number of experimental data from which the chemist is able to deduce the structure of the substance by solving an exceedingly complex three-dimensional crossword puzzle

The ring magnet is an important storage element in modern computer technology.

on a molecular scale. Our planet together with near-space has been turned into a laboratory. An endless chain of data is transmitted from satellites to ground stations. Ever since, in the early nineteen-thirties, Karl G. Jansky of Bell Telephone Laboratories discovered that radio waves, of wavelengths of a few millimetres to several metres, can penetrate the earth's atmosphere radio-astronomers have been kept busy with interpreting the flood of data coming from outer space. The investigation of extra-galactic radio waves forms a very important part of astrophysics today. In short, we can say that work in the exact sciences would hardly be possible these days without a formidable array of automatic calculating machines.

The computers which we have talked about are known as digital machines. They count so to speak in the 'two-finger-system' ('digitus' is the Latin word for 'finger') and do this step-by-step. In addition to these there is another type of computer which does not count but measures—the analog computer.

Although the finished article may no doubt be very confusing to the layman the principle of the analog computer is really quite simple. A very simple analog machine is the spring balance which is nothing but a metal spring which is stretched more the more weights it carries. If this is done within the elastic limit of the spring then this simple device can be used for analog calculations. The explanation is quite simple. If we attach a body to the spring of three weight units then it will extend by a certain amount which on a suitably calibrated scale amounts to three scale divisions (see page 284). A body of five weight units extends the spring by five scale divisions. If now both bodies are attached to the spring at the same time the reading will be eight divisions. Thus we have used the spring and its scale to carry out an addition of three plus five. With a finer scale and a good supply of weights one could use the spring to carry out numerous additions and subtractions without difficulty.

The principal difference between digital- and analog computers lies in the fact that for the latter, mathematical quantities have been transposed reversibly and uniquely into physical measurements whereas in the former, one is satisfied with a machine copy of counting—the original mathematical activity.

John von Neumann, the well known American mathematician, who was born in Hungary, and who studied in Germany and in Switzerland, contributed considerably to the development of computers. He gives the following description of the analog computer in his fragmentary booklet *The computer and the brain*:

'In an analog machine each number is represented by a suitable physical quantity, whose values, measured in some pre-assigned unit, is equal to the number in question. This quantity may be the angle by which a certain disk has rotated, or the strength of a certain current, or the amount of a certain (relative) voltage, etc. To enable the machine to compute, i.e. to operate on these numbers according to a predetermined plan, it is necessary to provide organs (or components) that can perform on these representative quantities the basic operations of mathematics...

Thus it is obviously not difficult to add or to subtact two currents (by merging them in parallel or in antiparallel directions). Multiplication (of two currents) is more difficult, but there exist various kinds of electrical components which will perform this operation. The same is true for division (of one current by another).

Analog computers are the specialists of the computer family. The range of many of these instruments is very limited. They fail when used even on a closely related mathematical problem. But being designed for a particular task gives them naturally great advantages, which applies to any specialized instrument.

The analog computer produces a physical solution to every mathematical problem. Mathematical quantities are translated into measured quantities and vice versa. This makes the analog computer a physical rather than a mathematical machine. It makes use of the continuity principle of classical physics, the application of infinitesimal calculus in the description of scientific and technological problems. This principle states that physical parameters (the instantaneous temperature of a body, its instantaneous velocity, etc) can be described by differential coefficients in such a way that they become measurable. The variable parameter is thus related to the elements of the set of real numbers which lies between any two numerical values forming the range of measurements

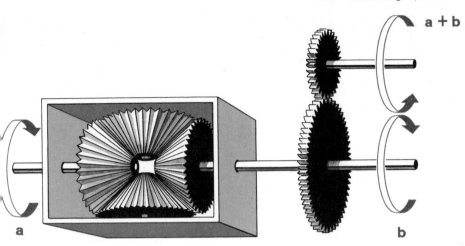

Analog addition of two numbers a and b by means of a differential. This analog adds angles of rotation. (Similar differentials are used in the gears of motorcars in order to transmit the engine power to the rear—or front wheels.)

(Differential coefficients and real numbers are discussed in detail in *Modern Mathematics*, chapters 10.2 and 5.3).

The mathematical aspects of this analog translation are not really of direct importance. What is important for science and technology is that the original process should be simulated by an analog in the computer. Although both processes follow the same course, the simulated process should naturally be easier to put into practice than the original process. We are already aware of the fact that one and the same scheme can be technically realized in different ways and thus with varying degrees of usefulness. Again these are isomorphous systems (see page 229).

The wind tunnel is a typical analog machine in which small scale models of aeroplanes can be tested. In the training of pilots 'simulators' reproduce almost perfectly all kinds of flight situations by means of an analog computer. By means of various couplings an imitation of a cockpit moves in a most realistic manner only a very small distance above the ground. The trainee pilot uses the normal control mechanism to 'fly', with the difference that this mechanism is linked to an analog computer. Appropriate film projections produce the illusion of real flying almost perfectly.

Whilst the analog computer copies dynamic processes by means of revolving wheels, differential gears and electrical potentiometers, and by producing continuously varying model images, the digital computer counts discrete numbers step by step, discontinuously, by means of flip-flop circuits. In a way one might compare the analog computer with the smooth tone of a trombone and the digital computer with the discrete sounds of the cymbal.

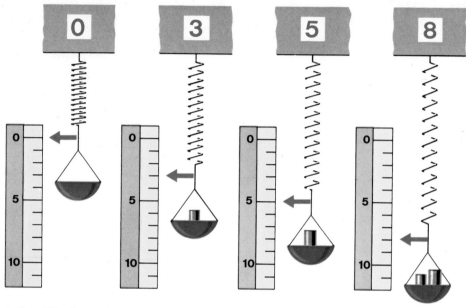

Analog addition by means of an elastic spring. Example: Three plus five equals eight.

The expert has to decide in each individual case whether, in a problem which is to be tackled by a computer, one should use digital or analog computers. If a number of variable factors enter into it then it may be advisable to use the analog. This is particularly so in the

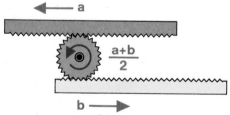

Analog addition of $\frac{a+b}{2}$ by means of the displacement of two rack-rods; they rotate a toothed wheel placed between them.

social sciences and economics; but also in the natural sciences and engineering many problems can be simulated usefully and with adequate precision. In practice it is often the case that various factors (parameters) which enter into the problem cannot be determined with sufficient precision. In this case it is enough to work with approximate values. Errors of measurement also occur when taking readings on the computer. Analog computers are therefore not as precise as digital machines but then in practical problems high precision is not always required. In the same way as it would make little sense to expect a kitchen knife to be as sharp as a razor blade, it is equally absurd to set the analog computer to highest precision if only approximate values are to be processed which are

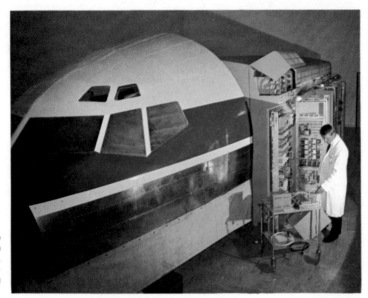

The simulator for the training of pilots is a typical analog machine. The model of the cockpit is linked to an analog computer (right).

The analog computer as a table model, mass-produced by a Japanese computer firm.

285

Flight simulator of an American research establishment for the training of pilots for vertical take-off.

quite sufficient for a practical solution. As already pointed out the great advantage of analog machines is their specialization, the simulation of a particular problem in terms of a model.

Digital machines are definitely more universal. Their advantage is that they can be used for all types of mathematical problems which they can solve with highest precision; they only have to be programmed suitably. It is these key-words which we are going to take up in the next section when discussing pro-grammed digital computers.

11.2 'Stored' machine instructions
Programmed digital computers

Logic circuits and computing circuits of digital computers are no strangers to us. Small, clear connections of bistable elements have helped us to calculate with truth definite statements and with binary numbers without difficulty. Naturally these processes have to be automated in large electronic information- and data-processing installations. The economic advantage of the digital computer lies in the fact that one does not have to build a special plant for every problem. One simply feeds the computer with the appropriate program, a list of instructions which are then played through. This is like the metal comb of a musical box which plays back a tune when it is plucked by pins fixed on a drum. The instructions to a computer are rules for the processing of information; they are known as machine instructions.

How do I tell my computer? is the first question which the expert—in this case the 'programmer' has to ask. He wants to know how a machine can express itself. A digital computer cannot (as yet) be addressed directly; it does not react to it—at least for the time being. As on a teleprinter, information can be fed in through a punched tape. This incidentally also explains the fact that a programmer in Glasgow can tell a computer in London what to do. The message can be sent by teleprinter. Instructions to a machine can also be fed in by means of a pile of punched cards. In every case the information is punched on cards or tapes in binary code: 'hole' means '1' and 'no hole' means '0'. In teletype the letter f

for example is, by definition, encoded in the binary system by the group of five digits as **01101**. The encoding on a punched tape takes the following form:

1. field: no hole (**0**)
2. field: hole   (**1**)
3. field: hole   (**1**)
4. field: no hole (**0**)
5. field: hole   (**1**)

If the work field permits the five binary digits to be placed next to one another (in parallel) on the tape, then a sequence of letters or numbers can be recorded in five tape tracks and fed into the computer over five channels. One then speaks of a

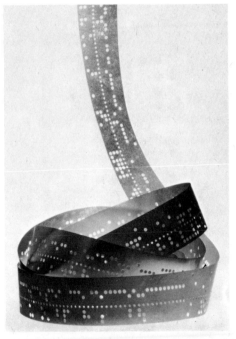

Information can be fed into a computer via this eight-channel paper tape.

'five-channel code'. The message 'Norbert Wiener' for example takes the form

0 1 1 0 0	N
1 1 0 0 0	O
0 1 0 1 0	R
1 1 0 0 1	B
0 0 0 0 1	E
0 1 0 1 0	R
1 0 0 0 0	T
0 0 1 0 0	(space)
1 0 0 1 1	W
0 0 1 1 0	I
0 0 0 0 1	E
0 1 1 0 0	N
0 0 0 0 1	E
0 1 0 1 0	R

In this way the data can be read into the machine through punched cards or punched tape. It is obvious that the read-

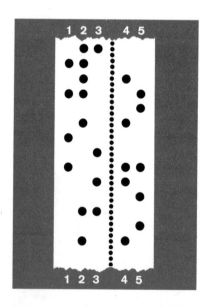

One can 'write' Norbert Wiener on paper tape by punching holes. The figures 1 to 5 represent the numbers of the channels. Between channels 3 and 4 is the perforation for moving the tape.

out from the machine follows a similar pattern. The decoding can be done by an automatic typewriter by translating the code into normal type.

Although we know what means of expression are at our disposal in order to make contact with a computer, the important problem is no longer the encoding. We have to be able to give the machine clear cut instructions which it has to carry out. Simply to feed the encoded words 'Norbert Wiener' into the computer does not represent an instruction.

For the moment we shall ignore the content of the message and concentrate on the fact that it can be read into the machine in the form of perforations i.e. a sequence of holes (**1**) or no holes (**0**). Then the computer has to take note of this sequence of signals; it is being recorded and stored at the input store. This recording is done with bistable storage elements with which the state **1** or the state **0** can be realized alternately.

We have already seen that flip-flops are capable of recording binary numbers. In the case of the addition the first number (a) is registered first of all before in fact carrying out the operation (+b) on the machine (see page 277). The bistable flip-flops can therefore be regarded not only as building elements of computing circuits but also as storage elements for computers. However, each flip-flop can only store 1 *bit* of information, either state **1** or state **0**. For reasons of economics they only act as a storage 'through-station'. The storage capacity of a whole 'battery' of flip-flops is of the order of several hundred *bit*. The storage time is not more than a fraction of a

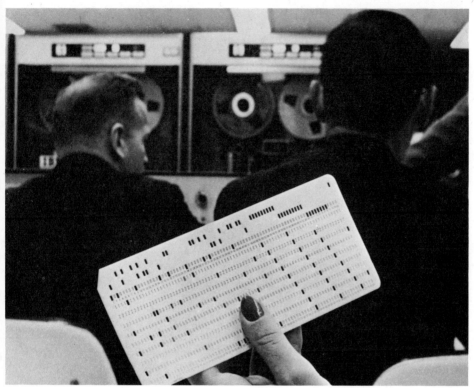

A punched card.

second. Flip-flops can be used as input stores, output stores and intermediate stores, the last storing intermediate results of calculations. These are only capable of storing the information to be processed temporarily, for a short time, before passing it on. Such a through station for the flow of information is therefore called high-speed store or working store. In this connection one can also talk of the register of the computer. A special type of intermediate store in the computing mechanism is called an 'accumulator'. The accumulator content can be read off directly from the console of many computers. Results and intermediate results

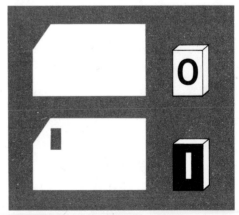

Information can be encoded in simple binary form on punched cards. No hole, in certain places, means 0, hole means 1.

11. A,B,C of computer technology

read- and write-heads

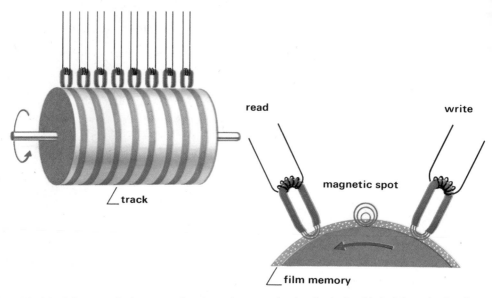

track

read

write

magnetic spot

film memory

Principle of the magnetic drum store. By means of magnets (read-and-write heads) the information is written on the storage layer, or read off from it (magnetic spot ↔ **1**, no magnetic spot ↔**0**). When writing, the heads produce a magnetic field which corresponds to the magnetic spot.

This magnetic disc store resembles a chromium plated juke box. But these discs yield bit instead of beat.

can be displayed here. Accumulators are single-number stores. This has become clear to us in our flip-flop addition.

Besides these high-speed stores where the information flux is only stored for a short time there are also stores with longer storage times. Here information can be stored as in a depot. They form so to speak the data store of the machine. There are storage cells with unique place numbers (addresses) which can store binary-coded machine words for long periods of time. This is reminiscent of storing wine bottles in a cellar or folios on book shelves. They are the auxiliary or backing stores of the installation where hundreds of thousands of *bit* of information are stacked; some have a *bit*-capacity of several millions. Such auxiliary stores are like huge warehouses or gigantic well arranged archives for the communication material.

A useful method of data storage in computers is the magnetizing of tapes, discs, and drums (see figures). How can information be stored magnetically? A magnetizable surface can be covered with magnetic spots by an electromagnet. As in the case of the punched tape 'spot' expresses state **1** and 'no spot' state **0**. In a manner similar to tape recorders, close above the magnetized material are the 'write heads' for the recording (storage) of data and 'read heads' for the play back of the stored communication. As with the tape recorder, information in the form of 'magnetic spot'—'no magnetic spot' can be erased when it is no longer required. Magnetic tapes,—discs and—drums are mainly used as auxiliary stores. As the owner of a tape recorder can well understand, tapes have a considerable

store access time. This means that to pass on a certain information from the store requires far too much valuable time—of the order of several seconds. This can be painfully long if we remember the enormously fast computing rates (see page 254). Magnetic discs however require only something of the order of tenths of seconds, whilst magnetic drums act like lightning with access times of milliseconds.

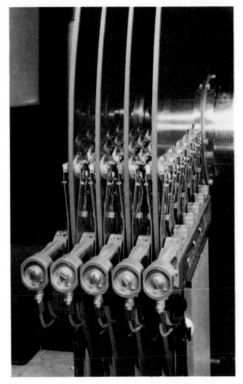

Read-and-write heads of a magnetic disc store.

A type of store known as a core store operates almost as fast as the flip-flop, that is within the microsecond range. The figures illustrate how tiny little ring magnets of 1 to 2 mm diameter are

Punched tape installation (right) and magnetic disc store; the building blocks of a modern information processing device.

The read wire which traverses the matrix diagonally transports the information in the form of induced impulses (see *Modern Physics* for a discussion on electromagnetic induction). The storage and reading process is described by the sequence of diagrams on page 295.

Each toroidal magnet can again only store 1 *bit* of information assuming either state **1** or state **0**; it is a bistable storage element. Each network of these magnets forms a matrix with 1000 elements. The matrices can be grouped into stacks in which the machine words composed of **1**- and **0**-signals can be retained. If, for example, a machine word is made up of forty signs then it requires 40 *bit* to encode it. This necessitates a stack of forty ring-magnet matrices. If each matrix contains

threaded onto a postcard sized frame at the intersection of a rectangular wire matrix. Short current pulses transmitted along these wires can magnetize these toroidal cores in a certain direction, or reverse their magnetization. The magnetization of a storage element is accomplished by simultaneously passing a current through the appropriate column- and row wires. The current is always of such a strength that if it were to flow in a column or in a row only it could not produce magnetization. Only at the intersection of the two sets of wires is the combined current sufficiently strong to alter the magnetic state of the core. A third wire, the inhibit wire, carries an opposing current pulse if the core stores a **0** and no current if the core stores **1**.

Twelve matrices with a total of 196608 ring magnets are stacked to form a storage block (bottom). Above, the small storage block consists of four matrices which can accept 1024 *bit* of information.

These tiny rings, of 0·2 mm diameter, do not come from the 'toy box' of an ant heap. They are ring magnets from the store of a computer. Compared with them, an ant appears like a huge monster.

a thousand cores then it is possible to store a thousand machine words in the stack, each with forty-digits. Every word has its own definite address in this storage system. For example the place number 6034 indicates *a storage cell in the sixth stack where always the thirty fourth magnet of the forty matrices is available.* In computer technology these stacks are referred to as 'storage blocks'. Thus machine words are information in binary code stored at definite addresses. In this way one can store numbers and instructions in the computer which are always available when required. Naturally, the instructions are stored separately, not together with the data, and thus form a kind of 'program library' in the machine (see page 301). A program in the form of a list of machine instructions goes straight into the stores of the computer. This is necessary because the short access time

293

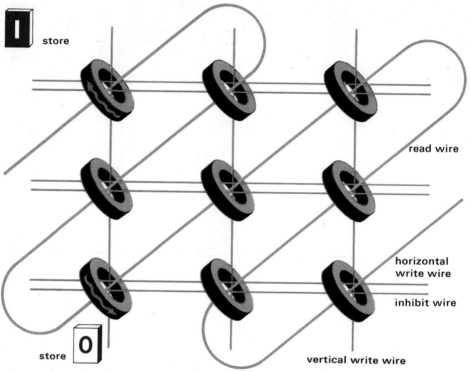

store

read wire

horizontal write wire

inhibit wire

store **0**

vertical write wire

Diagrammatic representation of a magnetic core matrix with nine storage elements each of which can express the value **1** or **0** magnetically. The binary states of the ring magnets at the intersections of vertical and horizontal write wires can be changed by passing a current through the wires.

of the working store is tuned to the speed of operation of the arithmetic unit. On the other hand the read-in through punched cards and punched tapes takes place at snail's pace, perhaps a few hundred cards per minute, or a few hundred signs per second for the tape. The idea of placing the program in the store stems from John von Neumann.

The most important parts of a machine instruction are the operation part and the address part. The operation part of the instruction contains the mathematical operation (addition, multiplication etc)

which is to be carried out by the computer. The address part on the other hand denotes the place number of the storage cell in which the quantity on which the operation is to be carried out (a numerical value, the operand) can be found. The values with which one wishes to calculate, the operands, have to be fed into the store. Operations are carried out with operands. To begin with both elements are in the machine store.

If we represent the addresses of the operands by the variables X_1, X_2, X_3 etc then the stored numerical values can be written as $\langle X_1 \rangle$, $\langle X_2 \rangle$, $\langle X_3 \rangle$, etc. In the same way the value in the accumulator can be indicated by $\langle ACC \rangle$ (see page 289). Machine instructions can be commands for the transport of numbers, the transport of operands and commands to carry out an operation. For example this could take the following form:

'Bring $\langle X_1 \rangle$ (from cell X_1) into the accumulator.' In other words: 'load the accumulator with $\langle X_1 \rangle$' In an abbreviated way this instruction would be: 'B$\langle X_1 \rangle$' or 'LD $\langle X_1 \rangle$'. 'B' or 'LD' indicate the operation, and $\langle X_1 \rangle$ the operand. Thus the instruction, suitably encoded of course, can be understood by the machine in this short and abbreviated form. So much for the example of a transport instruction.

An operation instruction can take the following form: 'ADD$\langle X_2 \rangle$ to $\langle ACC \rangle$'. (Meanwhile $\langle X_1 \rangle$ is in the accumulator i.e. $\langle X_1 \rangle = \langle ACC \rangle$.) This instruction can be abbreviated to 'A $\langle X_2 \rangle$' or '+$\langle X_2 \rangle$' where 'ADD' or 'A' or '+' are the signal for the addition.

This kind of program formulation uses a machine language. It is tailored to a particular type of machine and represents a computer dialect which even a machine constructed along very similar lines can no longer understand. A particular machine will only react with a multiplication to the instruction 'x $\langle X \rangle$' whereas another one will only understand

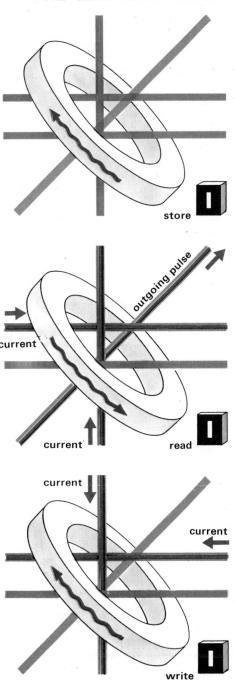

store

read

write

In order to read the 1-value of a ring magnet the magnetization has to be reversed. The currents in the wires induce a current pulse in the read wire (centre). Part of the energy of this pulse can be used to store the 1-value in the same magnet a microsecond later. This part of the current pulse has to be amplified by transistors.

295

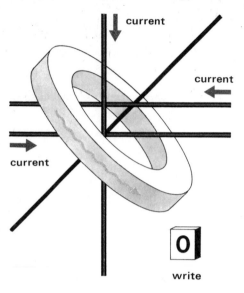

current

current

current

0

write

'·⟨X⟩' and a third one only 'MULT ⟨X⟩'. The expert groups machine-orientated languages under the heading of assembly languages. Less dependent on machines and therefore more useful are problem-orientated languages. We shall come to them presently but for the moment we shall side-step our discussion.

In order to automate the process of machine calculations in a meaningful way three conditions have to be satisfied. First of all it is necessary to encode all

In this way an **0**-value can be stored in the ring magnet. A current flows through the vertical as well as both horizontal wires.

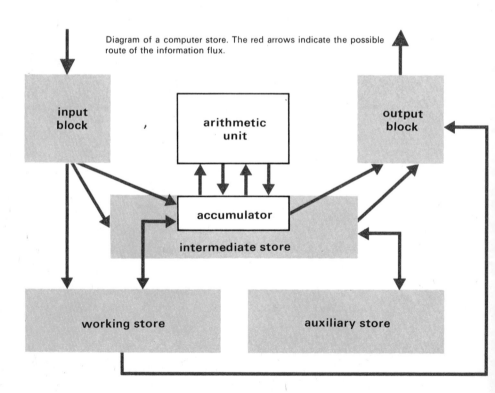

Diagram of a computer store. The red arrows indicate the possible route of the information flux.

input block

arithmetic unit

output block

accumulator

intermediate store

working store

auxiliary store

296

The programming of the computer is done at the control unit.

machine instructions in order to render them intelligible to the computer. Secondly there is the storage of instructions for operations and of operands. We have not yet mentioned the third condition: in order to automate the computing process we require a program control. (The emphasis now lies on control.) It

is carried out from the control desk of the computer, the actual 'bridge' of the plant (see figure).

By means of this control device the various stored instructions can be put into operation according to the program. The computer is addressed by operating various buttons on the console, one of them being the starting button. Once this button is pressed everything then goes automatically, step by step. The first instruction is carried out; its address is say Y_1. If the machine is not given a special instruction it selects instruction Y_2 from the store and carries this out.

The output of data from the computer can be printed out by an automatic printer. (Approximately 1000 type-written lines per minute.)

It then carries out instruction Y_3 then Y_4, Y_5, etc. Only when the computer comes up against the instruction 'STOP' does all activity cease. The instruction 'STOP' is a very important one. It reminds one of the magic formula of the old sorcerer from Goethe's *Sorcerer's Apprentice*:

'Take yourselves off into the corner, brooms...'

To carry out one instruction after the other and to stop at the STOP command: this is the monotonous way of the working of a computer which is controlled by a linear program. An ordinary installation runs through a sequence of around fifty instructions in a hundredth of a second.

In many programs it is necessary to execute certain instructions several times in succession. This can also be accomplished by the programmed digital computer. One has only to give it a jump instruction and immediately it jumps back. Because it carries out this operation unconditionally one speaks of 'unconditional jump instruction'. If the computer is given the jump instruction Y_7 to Y_4, it jumps back and repeats the instructions Y_4, Y_5, Y_6 over and over again until a new jump instruction this time a conditional jump instruction carries it outside this roundabout. The repeatedly run through 'program loop' can then be broken. This can be illustrated by a very simple example:

How often does one have to add 3 to 2 in order to get a number which is greater than 13? As the figure shows we could make an analog of this problem with a simple scale. To start with we mark off two units on the scale. Then we add units of three until the division 13 has been

The 'bridge' of a modern computer installation. The magnetic-tape stores can be seen in the background.

passed. The number 14 (which is greater than 13, or in short 14 > 13), is reached after four times adding the unit of three. In arithmetical notation this is

Step 1: $2+3 = 5$

Step 2: $(2+3)+3 = 5+3 = 8$

Step 3: $(2+3+3)+3 = 8+3 = 11$

Step 4: $(2+3+3+3)+3 = 11+3$

$= 14.$

This sort of problem can of course be generalized. How often does one have to add a number b to a number a to make the sum greater than a number c? (a, b and c are supposed to be variables replacing natural numbers.) In general we can therefore write:

1. $a+b$

2. $(a+b)+b = a+2b$

3. $(a+2b)+b = a+3b$

4. $(a+3b)+b = a+4b$

5. $(a+4b)+b = a+5b$ etc.

Depending on the actual values of a, b and c we may need either a few or many steps in order to solve this problem. A

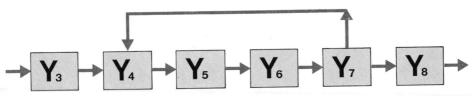

A programmed digital computer can carry out jump instructions. Here the computer jumps back from instruction Y7 to instruction Y4.

299

large number of steps requires a large number of machine instructions and consequently a large number of storage cells in the computer if one is restricted to a linear program. It is far more useful and economical to give the computer jump instructions.

This can best be understood with the help of a flow diagram (see page 303). The individual steps in the program can then be clearly depicted in a schematic diagram. The flow diagram appropriate to our problem shows several rectangular boxes each with one single input and one single output. (An arbitrarily long chain of such boxes between the triangular START- and STOP-boxes can represent a linear program.) A box of oval shape (see diagram) has one input and two outputs. This box contains a question which may be answered with 'yes' or 'no'. The course of the program depends on this answer.

In order to illustrate this we will now return to our numerical example ($a = 2$, $b = 3$, $c = 13$). Having formed the first sum $2 + 3$ the question in the oval box has to be answered by 'no'. 5 is not greater than 13. In the program we shall follow along the output on the right. The two instructions in the program loop (1 into the counter, 2 ($= a$) to be replaced by $5 (= a + b)$ are now carried out. The new sum is now 8, which is still smaller than 13. The answer to the question again has to be in the negative and we go back into the loop. Only after the fourth passage through the loop will the answer be 'yes'. The counter records 4; the machine stops.

Such flow diagrams are valuable maps for the interlinking of operations which the computer has to carry out. The programmer is always recommended to map out a flow diagram in order to translate the problem into a correct machine program. Because certain programs are frequently used, and by different types of machines, it is recommended to write them in a problem-orientated language. Although such a language is artificial, just as a machine-orientated language, it differs from the latter because it is not devised for one particular type of computer (see page 295). In a problem-orientated language mathematical rules are adhered to which can be translated into machine instructions without difficulty.

One of the best known and widely used computer dialects is FORTRAN (from '*fo*rmula *tra*nslator'). It has been developed by the American computer manufacturers IBM (International Business Machines Corp.). Understandably a programming language developed by a private firm is not concerned with complete machine independence. Obviously the management will be satisfied if FORTRAN is successful with IBM-installations. An instructive input in FORTRAN is, for example, as follows.

READ V_1, V_2, V_3

Hence the lingo of programmers to 'read' into the computer. The corresponding output instruction in FORTRAN is

PUNCH V_1, V_2, V_3

V_1, V_2, V_3 are variables for elements forming the input. PUNCH is simply the instruction to punch a card or a tape.

Another well known computer problem-orientated dialect is ALGOL (from '*algo*rithmic *l*anguage'). An algorithm is a general unique calculation method (see

An optical display helps to show the input and output of information. It will enlarge the toolbox of engineers and architects.

Modern Mathematics; chapter 11.2). The instruction for the delivery of the result in this case is

PRINT (V_1, V_2, V_3)

For many types of computer translation programs have been worked out; they are called 'ALGOL-compilers'. These compiler programs are also stored in the store of the machine. This makes it possible to read into the computer the ALGOL program which it translates automatically into its particular machine code program. If ALGOL-texts are punched on tape one speaks of an 'ALCOR-machine representation'. Several computer manufacturers and large computer centres have combined to form the 'ALCOR-group' in order to guarantee a uniform machine representation. Since ALGOL is a language which is independent of a machine it never refers to possible technical realizations of the information processing device such as accumulator, storage place, etc.

On the other hand clearly defined words in ALGOL-compilers permit fixed 'subroutines' to be inserted which come from the program library of the store. Such subroutines are formed by frequently used algorithms ('standard functions') like SIN (E), the sine-function, or SQRT (E), the positive square-root. These subroutines are also called 'procedures'. E stands for an arithmetical

301

expression (see *Modern Mathematics*, chapter 3). Like FORTRAN, ALGOL is an artificial language of instructions which is clearly related to the usual artificial language of mathematicians (i.e. their language of formulae). It can easily be learnt by experts wherever they may live.

$y = x_1 + x_2$ becomes in ALGOL

$Y := X_1 + X_2$ where ': ='

indicates the assignment statement (which may be read as '...follows from...'). $y = (x_1 + x_2)^2$, which is read 'y equals x—one plus x—two, all squared', is expressed in ALGOL: $Y := (X_1 + X_2)$ 'POWER' 2.

The many expressions like PRINT, READ, BEGIN, POWER etc which are often truncated (like SQRT for square root) often give the layman the impression that programs in such artificial languages are nothing but broken English. Some people find this comical and amusing, some even have a feeling of superiority over the computer. With the same justification one might find the orders of a foreman of a building site amusing or the gestures of a famous conductor or a text printed in braille. The same applies to man's feeling of superiority compared with a combine-harvester or a dredger.

It would be idle to include in our discussion a language course for ALGOL or FORTRAN. A passing acquaintance is quite sufficient if it makes us realize that there is no magic involved and that this is not a secret writing for the initiated few (see page 88). As in every artificial language one is dealing with strictly controlled signs including inverted commas, brackets, commas, semicolons etc. We shall give a few examples to illustrate this.

In the program declarations one can find, for example, numbers preceded by words like

'REAL' X, Y, Z;

or 'INTEGER' M_1, M_2;

Also truth-definite statements can be expressed in a similar way. Here the agreed way of writing is as follows:

'BOOLEAN' A, B, C.

(After the English logician George Boole, 1815–64.) The Boolean variables A, B, C, as we know, can be linked logically. $A \lor B$ is, in ALGOL, A 'OR' B, $A \land B$ becomes A 'AND' B and $A \to B$, becomes A 'IMPL' B. We have already discussed the corresponding circuit connections.

A jump instruction is indicated by 'GO TO'. For example a conditional jump instruction is:

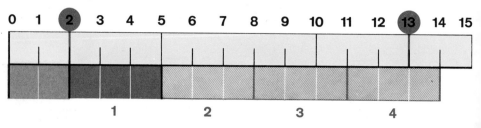

How often does one have to add 3 to 2 in order to obtain a number which is greater than 13? This problem can be analoged with a scale and building blocks.

'IF' A+B 'GREATER' C 'THEN' 'GO TO' PRINT;

(If the value of A plus B is greater than the value of C, print.)

In addition to FORTRAN and ALGOL there are two other languages of some importance. COBOL is used in formulations of problems in economics and management and COMIT in linguistic programs. All these languages are languages of instructions for information processing installations, for program-controlled digital computers or digital information transducers.

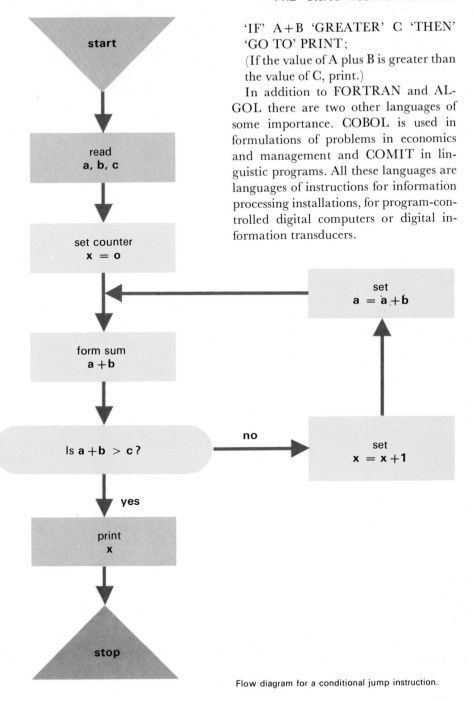

Flow diagram for a conditional jump instruction.

303

12. INFORMATION 'ROUND ABOUT'

12.1 A machine partner for the game of Nim
The computer 'Nimitron'

Digital and analog computers form part of the vast machinery of modern technology. These automated information processing devices are cybernetic machines. We discussed them without constantly using the very popular word cybernetics and without constantly bringing cybernetics into the language-game. As the reader will recall cybernetics was defined as the mathematical description of the recording, transformation, storage, transmission and dissemination of measurable information within a system or between one system and another. Seen in this light cybernetics is the mathematization of information transformation and its technical realization.

For the purpose of our discussion we have drawn from the tool chest of modern mathematics. In particular we have used information theory, the youngest branch of the theory of probability, and have thoroughly discussed its fundamental aspects. We have used the elements of classical statement logic for the interconnections in thinking tools and computing devices. As a purely formal system it is also known as Boolean Algebra (see also page 302). If Boolean Algebra is realized in technical installations—mainly with electronic building elements—the expert refers to it as 'switching algebra'; it is part of modern electrical engineering.

We have of course seen that the technology of cybernetic machines makes use of electrical phenomena in order to represent, store and process information.

There is one important point about cybernetic machines which still requires explanation. In the flow diagram on page 303 a program loop is shown which, according to instructions, can be run through several times by the computing device until the required value (greater than c) is obtained. Before every run through the loop the actual value $a+b$, attained at that moment, is compared with the desired value $a+b > c$. If $a+b$ is greater than c (yes) then the calculation comes to an end. In the opposite case (no) the loop is traversed again. The machine carries out an 'about turn' instruction; it reverts back to previous instructions.

This retracing of the computer steps reminds one somewhat of a number of calls by an obstinate insurance agent. With every call he produces better arguments until eventually he secures the desired contract. One could regard these facts also as a kind of mechanical check-back system: 'Here is my present value of $a+b$; does it satisfy the requirement $a+b > c$? If not I shall run through the loop once more and call again.' This check-back game is repeated until the desired value is reached.

We shall illustrate a similar automatic check-back system of a machine using a different type of computer circuit. In order to do this we can make use of a remarkably versatile 'games machine' which was built by boys from Exeter School. Because this mini-computer can play the game 'Nim' the boys called it 'Nimitron'. This digital machine has been specially built for the purpose of playing the part of a Nim-player.

Nim is a relatively simple yet very amusing game for two players which always ends with one partner winning. A draw cannot occur if the game is played correctly. It is suspected that Nim comes from ancient China. Although it may sound somewhat oriental the name is really due to the American mathematician Charles L. Bouton who, at Harvard University, at the beginning of this century analyzed it theoretically. When choosing a name for this game Bouton probably used the Old-English verb which means 'take away' or 'steal'. In fact the point of the Nim-game is to take away counters. Nim could stand for 'remove the right number of counters from a pile'.

How does one play Nim? From several piles of counters the two players S_1 and S_2 remove counters alternatively. In each move at least one counter has to be removed but it is also permissible to remove several as long as they are taken from the same pile. A player may even remove a whole pile. The player who takes the last remaining counter is the winner. (One can naturally play the opposite variant where the player who has the last move loses. We shall, however, not consider this any further in our discussion.)

A popular starting position in this game is the following: Twelve counters are divided into three piles α, β, γ so that

there are five counters in the first pile, four in the second and three in the third: $\alpha = 5$, $\beta = 4$, $\gamma = 3$. This can be expressed even in a briefer way by the group of three figures $(5, 4, 3)$. After a few rounds of the game, starting with $(5, 4, 3)$, one soon finds that there are certain moves which will ensure a win. For instance if S_1, who starts the game, takes two counters in the first move from the third pile he cannot lose provided of course he plays sensibly afterwards. Because if S_1 changes the initial position of $(5, 4, 3)$ to $(5, 4, 1)$ then no matter what S_2 does in the second move, whether he removes only one or several counters or even a whole pile, S_1 can always reply in such a way that he will be in a winning position.

The Nim game is characterized by such unique winning positions. C. L. Bouton called them safe positions. If, say one of the three piles has been completely cleared ($\alpha = 0$ or $\beta = 0$ or $\gamma = 0$) then the two remaining piles must have an equal number of counters. Such positions are for example $(0, 1, 1)$, $(4, 4, 0)$ or $(2, 2, 0)$. Also $(3, 2, 1)$ is a definite winner.

Let us take an example. S_1 moves and changes the initial position $(5, 4, 3)$ to $(5, 4, 1)$. S_2 removes one counter from α creating the position $(4, 4, 1)$. If, in his second move, S_1 clears γ he creates another safe position $(4,4,0)$ for himself. No matter what S_2 does subsequently S_1 will always have the advantage. The reader should try to finish the game and he will find that S_2 cannot win as long as S_1 makes no mistake.

How can one recognize a winning position in this game? This can be done quite simply. Change the three numbers

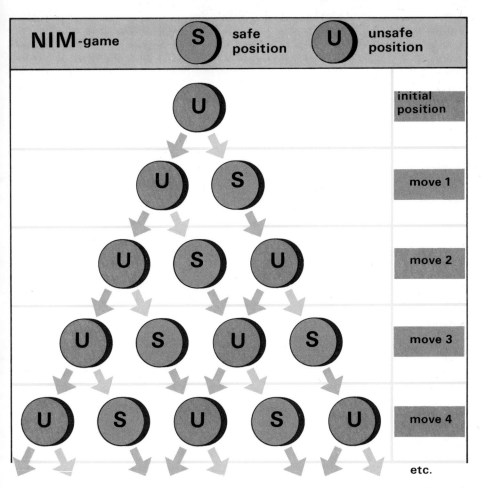

Scheme of the Nim-game. The blue arrows signal the transition from an unsafe position to a safe position (winning position). If the starting position is unsafe and if the first player manages to get into a safe position in his first move, the second player can only win if his partner makes a mistake in the subsequent moves.

of counters to the binary system and add the numerical values of each binary digit without a carry. If each sum is even i.e. if it comes to **o** then the position is safe. If, however, only one of the sums has the odd value **1** then one has an unsafe position.

This point will become clear from an example. We know that $(5, 4, 1)$ is a safe position. In the binary system 5 becomes '**101**' (one-zero-one), 4 becomes '**100**' (one-zero-zero) and 1 remains the same '**1**' (see page 267). The addition without a carry takes the form

307

$$\begin{array}{r} \mathbf{101} \\ +\,\mathbf{100} \\ +\quad\mathbf{1} \\ \hline \mathbf{000} \end{array}$$

We know that in the binary system $\mathbf{1}+\mathbf{1} = \mathbf{10}$ where $\mathbf{o}$ represents the digital sum and $\mathbf{1}$ the carry. In this addition without the carry all three digital sums are even ($\mathbf{o}$). Thus the position (5, 4, 1) is a winning position.

The following addition (without a carry) shows that the position (5, 4, 3) is not safe.

$$\begin{array}{r} \mathbf{101} \\ +\,\mathbf{100} \\ +\quad\mathbf{11} \\ \hline \mathbf{010} \end{array}$$

Since the middle digit $\mathbf{1}$ is odd this represents a losing position.

Thus the '$\mathbf{1}$' or '$\mathbf{o}$' method can tell us whether a particular position is safe or not; it is a purely mechanical process, a simple binary addition without a carry. A machine built with bistable switching elements will be able to tell us whether a position is safe or not. If, in addition, the very simple rules of the game are read into the machine it is then in a position to turn any situation into a safe one. It has become a perfect automatic Nim-player which can win from a human player.

The mathematician who is interested in the theory of games would summarize the characteristics of Nim which we have sketched out above in the following manner. Nim is a 'finite two-persons null-sum-game with complete information and optimum strategy'. Such a characterization is the concentrate, expressed in artificial language, of a reflec-

tion which is as abstract and generalized as is possible. (The basic ideas of the theory of games have been discussed in *Modern Mathematics*, Chapter 8.2.)

Here John von Neumann also contributed decisively to the formulation of this field of the exact sciences. We wish to add a small note to the description 'two-person-null-sum-game' which was coined by von Neumann. The sum of the winnings of two players S_1 and S_2 (or two teams) at the end of each game is always zero, which means that there is a clear winner and a clear loser. If S_1 decides the game in his favour then S_2 defeated and vice versa. One might be tempted to develop more complex models of this form of game within the sphere of military planning. In this context expressions like 'null-sum-game' or 'optimum strategy' sound rather more military than mathematical. But what the mathematical theory of games has achieved is that at least one thinks a little harder about situations of conflict.

But let us return to the completely peaceful Nimitron, the small computer which can act as a games partner. We shall discuss its construction by means of a block diagram.

The information regarding the actual position in the game is read into the machine via three inputs. They tell the computer the number of counters in the piles α, β, γ. The numerical values of α and β are added as binary numbers without a carry, for instance by means of flip-flops. (This particular circuit element is known as parity unit. The value of the sum without the carry which we denote by σ (Greek letter 'sigma') is transmitted to the comparison unit.

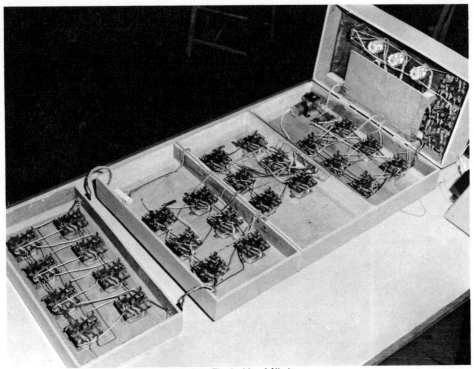

To the layman this is a confusing mass of wires. The inside of Nimitron.

Here the magnitude of σ is compared with that of γ, the number of counters in the third pile. In this comparison three situations can arise to which the computer will react in three different ways.

(a) If the value of γ is greater than that of σ ($\gamma > \sigma$) the σ-value is passed to the output. The output is that value of σ which tells what move Nimitron wants to make, in other words 'I want to take so many counters from γ that only σ counters remain there.'

(b) If γ and σ have the same value ($\gamma = \sigma$) then, as we know, this is a winning position. The goal—achieving a safe position—has been reached. The machine could simply pass if it were not for the rule of the game that at least one counter must be removed from a pile in each move. The obvious way would be to make an arbitrary move, a random move. This however requires a random signal generator to be built into the Nimitron circuit, a kind of electronic game of dice. The builders of Nimitron have however chosen a far simpler way which can also be much more easily realized technically. In this move the machine removes a single counter from one particular pile just to satisfy the rule of the game.

(c) The last possibility is that the value of

309

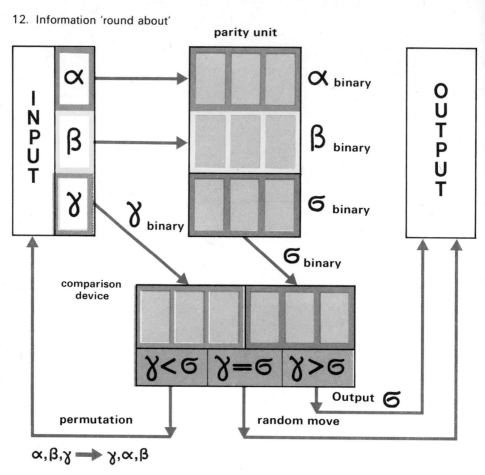

Block diagram of Nimitron. The most important building blocks are formed by a circuit, which allows two binary numbers to be added without a carry (parity unit), and a comparison device.

γ is smaller than that of σ ($\gamma < \sigma$). In this case the machine takes a step backwards by cyclically interchanging the three inputs α, β, γ. In other words the inputs α and β move down and input γ takes the place originally held by α (see figure). Normally the cases (a) or (b) will now apply for which clear machine instructions are available. Should however case (c) occur again the machine takes another

step back and another cyclic interchange takes place. The inputs γ and α move down and the input β goes to the top. This automatic retracing of the computer steps is of particular interest to cybernetics. In order to attain its goal the machine changes the input to the comparison unit systematically. The situation is similar to the automatic feedback system of the program loop discussed on page

303. Nimitron also has a feedback mechanism.

A few situations arising in a game of Nim are shown in the diagrams. An example of case (a) is shown in the figure on page 311. How does Nimitron behave when faced with the initial position (5, 4, 3) which we discussed above? The inputs $\alpha = 5$ and $\beta = 4$ in binary form '**101**' and '**100**' go to the parity unit where they are added without a carry

$$
\begin{array}{r}
\mathbf{101} \\
+\ \mathbf{100} \\
\hline
\mathbf{001}
\end{array}
$$

This value, $\sigma = \mathbf{001}$ (or just $\sigma = \mathbf{1}$) passes to the comparison device. The other input to this device is formed by the value of $\gamma = 3$ or in binary form $\gamma = \mathbf{11}$. The comparison of the values ($\mathbf{11} > \mathbf{1}$ or $3 > 1$) shows that γ is greater than σ ($\gamma > \sigma$). Thus the value $\sigma = \mathbf{1}$ passes to the output box. The Nimitron output $\mathbf{1}$ is indicated for instance by a series of lamps where only the last one is on. By this, the machine tells us: 'My move is such that from the γ-pile so many counters are to be removed that precisely one is left over'. This move of the computer has placed it into a safe position, the winning position (5, 4, 1).

Example of case (b), figure on page 312. The computer finds a safe position (4,4,0) i.e. the input is $\alpha = 4$, $\beta = 4$, $\gamma = 0$. If the values of α and β are added in the

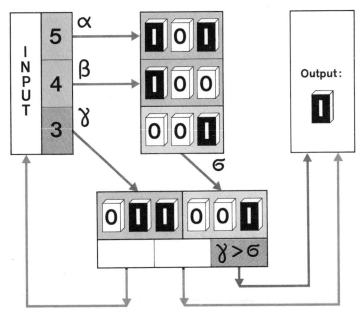

Nimitron reacts to the input (5,4,3) with the output: 'remove so many counters from the pile γ so that only one is left over.' In this way the machine produces the safe position (5,4,1).

binary system without a carry the resulting sum is zero:

$$100$$
$$+ 100$$
$$\overline{000}$$

The inputs to the comparison device are two equal-valued signals $\sigma = 0$ and $\gamma = 0$; of course $\gamma = \sigma$. As already discussed, in this safe position Nimitron has to remove a counter. Since the pile γ is already depleted the counter can be removed either from α or from β.

Example of case (c), figure on page 313. The position (5, 2, 1) is not safe which can be established readily by finding the sum $101 + 10 = 111$. The comparison of $\gamma = 1$ and $\sigma = 111$ leads to the situation $\gamma < \sigma$ which actuates the feedback mechanism. The input signals are interchanged

cyclically; (5, 2, 1) becomes (1, 5, 2). The comparison of the values gives $10 < 100$. Again we have $\gamma < \sigma$ therefore another cyclic interchange is necessary. This time the input (1, 5, 2) becomes (2, 1, 5) and we have $101 > 11$, that is γ is greater than σ. This corresponds to case (a). The value of $\sigma = 11$ (three) determines the move of Nimitron. The position (2, 1, 5) changes to the safe position (2, 1, 3) which, in the original notation, is (3, 2, 1). We have already met this position as a winning one (see page 306).

Although Nimitron is a machine it is an excellent opponent in the Nim game. But it is by no means unbeatable. This lies in the character of the Nim-game. If the player is in a safe position then provided he plays correctly the machine must obviously lose. But if the partner

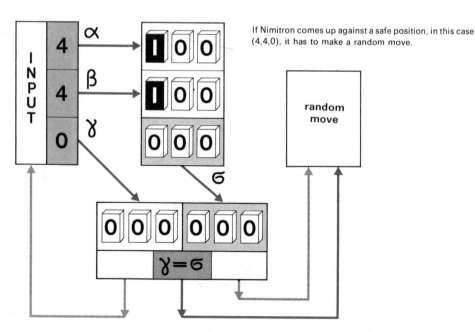

If Nimitron comes up against a safe position, in this case (4,4,0), it has to make a random move.

random move

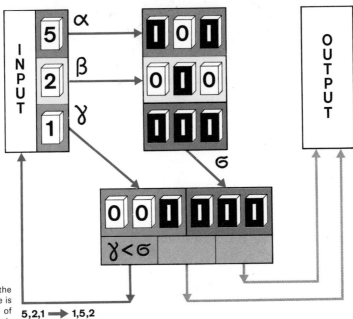

If the α-value from the parity unit of the machine is greater than the number of counters in the third pile (γ), then Nimitron has to take a step back and change its input.

5,2,1 ➡ 1,5,2

of the computer makes only the slightest mistake either due to carelessness or lack of concentration, then the computer immediately turns it to its own advantage and will win.

Incidentally, Nimitron has several big brothers, the two most famous ones being 'Nimatron' and 'Nimrod'. Nimatron, the stately one-ton robot was built back in the nineteen-forties according to a plan by the American physicist Edward U. Condon. It managed to win ninety per cent of all games of Nim played at the world exhibitions of New York and Brussels. An equally skilled Nim-robot which figured in the 1951 'Festival of Britain' is Nimrod: it is named after the legendary founder of Nineveh, a descendant of Noah's, of whom the bible says:

'Nimrod the mighty hunter before the Lord'.

A machine which is capable of automatic feedback and, like Nimitron, interchanges signals at the same time forms a sound cybernetic system. With such a feedback the computer changes accidental arrangements of signals in such a way that it can reach a definite goal which is expressed in the program. The installation automatically compares an accidental actual value, or an accidental actual situation, with the required value, or the required situation respectively. The machine refers back, systematically alters the accidental input conditions and, after one or more such back jumps, attains the required state. The technical writer A. Ducrocq once characterized the 'program of cybernetics' very vividly as the 'relegation of chance events'.

This method is widely practised in cybernetic machines which are far more complex than the small automatic Nim-player Nimitron. At first sight the circuits appear far more complicated but in most cases they are merely more complex. There are more branches, more loops indicating feedback, but the basic build-ing blocks of all these circuits are in most cases very similar. Their manner of operation can be explained in a similar way.

We shall come across this looping in the circuit structure, which indicates feedback in a cybernetic system, especially in circuits of systems where control pro-cesses of all kinds play a part. This will be discussed in the next section.

12.2 In which the experts talk of control circuits
Cybernetics as the science of control

In discussing the computer Nimitron we have mentioned its capacity of auto-matically retracing its steps which, as it were, relegates random events. In the flow diagram the situation is this: the information in the system does not simply flow along straight fast roads, or branch off into side roads. In certain situations diversion signs appear which have the effect of making the information flow back. It is like going on a ring road or a large roundabout.

It is this backward and forward move-ment of information which characterizes a cybernetic system. One has, so to speak, an information circuit which is somewhat reminiscent of our blood circulation. It is not surprising that some poetically in-clined cyberneticians refer to information as the 'blood' of their science. Information technologists on the other hand are far more prosaic. If in any installation only series and parallel connections of ele-ments occur they refer to the circuit as ladder networks. If on the other hand cyclic or back-stepping connections occur they speak of bridged networks. Now information can also be sent round the roundabout.

The bridging connection permits a kind of reaction to (chance) initial con-ditions. Herman Schmidt (born 1894), a German technologist, spoke of a kind of 'circular relation'. Already at the begin-ning of the forties Schmidt tried to give a general treatment of this problem which one refers to as control. With his tech-nological and biological colleagues he discussed at that time 'control as the fundamental problem in technology and physiology'. Since at times cybernetics is also referred to as the 'science of control' Hermann Schmidt may therefore be regarded as one of the forerunners of Norbert Wiener (see page 14).

The important characteristic of any control process is the ability to signal back or to couple back. The proper expression is 'feedback'; it is used in practically all scientific literature. We shall illustrate the jargon of control processes by quite a simple commonplace example.

Mr Smith is having a shower to remove the sweat of his day's work in as pleasant a way as possible. He contentedly lets the warm water flow over him. But after a little while he starts to shiver. What is he to do? He takes hold of the hot-water tap and carefully turns it further on—just a little. After a few seconds Mr Smith finds that he overdid it; the water is a bit too hot. He therefore turns the tap down a little and waits. If he feels happy then he has attained the right water temperature. But if he is not content he has to turn the tap again perhaps even several times. If for some reason or other the water-supply to the shower is not uniform or if the water is not of constant temperature and if, moreover, Mr Smith happens to be very sensitive to small fluctuations in the temperature of the water then he will have to go on turning the tap continuously.

We can look at Mr Smith's shower in a different way, namely as a control circuit. Why do experts refer to this as a control circuit? The block diagram reduces the system 'Mr Smith is having a shower' to a simple bridged network. Mr Smith expects a definite temperature of the water which makes him feel warm. This is the desired value (set point). Mr Smith's sense perception, his sensitivity to temperature, is good enough, for comparison purposes, to establish a certain deviation in the setting of the system. This deviation, also referred to as control error c, is the difference between the desired and actual condition of the water or, more precisely, it is the difference between the required value a and the actual value b. Hence the deviation is $c = a - b$.

The smoothing out of this difference is the task of the controller. In our example Mr Smith corrects the deviation by turning the tap up or down depending on whether the water is too cold or too hot.

This action generates the corrective signal which acts on the process system (or controlled system). The latter in our example is Mr Smith himself.

The action of Mr Smith produces a corrected signal b which corresponds to the actual value b of the water temperature. The information about the actual value b is now returned to the sensor; it represents the feedback of the system. Only when $b = a$ (or $c = o$) has Mr

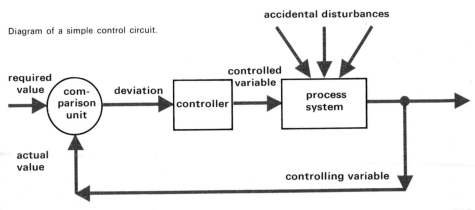

Diagram of a simple control circuit.

Smith succeeded. The actual value equals the desired value. In every other case (b > a or b < a) the cycle is run through again.

Because of the feeding back of the information in this control system one speaks of 'feedback control system'. Feedback control occurs frequently in everyday situations. A good survey is given by Pierre Bertaux (comp. page 184):

'The nucleus of any control is the feedback. Automatic control circuits are based on this principle starting with James Watt's good old governor. If the steam engine goes too fast the regulator throttles the steam supply. If I run down some stairs then a feedback mechanism operates in my brain which tells me: "Careful, stairs" and actuates my legs. As a concept, feedback holds a key position in cybernetics. Control mechanisms operate everywhere. The continued existence of most systems is based upon the indispensable condition of their proper functioning, as for example in the fields of management and economics. In a factory the manufacture of an article is determined by the sale. The director who keeps an eye on the sales figures and accordingly fixes the weekly quantities in which the article is to be made, is in fact nothing else but a feedback-, or control mechanism built into the factory.'

The purpose of control circuits is to create order, to smooth things out. If Mr Smith does not regulate the warm water supply correctly then he will have either a cold shower which will make him shiver or a hot one which may scald his skin. If the director of the factory, mentioned in the quotation from Bertaux, does not plan his production properly he will either accumulate stock and not be able to sell it, or he will lose a great deal of business.

Feedback in control circuits on the other hand carries also the danger of instability. The greater the feedback the greater is also the danger of moving away from balance. This can again be illustrated by a very simple example. Everybody who at one time or another has carried a full cup of coffee over some distance will know that it is not at all easy to avoid spilling some of it into the saucer. Here again we are dealing with a control circuit. One constantly watches the liquid surface and tries by balancing the cup to prevent the coffee from spilling over. But an exaggerated movement of the hand can have exactly the opposite effect. Instead of reducing the deviation it is in fact constantly being increased; the coffee spills over. Such an overrun control is characterized by the fact that the feedback signal came too late, that it lags behind. This makes the controlled system unstable and it goes on increasing its pitch until in some cases it can destroy itself. A control catastrophe occurs. This catastrophe is relatively harmless in our example; in the worst case there will only be a few coffee stains on the carpet. In technological control processes such a catastrophe can be absolutely devastating. Steam boilers can explode, electric motors can burn out etc.

Such catastrophes can also occur in the ailing human body. A nervous disorder which is particularly interesting to cybernetics is 'purpose tremor'. In his book *Cybernetics* Norbert Wiener discusses his

Watt's centrifugal regulator (governor): A steam engine causes a pair of metal balls to rotate. The faster the engine goes the quicker do the balls rotate and the farther are they driven apart by the centrifugal force. If the engine goes too fast i.e. if the balls are too far apart a throttle automatically reduces the supply of steam. Engineers refer to this as an epicyclic gear.

definite conviction that goal seeking movements are control processes. During a movement the aiming is brought about by the fact that one constantly registers deviations from the correct line which are correspondingly balanced out. One constantly compares the actual and desired values. Even if we merely try to take hold of a pencil which lies on the table in front of us we carry out such an aimed movement. Is it possible that in this case disturbances can occur in a

feedback circuit? Wiener therefore put the question to a psychiatrist: 'Is there any pathological condition in which a patient, in trying to perform some voluntary act like picking up a pencil, overshoots the mark, and goes into uncontrollable oscillation?' This is indeed so in the case of purpose tremor. The patient tries in vain to take hold of an object. However hard he may try, his hand oscillates more or less strongly above the aimed at body. This intense vibration only occurs in directed movements and not when the hand is stationary.

A knowledge of control processes in the human body gives the doctor a chance to prescribe a cure. A control catastrophe of a biological-cybernetic type is the stammer, one of the best known speech defects. The out-of-control production of sounds reminds one of the spilling of coffee. Here too feedback comes too late, the control mechanism lags behind. Medical research has established that stammer is due to wrong connections in the nervous system.

A convincing experiment confirms this control catastrophe which can also be brought about artificially in a completely healthy and normally speaking person. The test subject is asked to make a tape recording of a not very difficult text. This is played back to him via earphones with a delay of about a tenth of a second. This delayed hearing of what he had just said confuses the speaker so much that he begins to stammer. One has forced upon him an unstable feedback circuit.

It is perhaps not very surprising that a control mechanism also applies to speaking. After all in a conversation, communication is supposed to function. There

317

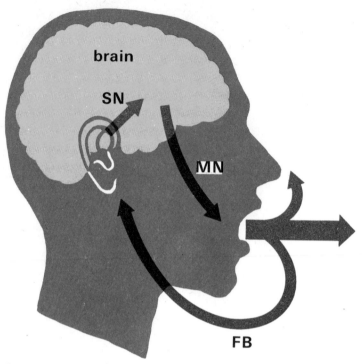

A control process also takes place when speaking. The sound does not only impinge on the ears of the listener but through feedback (FB), via the air and bones, on the ears of the speaker. Sensory and motor nerves (SN and MN) close this control circuit.

is a very wide gap between whispering and shouting and in order to make himself understood the speaker has to fit in somewhere between the two. The feedback does not only come from the listener (receiver) who may put his hand to the ear thereby increasing the receiving area of the ear or who may painfully distort his face etc. The important thing is that the sounds produced by the speaker (transmitter) are also received by his own ears. The feedback path is provided by the air surrounding the the speaker and through his bones. The signal is transmitted from the ear to the brain by sensory nerves and the brain is linked to the speech organs by the motor nerves. In this way the control circuit is closed (see figure).

An apparently simple model of a control process which easily leads to disturbances is that of two pedestrians walking towards each other and who want to pass one another. It happens frequently that both correct their movements like mirror images and therefore never avoid one another. Here too the control catastrophe is mostly quite harmless unless the two people concerned are in a tremendous hurry.

When explaining processes taking place in the human body we have used the expression 'control mechanism'. Some readers may find this inapt or perhaps even monstrous; after all man is not a machine. To be sure this picture may not have been drawn correctly but in a different sense from what one usually assumes. Let us look at it in the sense of the physiologist Hans Schaefer (born 1906). 'Technological control installations are built in analogy with man; but biological control installations are not built in analogy with technology.' Therefore Schaefer may write down the unusual sentence: 'Biological controllers are more mechanical than technological ones'. To him the biological control mechanism is 'the perfection in mechanism'; because it is 'the machine working without interference and correction towards constancy of form'.

We can add to this the conclusion arrived at by the psychologist Wilhelm Arnold (born 1911) who placed the technological controller into an unusual light: 'Basically the desired value in a technological control circuit is determined psychologically by the psyche of the technologist. It is mechanical only in the way it functions. The biological control circuit, however, is not determined by external factors and thus is far more automatic than the technological one.'

This amazing conclusion has made us prick our ears to know something about the future aims of automata which will be the subject of our next chapter.

13. FUTURE AIMS OF AUTOMATA

13.1 Life as the 'hardware' of technologists?
The homeostat and the self-reproducing machine

Our excursion into the land of 'intelligent machines', of self-controlled mechanisms or cybernetic machines, is coming to an end. It was a serious tour into the realm of technology, without excitement and without drawing any analogies between technological structures on the one hand, and animals and man on the other. We were out more to demonstrate how man with play instinct and constructive fantasy systematically enlarged his 'tool box' and formed tools which make it easier for all men to master their surroundings. In a fully industrialized society, no man needs others to slave for him any longer. One reason for this is that nowadays machines can do the work much more cheaply than man can. In addition to machine slaves we have also thinking slaves. Within the field of mental activity there are certain types of work which are more or less dull or at least consist of nothing but tedious routine work. It is here that the thinking slave 'computer' becomes an invaluable tool.

One surely can visualize something more worthy of human beings than adding long columns of figures, the evaluation of rows of measurements according to mechanical rules, or carrying out the same sort of routine over and over

This comic wire parrot is an advertisement of the computer manufacturers Honeywell. This chapter shows that the 'cybernetic zoo' also contains other 'animals'.

again. What is important for society nowadays are not questions like 'man or machine?', or even 'man equals machine?'. No, what one has to consider and master are the problems associated with 'man *and* machine'. Computers are here to be used by man. We have to learn to think with thinking tools. This requirement must be the basis of any highly industrialized society in the cybernetic age, of any society which wants to be 'with it' and must be 'with it' unless it is satisfied to play second fiddle. To be ruled by a computer is no less ridiculous than to be ruled by a car, television or telephone.

In this way man becomes free to do what no machine can take from him. This liberation of man by modern computer technology is what Norbert Wiener so aptly phrased 'the human use of human beings'. Here lies the socio-political task for the future; to make use of the humanizing effects of modern technology in the right manner.

The American psychologist Nehemiah Jordan added to this thought in the following way: that if man is being used like a machine he realizes his own lack of effectiveness. Furthermore he discovers that he is being used in a stupid way. Jordan goes on to say that the system man-machine incites the human components to rebel against this system. So, if we don't learn to use these 'new machines' coolheadedly then one day computers may perhaps be destroyed

321

senselessly as were automatic looms during the last century.

Moreover, around the middle of the sixties clear limits began to show regarding the use of these mechanical thinking slaves particularly in the field of translating machines. Machine translations from one language (e.g. Russian) into another one (e.g. English) even of relatively simple texts has so far not led to satisfactory results. Because of this the 'prosperous' USA does not want to and can not afford to finance machine translation (MT). In the opinion of the National Research Council an automatic translation machine would be uneconomical, even if it could be realized, compared with the human translator who is a relatively cheap source of labour.

At the moment in any of the industrial countries there is no dearth of human translators. There is no recruiting problem in the foreseeable future. Why then should translators not have computers made available to them to act as tools? Computers could provide the building blocks of words for the translation as do dictionaries or technical handbooks. The acquisition of the required information will take place much faster than the conventional looking up.

In 1953 the American physicist V. H. Yngve published an instructive experiment which can justify this kind of process. He had a mathematical paper translated by a computer as well as possible from German into English. Then Yngve tried out the slightly distorted text on two groups of people, mathematicians who did not understand German and non-mathematicians who were at least reasonably familiar with German. The mathematicians could not get on with the machine translation. The non-mathematicians on the other hand with their knowledge of German managed after initial difficulties to find their way through the text. The conclusion is that in order to understand a language a knowledge of the often fairly complicated rules of grammar tips the scales. A lot of noise was made in the fifties and at the beginning of the sixties about translation machines and the remarkable feats that could be expected from them. The Frenchman Abraham A. Moles went so far as to write that one can dream of the day when one simply has to feed the original text into a teleprinter which is provided with a number of knobs on which is written: English, German, Japanese. He certainly can dream about it but the chances of realizing his dream are very small indeed.

A very useful by-product of these machine translations was the understanding that one obtained about the structure of the vocabulary. If one analyses the grammar using mathematical methods, as has become usual in modern linguistics, then the computer can be very useful. Calculating machines belong to the tool box of mathematical linguistics. It may be pertinent to point out that from the shortcomings of machine translations one cannot infer the existence of deficiencies in our natural language. Yet there are technologists who make this absurd inference which cannot be right particularly when one considers over what long period of time this universal tool has fulfilled its function (comp. page 336). We shall not deny the reader an example of such thoughts. 'The complexity of our language which is the basic reason for the difficulties in machine translations does not necessarily speak in our favour. Moreover it is the proof of the existence of deficiencies in human logic which is by no means something we should be proud of.' Strange things blossom forth at times from the pen of technologists!

The wild fantasy has meanwhile been replaced by cool reasoning. At times one might almost say that the 'cybernetic credo' of the fifties has given way to a kind of hang-over. But we don't need to go to such extremes (comp. also page 336). It is important that one should recognize the methodical limits of a particular process. Cybernetics is just not a scientific panacea.

Machine translation has clearly highlighted the limits of 'cybernetization'.

Also Y. Bar-Hillel has retraced his optimistic 'formula' of 1952 when he said with reference to MT: 'if a human being can do it, a suitably programmed computer can do it too'. The suitable machine program required for this has not been written so far. What then are the difficulties? In a German educational television lecture Bar-Hillel admitted:

'It became more and more clear to me that man's ability to translate and, in the course of time and with more experience, to translate better and better, rests on some kind of innate organization. At the moment there are no indications that we shall understand this innate organization in the foreseeable future to such an extent that we shall be able to make use of this understanding for building models

The philosopher Y. Bar-Hillel is a machine translation expert.

and for programmed simulation. To put it into somewhat more philosophical terms: It seems that we human beings in order to acquire that particular disposition of the first kind, which is called "competence" in a given language, make use of an innate disposition of the second kind whose anatomical and physiological aspects are as yet completely unknown to us. The fact that this disposition of the second kind has been denoted, more than fifty years ago, as "Faculté de Langage" by the well known Swiss linguist Ferdinand de Saussure does not alter the facts. I think it is better for us to admit that with such an abysmal lack of knowledge not even a cybernetic wizard would be able to conjure a live rabbit out of a hat.'

Not many experts on cybernetics exhibit this philosophical humility. The 'sorcerer's apprentices' are still at work here. A key position in this MT-problem is naturally the investigation of the human brain. We know practically very little about the structure of this subtle and specific mechanism called brain—even if some technologists talk about it as if they themselves 'wired up' this delicate system. In fact we have to concur with Bar-Hillel in admitting that cybernetics was not and is not capable 'of producing a copy of this specific structure or to simulate it by a suitable computer program'. In this connection it is interesting to know that, from the beginning, Norbert Wiener, the father of cybernetics, was sceptical towards the MT-project.

To many journalistic writers as well as experts in cybernetics the idea that 'man enlarges his toolbox' in connection with 'intelligent machines' is far too narrow. They would like to open up much bolder perspectives. But Norbert Wiener was far more concerned with creating a common jargon which would be useful to describe technological as well as biological systems.

Nowadays, and very appropriately, not only the technologist but also the biologist speaks of information (see *Modern Biology* in this series). Bistable switching elements also have their place in biology. The idea of a black box is as useful in biology as it is in nuclear physics. The control circuit has become one of the most useful concepts in technology, biology, medicine and psychology.

Statements like 'information is being processed in the computer as well as in the human brain' have quite legitimately become part of the language of science. On the other hand formulations like 'the human brain is nothing but a complex computer' are rather problematical. Such generalizations appear just as questionable as old and well known assertions according to which the brain 'is nothing else but a system of moving atoms'. The use of the speculative series of words '... is nothing else but...' always seems to hint at an enforced assimilation against which Ludwig Wittgenstein warned us forcibly (see page 33).

But it is possible to make comparisons, to establish similarities, without constantly quoting '...is nothing else but...' For every fact there exists more than just one way of looking at it. In the exact sciences one also finds it useful to observe one and the same fact from different points of view. In most cases one cannot see straight away which approach is the most fruitful. The most important self-controlling mechanisms which we have come across so far were program-controlled. They work to a program, possess a memory and a feedback system. These mechanisms move, so to speak, on solid rails just as a railway engine. The timing is fixed beforehand, all goes according to plan. This does not imply however, that everything is rigid and that no deviation is possible. The feedback takes care of that.

And yet all possible situations that might arise have been considered beforehand. Situations which the designer has has not taken into account don't play a part. Such program-controlled machines are therefore referred to as deterministic machines. The built-in feedback in these machines enables them to test the actual state of a system and to take the corresponding switching action. They are the right kind of devices to relieve man of the drudgery of routine work. We shall enlarge a little on the present state of the art in the subsequent part of the book.

In the previous chapter we have become used to the unusual idea of considering the biological control circuit as being more mechanical and functioning more automatically than the technological one. In this connection it was useful to speak of a biomechanical process. The automation of biological control circuits has nowadays become a particularly important characteristic of 'life'.

Biomechanical feedback systems ensure the stability of conditions within the organisms which are important to life (blood pressure, body temperature, oxygen concentration in blood, etc) in the hostile surroundings.

Such an automatic maintenance of the conditions of a system at preset levels is called homeostasis. This artificial word is derived from the Greek 'homoios' which means remaining constant. It was introduced into science by the American physiologist Walter B. Cannon at the beginning of the nineteen-thirties. Is a technical realization of homeostasis in organic systems possible? Is it possible to construct a technical control mechanism which is able to react similarly to an organism in hostile surroundings? In fact the English neurologist W. Ross Ashby succeeded in the early fifties in developing a mechanism which can maintain any preset condition in a stable state against all kinds of disturbances coming from the surroundings. This unusual machine was called homeostat.

How does such a homeostat operate? How can it automatically regain its disturbed equilibrium? Ashby's machine consists roughly speaking of two coupled installations which we shall call box H_1 and box H_2. The H_1-box contains the system which is susceptible to disturbances; it is made up of four electromagnets. As discussed previously (chapter 4) such a magnet consists of a current carrying coil of wire surrounding a soft-iron core. In Ashby's homeostat the four cores are free to move. On switching on the current the cores are drawn into the coil.

The displacement of the cores actuates a simultaneous control of the current to the magnet. If a core is displaced it changes the position of the movable contact of a slide-wire rheostat placed in series with the magnet. Thus the current through the rheostat, and therefore also through the magnet, varies according to the position of this contact.

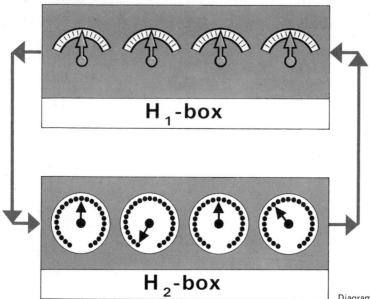

Diagram of W. Ross Ashby's homeostat.

The positions of the cores of the four magnets are indicated on scales attached to the outside of the H_1-box. Certain positions of the four pointers indicate certain equilibrium conditions of the homeostat. For example a stable equilibrium state of the device exists when all four pointers are in the middle of the scale (see figure). For such a position the system is at rest; the cores don't move. In such a state the H_1-box produces no output for the H_2-box. In all other unstable cases the H_2-box will be activated by an output from H_1.

What happens if the output of H_1 sets the H_2-box into action? A complex switching system—four switches each with two dozen positions—will make H_2 react in many-thousandfold ways. Which of the large number of switch positions prevails is purely a matter of chance. But in each case the H_1-box now receives an input from H_2 which causes the iron cores to be displaced. If the input to H_1 has produced a stable state, which is hardly ever the case right away, then there will be no output signal. Generally, however, it will still be unstable and the output signal activates the switches in the H_2-box which adjust themselves to another chance setting. This in turn produces another input to H_1 and so forth until H_1 reaches an equilibrium state.

In this discussion we are not interested in the technical details of Ashby's homeostat. What does interest us however are two important points. One is the fact that there is a feedback between the two boxes and the other is the chance connection in the H_2-box. The latter carries out a kind of search by jumps for a chance hit. This process is described by the expression 'step-function'. Ashby calls a system which scans possible switch positions in the search for stability 'ultra-stable'.

Ultrastability is an important property of artificial cybernetic systems which are also referred to as 'self organizing systems'. The Ashby-machine is one such example because it is capable of changing a chance pattern in the arrangement of its elements (magnetic cores), discontinuously and by chance, into another such pattern. One might say that chance helps to push back chance (comp. page 314). The important point is that eventually in this way a definite stable state is reached. If we compare a biomechanical regulator with the ultrastable homeostat by considering both as black boxes then the similarity in behaviour must astonish one. Ashby's automaton is indeed an amazing device which, in the way it functions, shows certain similarities with living systems. Nevertheless one has to be careful of using the ready made expression '...is nothing else but...' too eagerly. To simply equate uncritically 'organism' and 'self organizing (technical) system' is somewhat premature.

In order to give the reader some idea of the vast range of opinions about homeostats we shall restrict ourselves to quoting two extreme comments. The first, by the philologist Pierre Bertaux, will no doubt meet with the approval of most technologists.

'The innovation in Ashby's homeostat lies in the fact that not only has it at its disposal a large number of possible solutions but even manages to deal with unforeseen circumstances by arranging its internal states (the position of the switch units) so that the simplest stabilization becomes possible. When confronted with a situation not foreseen by its inventor the homeostat is capable of inventing a new answer or to use a new solution. It is also a machine which can adapt itself to situations which the designer had not foreseen. The homeostat, like a living creature, is adaptable and capable of inventing; it can master new problems. The power of adapting to the surroundings, which until now has been considered a special ability of living creatures, can now also be formulated mathematically and realized in the form of a machine.'

Biologists and particularly psychologists will by and large doubt the inventive ability of the homeostat to which Bertaux referred. The step-function of the homeostat, its chancelike mustering of probable states, reminds one very much of playing blind-man's bluff, or groping in the dark. A control engineer would no doubt say that the homeostat 'selects its own' switch positions or 'selects them automatically'. In this context the psychologist Wilhem Arnold has this to say:

'Can Ashby's apparatus really choose or can it make spontaneous decisions? The fact is that the various positions follow one another randomly until one is obtained which is stable. To be exact, therefore, the homeostat is not a control system but a mechanism which may take minutes, days or years in order to find stable parameter values. Compared with this irregularity in the succession of possibie settings, which applies in the case of the homeostat, the biological control processes are of quite a different kind. Biological control circuits can ensure the continuance of life—which is their main task—only if they act not after an indefinitely long time but within a definite time interval. According to circumstances this time interval can be short or arbitrarily long. What matters is not that biological control processes should be faster or slower than mechanical ones, but that the time parameter should be adapted biologically to the existing conditions.'

The psychologist, Wilhelm Arnold and many of his colleagues are of the opinion that an irregular succession of different possible settings, the chancelike picking of values cannot be called choice. 'Choice and decision are always related to conscious experience.'

A detailed discussion of these ideas would lead us far too far into the field of modern psychology which is really outside the scope of our theme. We merely would like to keep in mind that the chance correction, which the homeostat is capable of by means of Ashby's step-function, is according to the views of many scientists not sufficient to simulate correctly biochemical control operations mechanically.

Ashby's device only acts through chance. This cannot be altered. Its 'choices' are accidental actions, its 'decisions' are arbitrary, without motive or background. In short, Ashby's automaton is no more capable of making decisions than is a computer (see page 247). The way it makes these choices is by an irregular and clumsy scanning of possible switch positions. It does not suffice to say that the machine 'pushes back chance'.

The way it does this does not meet with the complete approval which would allow us to assert that it possesses life characteristics.

A mere chance connection fixed inside a machine can certainly not simulate the fact that an organism 'is forced to make a decision'. The machine lacks 'consciousness' or, to put it less strongly, it lacks the experience that the outcome of its decision can be positive or negative. The machine is not conscious of the fact that its decision can be nonsense; it does not know any dilemma. (Shakespeare's *Hamlet* is something much more than just a chance controlled collection of words.)

The man who knows that by making a decision the possibility exists that something could go wrong afterwards will be afraid when he has to decide. That this fear of making a decision is not only the privilege of man has been explained once very vividly by the behaviourist Konrad Lorenz in a discussion:

'It is significant of animal, as well as human neurosis, the fear, that one has to make one's own decisions. There is a beautiful experiment by Jules Masserman where a Rhesus monkey has to make a not very difficult decision between two possibilities. Whenever the monkey is made to press a certain knob a picture appears. He is then made to press a second knob when another picture appears. If he does the wrong thing he receives a slight electric shock. This monkey has to work five hours in the morning and two hours in the afternoon and for the rest of the time he is left alone. Experience shows that such a monkey dies after a short time of high blood

A homeostat from the laboratory of Prof. Heinz Zemanek (Vienna).

pressure, of coronary thrombosis, and of all those ailments that a manager suffers from. A second monkey sitting there and seeing the same things and receiving the same shocks, which are quite mild and humane, survives without any ill-effects. It is thus apparent that the freedom, that it is I who decides, is a substantial part of fear.'

In short one could argue in the following manner: Although the technical mechanism simulates quite convincingly a function of the living organism, the simulation of a structure does not seem to have been accomplished. (Such an argument naturally transcends the methodical limits of the black-box point of view.) Despite the many doubts which one could

bring forward about this way of simulating living systems one should not simply brush aside all arguments put forward by those who attempt to create life. W. Grey Walter, the British neurologist made points which are well worth discussing. If several properties of a system are known and if one has constructed the simplest model which can reproduce these properties then one is permitted the assumption that the original contains components which are comparable with those in the model.

There is no reason whatsoever why anybody should feel it necessary to go as far as the information scientist Karl Steinbuch (born 1917) in his *Thesis on Cybernetics*. 'It is being assumed that the occurrence of life and physical processes in the arrangement, and physical inter-

329

action of parts, of the organism will be completely explained in principle.'

As already mentioned what biologists have described, right up to our time, as life processes is a very complicated and presumably highly stratified world of phenomena. But this is no reason for modern biology to give up methodically. It could be quite meaningful, particularly in view of the new approaches in, say, molecular biology, to compare living and technical systems in a sober manner. It is certainly useful that large regions in modern science and technology can be described with the same kind of vocabulary.

Exact sciences cannot progress without systematic generalizations even if such generalizations always carry certain dangers with them. Modern biologists use methods which are far more akin to those of physicists and technologists than those of their colleagues in previous decades. This was put remarkably well by the Englishman John Kendrew (born 1917) who won the Nobel prize for chemistry. In essence he had this to say: In their investigations the old biologists tended to progress from the complicated to the simple. They began with the whole organism, dissected it, investigated the various organs and tissues in order, finally, to study the individual cells under the microscope. Their analyses so to speak took one 'downhill'.

The new biology, on the other hand starts at the other end. It progresses from the bottom to the top. It starts with the simplest elements of living creatures, the molecules in the cells, and with their interactions. It neglected complications. Now it has to deal with these complications and has to work its way up within the hierarchy of biological organization.

It is significant for this new-look biology that it makes not only the stabilization of system states accessible to a technical investigation and realization; this includes the stabilization of very complex molecular structures which are regarded as an important aspect of life. It will also be useful for science to investigate another important property of life namely the ability of these molecules to reproduce themselves in a hostile medium. Is this perhaps the decisive difference between a living organism and a machine?

In this connection one is tempted to relate a story which is supposed to have taken place in the seventeenth century at the Swedish royal court. When the famous philosopher and mathematician Descartes explained to the Queen his theory that animals are automata she took the wind out of his sails by pointing at a clock and saying sarcastically: 'See to it that it produces offspring'.

Nowadays intelligent queens find it far more difficult in this respect to deal with philosophers. The responsibility for this falls again on the great mathematician John von Neumann. He designed the blue-print of an automaton which can reproduce itself. This curious machine could even perfect itself from generation to generation by assuming more and more complex structures.

This reflection appears like castles in the air but the basic facts are still solid mathematical materials. Like Ashby's homeostat, von Neumann's blue-print model is a self-organizing system. Although von Neumann's machine is not yet a technical reality, not yet the hardware of the engineers—it is only a paper and pencil operation—on the other hand it is not just a paper tiger. In principle and with sufficient effort this software could well be turned into hardware. But there has been no compelling reasons so far to turn this plan into the very costly reality. Yet no expert today would doubt that von Neumann's paper tiger could be made to roar.

John von Neumann has in fact produced the precise mathematical image of such a self reproducing machine. Like a living organism such a machine has to be provided with food from which it builds up the new one. The 'diet' has to consist of components like wires, bistable switching elements, storage elements, photocells, electric motors, batteries etc. The infant automaton built up in this way could in turn, given the right nourishment, produce yet another machine etc.

Every machine element in this blue-print is an elementary cell. There are for instance 'active' machine elements which can carry out logical operations and regenerate electrical impulses (e.g. impulses which have become weak can be regenerated by sending them into a flip-flop which not only switches them into the appropriate channel but also gives them energy.) Other elementary cells of the machine are transmission and executive elements which, symbolically speaking, form the nerves, the muscles and the glands of the machine.

Of the approximately 200000 elements, which is the minimum requirement of such a machine in order to be capable of 'living' about 75 per cent are used to fix its own program, the machine structure.

John von Neumann (1903–57), the well-known American mathematician of Hungarian descent; he produced a blue-print model of a self-reproducing machine.

This reminds one of the 'copying process' in the 'chromosome-wing' of the living 'cell-factory' from where the blue-prints are transmitted from one cell-generation to another (see *Modern Biology*). In this parallel one should again remember that the processes taking place in a living cell must not be simply characterized as 'nothing else but a von-Neumann-machine'. A good description of the reproductive mechanism in von Neumann's blue-print model was given by the Soviet scientist I. A. Poletaiev (comp. page 179).

'The machine receives the input information which is written on a sequence of elements of the machine itself. Any desired operation with those parts which

331

surround the machine, the raw material, can be recorded in the program.

Corresponding to the program the machine can make up any possible scheme. For the machine to reproduce itself it would suffice to record in the program the building up of a replica of the machine, the copying of the program, the transmission of the program to the new machine and putting it into operation according to the program.'

This process of self-reproduction can be continued as long as new materials and food (leads, transistors etc.) are available and as long as the descendants of these automatons don't get into each others' way. How these machines would behave in these situations of conflict is an interesting aspect of this problem field. One might speculate that the more advanced machines, with corresponding extensions of their program, could use the 'incomplete offspring' of neighbouring machines as food. But this automaton-cannibalism brings us into the realm of science fiction. As I. A. Poletaiev sees it there are two main differences between the von-Neumann-machine and a live organism:

'The organism has no fixed structure. Its construction and function vary continuously with growth and development and with the accumulation of experience. The machine, on the other hand, does not replace its parts. It does not increase the number of its components. It lacks metabolism although its structure changes during the working process. The control devices can make it interchange its elements.

In contrast to living creatures the machine does not go in search of food, the raw materials. It cannot therefore exist without the help of man.'

In principle, both differences could be put right and the machine would then resemble an organism somewhat closer. But this structure would not be able to go beyond functional simulations.

Although cybernetics has made it possible for biologists and technologists to speak the same language in many respects, there is no doubt that life has kept its secrets. Life is still more by far than the hardware of technologists. And cybernetics has succeeded only in making its secret more exact.

13.2 ELSIE from the cybernetics zoo
Speculations and the machina speculatrix

We might say that the guiding line of our discussion was: 'Man enlarges his tool-box: he transforms it into a thinking tool.' Cybernetic installations as technological hardware will control all fields of work in varying degrees. Computers will be at the disposal not only of technologists and scientists, but also of politicians and tradesmen, police and army. Just as any typist today uses her electric typewriter without being afraid, she will use the computer tomorrow. An amusing note in a German daily emphasises the many-sided use of computers even in unusual places.

'The Munich Theatre have "engaged"

a computer which plays its part not on stage but in the administrative offices where it will evaluate all book-keeping processes, operations statistics, production costs as well as check the current household budget.'

The various types of computers will not only be important at the place of work. The time is not far off when most people will only work four days a week and will have between two and four months holiday. A modern games and toy industry will presumably flourish in this leisure society. Cybernetic toys will then not only delight and occupy many children but also adults. A cybernetic games and hobby paradise for young and old looms ahead. No doubt one will also find a good deal of crazy and useless stuff in the cybernetic toy cupboard.

One should not, however, underestimate its practical importance for the new play society. Playful discoveries of facts in modern mathematics, science and technology can, and should, be made in early childhood. The American psychologist Glenn Doman once remarked ironically: 'We have succeeded in keeping our children carefully isolated from learning in a period of life when the desire to learn is at its peak.'

An enlightened method of teaching will follow Doman's motto in all fields of knowledge everywhere. 'Learning is also the greatest game in life and the most fun.' In order to awaken curiosity, imagination and the urge to play at the right time in the child one has to provide a very wide and varied wealth of information even at the kindergarten age. To this cultural exercise belong particularly the activities of the exact sciences and modern tech-nology. The readiness of children of below or just school age to discover facts in a playful kind of way, something that is often only learnt in universities, is remarkably great.

Here lies the fundamental, even revolutionary task of modern education. It should not only develop new teaching methods but it should also open up new regions of knowledge to children. It has to relegate into last place the myth, thought up during the past century, that exact science and technology lack educational value. Mathematical, scientific and technological activities go far beyond that which is usually described by intellect and comprehension.

In all fields of research cybernetics has to fulfill a very important and practical task. This is to enliven in all stages of life the desire to learn and to stimulate constructive imagination. The programmed teach- learn-instructions for so called teaching and learning machines leave much to be desired in this respect. Programmed teaching by means of simple machines has not yet been able to bring about a pedagogic revolution. One still relies too much on purely quantitative methods in order to pass on knowledge and skill.

A preliminary stocktaking after more than a decade of programmed teaching leads to the following conclusion: The best and most effective teach-learn-instructions applied to the exact sciences were developed by Soviet educationalists. In Russia 'mechanization at any price' was not the sole aim; quantitative methods had their place but they were not used exclusively. This clearly very effective Russian compromise in education

333

will no doubt become accepted gradually in the western world.

Programmed learning has made education definitely richer and more colourful. As it was praised as being 'the greatest revolution of our educational system since the discovery of printing' it certainly belongs also to the theme of future developments.

Cybernetics, however, is by no means limited to teaching machines which are still capable of much development. There also exist machines which do not teach, in fact there are some which even have to 'learn'. Usually all these cybernetic machines are lumped together under the vague term 'robot'. In slavonic languages similar words are used to express heavy manual labour (for example the Russian word 'rabota'). Karel Capek, the Czech writer, coined this widely used expression in the nineteen-twenties. Since then robots in many different shapes and forms are capable of creating universal chaos in the utopian tales of science fiction.

A few remarks about those products of fantasy of science fiction literature, the 'poetic software' robot, may not be out of place. The idea that these machines are potential revolutionaries is mostly very exciting to authors. Thinking slaves with a higher intelligence quotient than that of their inventors revolt without feeling and respect against humanity. The inhabitants of the earth, the terrestrians, are already doomed to perish.

One now comes up with more or less original solutions to this conflict machine

The computer in the classroom will soon become the obvious instrument for programmed teaching.

versus man. The silliest but most often employed is that some terrestrian manages to immobilize this electronic automaton by simply 'pulling out the plug'. Another feeble solution is the 'Martian' one, that the rebel robot is attacked by some kind of plasma—or radiation gun—and is melted down. If this method does not produce the desired result then in terrestrian circles one gets ready for the 'overkill'.

The whole utopian misery is due to the fact that these robots are capable of making decisions, that they can suffer from neuroses, and that their complex nervous system is extremely sensitive to faulty connections. Yet everybody knows already that this machine creature carries the highest robot-law in the command store: 'Never kill a human being'.

The germ of those bad and flimsy flights of fancy has even attacked serious scientists. Hubert L. Dreyfus, professor at MIT, is not quite so scathing when he refers to 'intellectual smog'. This dirty smog coming from eggheads gathers at times to form such dark clouds that it comes remarkably close to reports of the sensational press. A strong criticism, at times even too strong, of these scientists was made by Mortimer Taube in his book *Computers and Common Sense—the Myth of Thinking Machines.*

For example an American expert on artificial intelligence wrote in 1959: 'We begin to understand the heuristic principles according to which human thinking takes place. To the same extent the mystery which surrounds such vague concepts as "intuition" and "judgement" begins to lighten.' Since then this passing enthusiasm has evaporated. What one 'begins to understand' nowadays seems to move in a different direction. The future has not started yet, and if the electronics expert Dean Wooldridge wanted to discern the vague glimmer of consciousness somewhere between the wires and transistors of the machine one has to say that in the meantime this glimmer turned out to be a Martian canal.

Is the whole cybernetic game nothing but bad science-fiction fantasy? Is the toybox of cybernetics nothing but a materialistic moth-eaten and dusty box? This would mean throwing out the baby with the bathwater. H. L. Dreyfus takes probably the most useful view that so far as our researches into artificial intelligences are directed towards play, to recognize the reasons for the present stagnation, which clearly has set in in the construction of thinking machines, then the value of such computerized pastimes cannot be placed too highly. Every step in this direction brings us nearer to the understanding of our own thinking processes.

Exaggerated speculations of scientists about artificial intelligences belong nowadays to bad science fiction in the same way as do weak stories about robots. After having said so many bad things about science fiction it is only fair to say that there exist also fascinating and convincing writings in this type of literature. But they fascinate more because of their sociological, political, biological, psychological and philosophical uncertainty rather than because of their technological implications. The utopian writings of the astrophysicist Fred Hoyle (*The Black Cloud*) and the physicist Leo Szilard (*The Voice of the Dolphins*) are also attractive to those concerned with information theory.

But let us return from our flights of fancy, the intellectual smog and poetic software, to the hardware of already existing robots. On first hearing the names of all these creations one inevitably gets the impression of a 'cybernetics zoo'. From the MIT laboratories of N. Wiener and J. B. Wiesner came an artificial creature which could play 'moth and bug'. With the switch of the machine pointing to 'moth' the little electric cart with motor and photocell moved towards every source of light. The mobile apparatus exhibited what is called 'positive phototropism'. If the switch points to 'bug' then 'negative phototropism' occurred. Every source of light made the cart move away from it. In France A. Ducrocq designed a cybernetic 'fox' which reacted to light-, sound- and touch stimuli. Tortoises which go by the names of ELMER, ELSIE, and CORA, and which look like old fashioned irons without a handle, were made by W. Grey Walter. And finally 'mice in the labyrinth' were contributed to the cybernetics zoo by the American C. E. Shannon and the Austrian Heinz Zemanek.

What is the point of all this? One might well ask. Have the eggheads become infantile by playing with a kind of model railway on a higher plane? But let us recall Dreyfus' remark about the value of computerized pastimes. The similarity in behaviour which exists between these robots and animals is at times really astonishing. Yet one does not really have to go as far as W. Grey Walter who is of the opinion that clumsy though these machines may appear they produce the uncanny impression of target acquisition, of mutual dependence and a remarkable wealth of ideas.

Let us take a clearer look at one of Walter's creatures for instance the tortoise ELSIE. Its name is derived in a way which is now familiar to us 'Electro Light Sensitive with Internal and External stability'. Together with its robot-colleague ELMER (short for ELectro MEchanical Robot) ELSIE is known in the literature as 'machina speculatrix'. (In addition to humorous abbreviations of double-Dutch-sounding designations W. G. Walter seems to take a fancy to Latin names for robots. For example he called Ashby's homeostat 'machina sopora' the 'sleepy machine', because, like a cat dozing in the sun, it only moves when disturbed only to fall asleep again after a little search for another suitable rest position.)

What is the purpose of a machina speculatrix, a reconnoitring machine? It looks out for light sources in dark rooms. How does it accomplish this? A glance at ELSIE'S anatomy reveals that it is a three-wheeler which carries two electric motors. One of them is responsible for the motion by turning the rear wheels of the cart and the other controls the steering of the front wheel, forwards, backwards, right and left. A chance setting of the steering mechanism causes ELSIE to move zigzag or in circles. This irregular movement (which reminds one of a drunkard) causes a resetting of a photo-electric cell, ELSIE'S eye. It searches around for a source of light in the dark room.

What happens when it does 'see' a light? Then it exhibits positive phototropism like the Wiener-Wiesner moth.

The British neurologist W. Grey Walter the inventor of the 'machina speculatrix'.

Random steering is now cut out and replaced by an ordered movement. ELSIE sets course for the light source. A well thought-out mechanism ensures however that the robot does not make blindly for the light; at a certain distance from the luminous object ELSIE switches over to negative phototropism. The robot is blinded by the light; it no longer reacts like a moth but rather like a bug. ELSIE begins to move backwards.

It could of course happen that ELSIE in its travel towards a lightsource, in other words in the stage of positive phototropism, is hindered by an obstacle. If the machine runs up against some kind of barrier then it senses this through a device which is sensitive to touch. This switches off the directional movement towards the light and swtiches on the random movement. ELSIE tries to circumnavigate the obstacle in an irregular manner. It moves about blindly until it again detects the light source; from this point on the regular movement sets in until the robot hits another obstacle. Eventually ELSIE will reach the position mentioned above, where it is blinded and the device switches over to negative phototropism. In this way the machina speculatrix moves round the light source until it has found optimum conditions where positive and negative phototropism balance one another (see page 336). ELSIE has then reached a state of homeostasis (see page 325). ELSIE derives its electrical energy from a battery which becomes discharged in the course of time. This in turn causes ELSIE'S vision to become so acute that it detects even the faint glimmer of light inside its own cavity. As a consequence ELSIE drives 'home' where it automatically touches a battery charger. After having been charged ELSIE is ready for another round of tasks. The 'home' of the machina speculatrix is a sort of service station for weak batteries which can be made use of

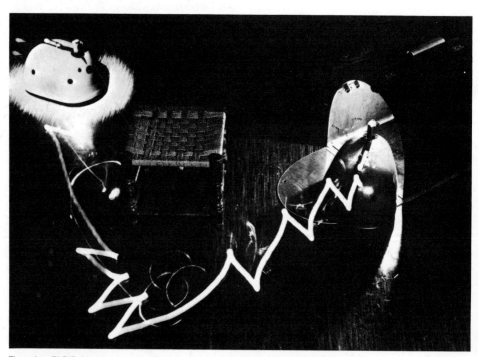

The robot ELSIE dances round an obstacle. At the right of the picture is ELSIE's cave.

automatically whenever required. (Which motorist would not be delighted if his car were a machina speculatrix, at least on very cold mornings?)

W. Grey Walter has fitted ELSIE with a headlamp which lights up when it carries out random movements and is extinguished when it heads towards a light source. What happens when it sees its own headlamp through a mirror? If ELSIE drives towards this light then obviously it will go out and if ELSIE switches over to random steering it will come on again. Are we dealing here with a control catastrophe similar to the case of stammer? This indeed is the case. In front of the mirror the creature hesitates, falters, trips and trembles like a leaf. This last sentence describes unstable feedback mechanism which we have met in a different context (see page 316).

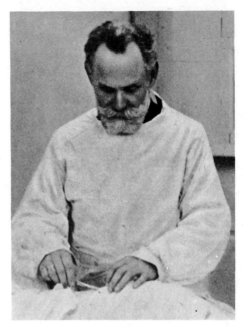

The famous Ivan P. Pavlov studied the behaviour of dogs.

The assertion that ELSIE reacts nervously in this situation, that it suffers from neurotic disorders must not be taken literally. As far as a comparison with living organisms is concerned considerations similar to those made in connection with Ashby's homeostat apply here as well. The random step function of Ashby's machine and the random searching round of Walter's machine permit the same kind of argumentation. Machina sopora and machina speculatrix are basically stupid blind-man's-buff players.

Anybody who is of the opinion, like Karl Steinbuch, 'that every intellectual function that we observe is nothing but recording, processing, storing and dissemination of information' will naturally doubt this harsh judgement. This description may be good enough from the point of view of control technology, but it is not sufficient for a psychological consideration which goes beyond the black box view. No one will doubt that in these intellectual functions all these processes do occur but that they could guarantee a complete description of intellectual activity is, to begin with, a private view, a kind of philosophy of life in the widest sense.

Researches into artificial intelligence have shown that automatons can be made which are capable of learning. And as far as learning is concerned things are rather similar to intellectual activity. Men learn in a variety of ways and the psychological field of learning is far wider than that of the control engineer. A basic

339

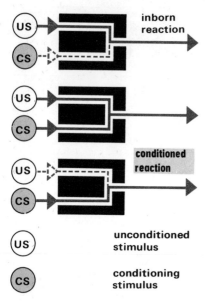

inborn
reaction

conditioned
reaction

US   unconditioned
stimulus

CS   conditioning
stimulus

Diagrammatic representation of the
formation of a conditioned reaction.

form of learning which applies to the latter as well as the former is the conditioned reflex or, more generally, the conditioned reaction. This behaviour was discovered at the beginning of this century by the famous Russian physiologist and Nobel-prize winner Ivan P. Pavlov.

His classic experiment with dogs has frequently been described. When seeing food a hungry dog secretes saliva and gastric juices. These gland reactions set in automatically at the sight of food (unconditioned stimulus). A bell is now rung every time food is shown so that the dog connects the unconditioned stimulus of seeing food with an arbitrarily selected conditioning stimulus of the ringing bell.

The actual mechanism of the inter-linking of these stimuli in the central nervous system has not been established yet. All one can do is to establish experimentally a change in the behaviour of the dog after repeated feeding. The animal reacts to the bell alone by secreting gastric juices and saliva. A conditioned reflex has been formed; the sight of food is no longer necessary to trigger off reflex action.

Owing to the fact that the behaviour of the dog has changed one can say that it has learnt something. Which normal dog would react in this way on hearing the bell signal which is not really connected with feeding? Only the correctly trained dog would behave like this. In addition to the conditioned reflex the unconditioned reflex is there as before. The reactions of the glands are inborn reactions of the dog. In order that the animal should not forget straight away the learnt conditioned reflex it has to be rewarded with food after the sounding of the bell. The feeding of the animal is a kind of diploma. In general one can express these matters in the following way: the conditioned reflex requires reinforcement in order to maintain it. This

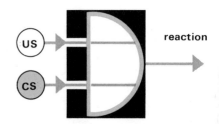

reaction

An organism which has changed its behaviour through a conditioned reaction—in other words which has learnt—reacts to normal or conditioning stimulus like an 'Or-box'.

reinforcement forms the positive influencing of the desired behaviour.

It is not difficult to see that this method of learning can also be simulated by a machine. One then deals with an automaton which is capable of learning but which is neither capable of spontaneous activity nor of conscious action. It cannot make decisions. Even if these machines were more complicated than the homeostat or ELSIE, to a psychologist they are just stupid, brainless apparatuses which don't possess intelligence. At best the robots may be regarded as 'intelligence amplifiers' as Ashby expressed it so well. The psychologist Arnold explained: 'the primary cause of machine activity is never the machine but only creative man'.

This creative man has to be used in a manner which befits man. This is one of the most meaningful challenges from the field of cybernetics, Norbert Wiener's 'human use of human beings'. This does by no means entail that future generations should consist of thinkers only. The number of unskilled and semiskilled workers will still go on rising. The manual worker will keep his place next to the white-collar worker in spite of all future plans. It has been shown clearly that far less manual work, even relatively simple work at that, can be automated than was assumed at first. Even for future generations manual work will still be needed. The 'homo faber' will survive on this planet.

The 'human use of human beings' will hardly show in manned spaceflight. Considering the gigantic cosmic distances, astronauts and cosmonauts will merely execute 'flea jumps' into near space and land on the moon and Mars and Venus

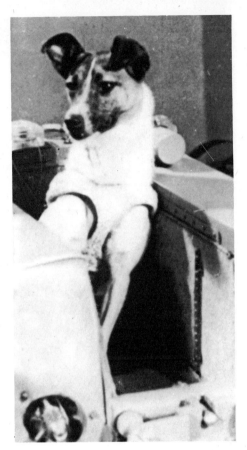

The Siberian dog Laika, which circumnavigated the earth in a satellite, showed conditioned reflexes. She ate only at the ringing of a bell.

etc. The exciting and scientifically interesting results will be produced by special tools like space probes, or space robots, or whatever else one wants to call them. The Swiss historian J. O. Fleckenstein noted: 'One knows nowadays that electronically controlled probes can almost yield as many results as a moon landing of terrestrians with a manned spacecraft. For where lies the border between man

341

13. Future aims of automata

The Russian physiologist I. P. Pavlov (centre) and co-workers in his laboratory. On the left is an animal used in the experiments. The photograph was taken in 1914.

trained as "super ape" to carry out the activity of robots and an electronic probe constructed to carry out man-like robot activity for which most of the complicated organs of homo faber so to speak become superfluous?'

Cybernetic tools, thinking tools, and toys will certainly contribute to the determination of the future of man but by no means to the extent that was prophesied some years ago. The many 'revolutions' announced with great noise have so far not been realized. They are more likely in modern biology rather than in technology. Many proponents of technical cybernetics have first and foremost to free themselves of the dangerous 'is nothing-else-but' point of view if they are dealing with living systems and if they are trying to step into the psychological

field and particularly that of thinking.

Perhaps cybernetics will be able to open a door for the game of games which Hermann Hesse has described so impressively in his novel *Das Glasperlenspiel* (translated by M. Savill under the title of *Magister Ludi*). According to the author's statement this game requires 'great attention, alertness and concentration', virtues which were taught particularly by philosophers since the days of the Ionic natural philosophy of ancient Greece. Philosophizing man who is supposed to pursue his intellectual activity, with attention, alertness and concentration is no doubt far more than a mere 'signal converter', more than a 'receiver', 'processing device' or 'store' of information. And yet technologists will, in certain respects, be an example to the coming generation of intellectuals. Let us end with the vision of Hermann Hesse the outlines of which become already clearly discernible.

'Young people who wish to dedicate themselves to intellectual studies consider them no longer as simply a sampling of Universities where famous professors without authority presented them with the remnants of past education; nowadays they have to learn as hard and even harder and more methodically than students of engineering had to do in the past in polytechnics.'

Solutions

Page 158

The sentences with missing vowels can be completed easily. The English example is *'Mr Smith is a gentleman'* and the German one is *'Hans ist hungrig und durstig'*. The sentences with spaces, where consonants have been left out, are hardly intelligible. The solutions are: *'it is the postman'* and *'der Hund spielt im Garten'*.

Page 216

not-A and B and C, or A and not-B and not-C.

Page 221

0000
1100
0100
1110
0010
1011
0011
1111

Page 262

A	B	A ∧ B
current	no current	current
current	current	no current
no current	no current	no current
no current	current	no current

INDEX

PHOTOGRAPHIC ILLUSTRATIONS WERE PROVIDED BY:

APN 165, 297 (bottom), 339, 341, 342; Joh. Barth (Joba) 56; Boeing 285 (top); Deutsches Museum 84, 250, 317; Digitàl 257 (bottom); Walt Disney Productions 264; dpa 24; Hans Erni (IBA) 40; M. C. Escher 174, 175; Exeter School 304, 309; Dr Fuchs Archives 49, 147; Herder Verlag 116; Hitachi 285 (bottom); Honeywell 292 (top), 257 (top), 290, 320; IBM 196, 222, 252, 253, 256, 257 (bottom), 259, 263, 287, 289, 293, 299; Massachusetts Institute of Technology 87; RCA 335; Ehrhard Schönberg, München, 168, 297 (top); Sessner, Dachau, 323; Siemens 248, 258, 262, 270, 271, 280, 291, 292 (bottom); Suhrkamp Verlag 21; Tripp, Bristol, 338; Ullstein 298, 301; UPI-Bild 83, 141; USIS 13, 255, 260, 286, 331; Verlagsarchiv 45, 337; Die Zeit, Hamburg, 251.